Elementary Matrix Algebra with Linear Programming

Richard J. Painter
Colorado State University

Richard P. Yantis
United States Air Force Academy

PRINDLE, WEBER & SCHMIDT, INCORPORATED

Boston   London   Sydney

Library of Congress Catalog Card Number: 70–136199
Printed in the United States of America.
SBN 87150–121–X

SECOND PRINTING: October, 1972

This book is fondly dedicated to our teacher

Alfred T. Brauer

Preface

This textbook has been designed to enable the beginning college student to learn the basic concepts of matrix algebra as quickly as possible and to use them in some elementary applications in business, economics, engineering, operations research, probability, and statistics. Chapters 1–4 contain the main theoretical development in the text. Chapter 5, on determinants, stands somewhat independently between the theory and Chapters 6–8, which embody the principal applications (so important in a book of this nature).

With the student in mind, the development of the text is based on three main themes:

1. The student learns new concepts faster when he is able to compare new ideas to those he already thoroughly understands.

2. It is important for full comprehension of the subject that the student be able to understand and perform the computational algorithms of matrix algebra.

3. Unnecessary symbolism and unfamiliar notation often inhibit the student's ability to learn basic matrix algebra.

Chapter 1 is a review of the operations and properties of the real number system. In Chapter 2, the algebra of matrices is developed by analogy with the structures in Chapter 1. Emphasis is placed on those properties for which no matrix analogue exists.

The development of matrix theory continues in Chapter 3 with the introduction of systems of linear equations and their solution by matrix methods. We examine and exploit the technique of Gauss-Jordan reduction. Because it is used to solve many of the standard problems of matrix algebra that we discuss, this technique provides a thread of continuity in Chapters 5-7. To avoid having students develop a strong dislike for the hand application of the Gauss-Jordan technique because of arithmetic difficulties, we have designed many of the problems so that all of the coefficients remain integers throughout the entire solution process. Chapter 4 concludes the theoretical development with the study of vector spaces (only as sets of row or column

v

matrices). The results of Chapter 3 are then reviewed in this new setting. Chapter 5, on determinants, may be omitted by those who wish to spend more time on the other applications. If the material on determinants is omitted, one should also consider omitting Section 6.7 which is concerned with eigen-vectors.

In Chapter 6, we apply matrix algebra to geometrical problems which arise in many varied contexts. Here the problem of coordinate change with a change of basis is analyzed. We introduce the concept of a linear transfor-mation from a vector space into itself and find its matrix representation with respect to a given basis. Matrix representations of the standard rotations, projections, and reflections in the plane are then developed. The dot product is introduced and used to define the concept of length and angle in a vector space. The chapter concludes with a study of the eigenvector problem and a short introduction to the terminology and matrix representation of quadratic forms.

Chapter 7 is an extensive chapter in which elementary geometry and matrix algebra are used to develop in the student a thorough understanding of and a computational facility with G. Dantzig's simplex method of linear programming—one of the most important practical mathematical algorithms ever developed. To set the stage, several real situations are modeled as linear programming problems. Small problems are solved geometrically. The algebra of an iterative solution by the simplex algorithm is then developed in coordination with a geometrical solution of the same problem. The relationship between the bases developed in Chapter 4 and the extreme or corner points of the feasible region is emphasized. The columns of the body of the simplex tableau are treated as coordinate matrices of the columns of the original tableau, but with respect to a new choice of basis. As in Chapter 3, many of the problem sets of this chapter have been designed in a semi-programmed fashion.

Chapter 8 provides a short but uncomplicated introduction to the ideas of stochastic matrices and Markov chains. It concludes with an application to the automobile insurance industry.

In addition, there are three appendices. In Appendix A, we consider the completeness property of the real numbers in order to round out the dis-cussion of the text in Chapter 1. Appendix B contains the proofs of those algebraic results that we have chosen either to omit in the main body of the text or to prove for only a special case. Here the summation notation is developed and used. Appendix C introduces the subject of vector spaces in full generality and provides varied examples.

We would like to thank Martha Reardon of the publisher's staff, Miss Marion J. Watson of Carleton University, and Dr. James E. Shockley of Virginia Polytechnic Institute for their invaluable comments, corrections, and constructive criticisms. We would also like to express our appreciation to Arthur L. Weber, without whose encouragement the chapter on determinants would never have been written, and especially to Dr. James Gentry, without whose eye for correction and good offices the revision and proofreading of the manuscript would have been a much less pleasant task.

RJP
RPY

Contents

[1]   Introductory Concepts

The topics included in this chapter—sets, functions, the real numbers, and formal logic—although introductory in nature, are matters with which every person interested in mathematics should be concerned. The elementary notions and language of *set theory* will be used throughout our discussions because of their simplifying effects upon the presentation and understanding of new ideas; the concepts of *function* and *number* are fundamental in both the theory and the application of mathematics; and *formal logic* is the filter which we use to separate truth from mere conjecture. We therefore recommend that the reader scan our introductory remarks, and that he devote serious study to those portions with which he is unfamiliar.

1.1   Sets

The words *set*, *element*, *belongs to* are, for us, undefined terms, and we lean upon your intuition when we speak of the *set* of, say, all pages in this book. We are also confident that you recognize page 1 as an *element* of that set, which is to say that page 1 *belongs to* that set.

A particular set is considered to be properly defined or specified when it is described in such a way that one can distinguish between objects which belong to the set and objects which do not belong to the set. For example, consider the set of all coins in your pocket. It is clear that, given an object, you can decide whether or not it is a coin in your pocket. On the other hand, some descriptions are so vague, or ambiguous, or so dependent upon personal opinion, that it is not possible to distinguish elements from nonelements. For instance, consider the "set" of the ten greatest American Presidents. We are a little uneasy when we ask, "What are the elements of this set?" Perhaps we could all agree to include Lincoln and we probably could agree to exclude Andrew Johnson. But the questions of including Lyndon Johnson, Truman, Washington or Wilson, are questions which are likely to arouse heated debate and unlikely to receive definite answers. Thus the phrase "the ten greatest American Presidents" does not properly define a set, because it does not clearly determine which objects are elements and which are not elements.

There are several symbols which we will want to use to denote sets. First, we will most commonly use a capital letter such as A or T to stand for a given set, and, second, we will frequently describe a set by writing down a list of its elements enclosed in braces—for example, the set consisting of the first three counting numbers (positive integers) may be denoted as

$$\{1, 2, 3\}.$$

In certain instances this listing of elements could be awkward, exhausting, or even impossible. For if we consider, even for a moment, the set consisting of the first 1000 counting numbers, the prospect of writing them all down in a list is not at all appealing. Instead, we write

$$\{1, 2, 3, \ldots, 1000\}$$

and hope that whoever sees this symbol will understand that the dots stand for all of the counting numbers between 4 and 999 inclusive. An extension of this device occurs when the set $\mathbb{Z}^+$ of *all* counting numbers is denoted as

$$\{1, 2, 3, \ldots\},$$

or when the set of even counting numbers is denoted as

$$\{2, 4, 6, \ldots\}.$$

Even though something is being left to the imagination, the context should make clear the proper interpretation of the three dots (...).

A third type of notation for sets, which is not ambiguous, is illustrated by the following example. Consider the set of all counting numbers denoted as

$$\{n \mid n \text{ is a counting number}\}.$$

In words: "the set of *all* objects n such that n is a counting number." Or consider the set T denoted by

$$\{t \mid t \text{ is an equilateral triangle}\}.$$

In words: "T is the set of *all* objects t such that t is an equilateral triangle." In general, then, this notation

$$\{x \mid p(x)\},$$

called the "set-builder" notation, will be considered to stand for the set of *all* objects x such that x satisfies the properties described in the sentence $p(x)$. That is, the braces { } denote *set* and the vertical bar | is read "such that."

We say that a set B is a **subset** of a set A if each element of B is also an element of A. For instance, the set E of all even counting numbers is a subset of the set $\mathbb{Z}^+$ of all counting numbers. We denote the situation that B is a subset of the set A by

$$B \subseteq A \quad \text{or, equivalently,} \quad A \supseteq B.$$

In words: "B is contained in A" or "A contains B." Please note that this definition of subset implies that a set A is always a subset of itself. We distinguish between this trivial subset of A and other subsets of A by saying that B is a **proper** subset of A providing B is a subset of A and, further, that A has at least one element which is not in B.

We say that two sets C and D are **equal** and can write

$$C = D$$

as long as the two sets have precisely the same elements. A moment's reflection will assure you that this is equivalent to saying, "C is a subset of D and D is a subset of C."

When we speak of the **union** of two sets A and B we mean the set C whose elements are exactly the elements of A, together with the elements of B. We denote the union of A and B as

$$A \cup B \qquad \text{(read "} A \text{ union } B \text{")}$$

and note that

$$A \cup B = \{x \mid x \text{ belongs to } A \textit{ or } x \text{ belongs to } B\}.$$

By the **intersection** of two sets A and B we mean the set C whose elements are precisely those elements which are both in A and in B. We denote the intersection of A and B by

$$A \cap B \qquad \text{(read "} A \text{ intersect } B \text{")}$$

and note that

$$A \cap B = \{x \mid x \text{ belongs to } A \textit{ and } x \text{ belongs to } B\}.$$

This definition of intersection leads us to consider a curious set. First, consider the set C of all cards in an ordinary deck of playing cards. If R denotes the set of all red cards (diamonds and hearts) and B denotes the set of all black cards (clubs and spades) then clearly $R \subseteq C$ and $B \subseteq C$. Moreover, $R \cup B = C$(Why?). But what is

$$R \cap B?$$

According to the above definition, $R \cap B$ *is* a set; and it is also easy to decide which objects belong to it and which do not, for clearly any object which you care to name does *not* belong to $R \cap B$. We call this set the **null set** and denote it by $\emptyset$. Of course, there are many ways to describe $\emptyset$ other than in terms of playing cards. Observe, for example, that

$$\emptyset = \{1, 2, 3\} \cap \{4, 5, 6\},$$

and also that

$$\emptyset = \{x \,|\, x \text{ is a motorcycle with 79 wheels}\}.$$

As a matter of some interest, observe also that $\emptyset$ is a subset of every set A; for it is true (Isn't it?) that each object in $\emptyset$ is also in A. (This could only be false if there were objects in $\emptyset$ which were not in A; since there are no such objects in $\emptyset$, the statement cannot be false.)

Exercises I.I

1. Describe in words the following sets (where $\mathbb{Z}^+$ denotes the set of positive integers):
   a. $\{x \,|\, x - 5 \text{ is in } \mathbb{Z}^+\}$.
   b. $\{y \,|\, y \text{ is a positive integer}\}$.
   c. $\{2x - 1 \,|\, x \text{ is in } \mathbb{Z}^+\}$.

2. Describe the following sets using the set-builder notation:
   a. The set of all positive integers which are multiples of 5.
   b. The set of all negative integers.
   c. The set of all triangles which are also rectangles.

3. a. Is $\{1, 2, 3\}$ a subset of $\{1, 2, 3\}$? A proper subset?
   b. Is $\{1, 2, 3\}$ a proper subset of $\mathbb{Z}^+$?

4. Let $A = \{1, 2, 3, 4\}$, $B = \{-1, 2, 7\}$, $C = \{1, 4, 6, 8\}$.
   a. Find $A \cup B$ and $B \cup C$.
   b. Find $A \cap B$.
   c. Find $A \cap (B \cup C)$.
   d. Find $A \cap C$.

e. Find $(A \cap B) \cup (A \cap C)$. Compare c and e.

f. Find $B \cup (A \cap C)$.

g. Find $(B \cup A) \cap (B \cup C)$. Compare f and g.

5. How many elements are in $\varnothing$? How many elements are in $\{\varnothing\}$? Would you say that $\varnothing = \{\varnothing\}$?

6. If E denotes the even positive integers and D denotes the odd positive integers, what is $E \cup D$?

7. If $A \subseteq B$, what is $A \cup B$? What is $A \cap B$?

8. What is $\varnothing \cup A$? What is $\varnothing \cap A$?

9. Show that if $B \subseteq C$ and A is any set, then $A \cap B \subseteq A \cap C$.

10. a. Show that for the three sets $A = \{1, 3, 4, 6, 7\}$, $B = \{3, 4, 7\}$, $C = \{1, 2, 3, 7, 10\}$,

$$A \cap (B \cup C) = (A \cap B) \cup (A \cap C).$$

b. Use the definition of set equality to verify the equation for any three sets A, B, C.

11. How many subsets are there of $\{1\}$? Of $\{1, 2\}$? Of $\{1, 2, 3\}$? Of $\{1, 2, 3, \ldots, n\}$?

12. It is sometimes helpful to use a *Venn diagram* to discuss sets. If A, B are sets and $A \subseteq B$ we show this diagrammatically as follows:

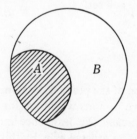 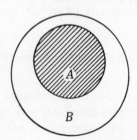

If we are interested in showing an element x in $A \cap B$ we have

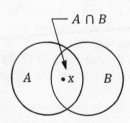

If we are interested in displaying all of $A \cap B$, we simply shade the area common to the circles representing the sets A and B. Thus we have

Draw a Venn diagram to illustrate the following sets:
a. $A \cup B$.
b. $(A \cap B) \cup (A \cap C)$.

Suggested reading

P. Halmos, *Naive Set Theory*, D. Van Nostrand Co., Princeton, N.J. (1960).

New terms

subset, 3*
proper subset, 3
equality (of sets), 3

union (of sets), 3
intersection (of sets), 3
null set, 4

1.2   Relations and functions

Using the terminology and notation of the previous section, we can now give definitions making specific two notions which are fundamental to all mathematics—*relation* and *function*. We lean once more on your intuition as we introduce first the term **ordered pair**. By this, we mean a pair of elements (a, b) from some set (a and b are not necessarily different elements) with the understanding that the pair (a, b) is different from the pair (b, a), unless $a = b$. This is why a pair is called **ordered**. Thus $(2, 5)$ denotes an ordered pair of counting numbers, and is different from the ordered pair $(5, 2)$. We say that the ordered pair (a, b) is **equal** to the ordered pair (c, d) provided that $a = c$ and $b = d$; that is, $(a, b) = (c, d)$ when the ordered pairs have the same first

* New terms are listed with page numbers in order of appearance.

elements (a and c) and have the same second elements (b and d). Thus $(2, 5) = (4/2, 25/5)$.

Next, let us consider two sets A and B and define the **cartesian product** of A and B to be the set of *all* ordered pairs of the form (a, b) where a is in A and b is in B. Our symbol for this cartesian product is $A \times B$, and thus, to use our set-builder notation, we may write

$$A \times B = \{(a, b) \,|\, a \text{ is in } A \text{ and } b \text{ is in } B\}.$$

For example, if $A = \{i, j, k\}$ and $B = \{\#, \&\}$, then $A \times B = \{(i, \#),$ $(i, \&), (j, \#), (j, \&), (k, \#), (k, \&)\}$. One may, of course, form the cartesian product of a set with itself. For two examples, consider that $A \times A = \{(i, i), (i, j), (i, k), (j, i), (j, j), (j, k), (k, i), (k, j), (k, k)\}$ and that $B \times B = \{(\#, \#), (\#, \&), (\&, \#), (\&, \&)\}$.

We can now give the definition of the term **relation** in a very easy manner. By a **relation** in $A \times B$ we mean, simply, a subset of $A \times B$. In other words, a relation in $A \times B$ is a set of ordered pairs whose first elements belong to A and whose second elements belong to B. In the special case that A and B are the same set, we sometimes refer to a "relation in A," instead of a "relation in $A \times A$."

Let us first consider some "family relations" in the Jones family. The Jones family is the set

$$J = \{\text{Mom, Dad, John, Bob, Mary, Sue}\}.$$

The relations which we consider will, of course, be subsets of $J \times J$, which in its entirety consists of 36 ordered pairs; for instance, (Mom, Sue) and (Bob, Bob) belong to $J \times J$, just to mention two examples. Now consider the relation defined by the phrase "is a sister of" in $J \times J$. This relation is the set

{(Mary, John), (Mary, Bob), (Mary, Sue), (Sue, John), (Sue, Bob),
$$\text{(Sue, Mary)}\},$$

since Mary is a sister of John, and Mary is a sister of Bob, etc. And, for a second example, consider the relation defined by the phrase "is a son of," which is the set of pairs

{(John, Mom), (Bob, Mom), (John, Dad), (Bob, Dad)}.

As a somewhat more mathematical example, let $\mathbb{Z}^+$, as before, denote the set of positive integers (counting numbers), and let M be the relation defined by the phrase "is a multiple of" in $\mathbb{Z}^+ \times \mathbb{Z}^+$; that is, M is the set of all ordered pairs of positive integers of the form (a, b) with the property that a is a multiple of b. For instance, the pairs (10, 5) and (12, 3) belong to the relation M since 10 is a multiple of 5 and 12 is a multiple of 3; but (5, 10) and (13, 7) do not belong to M.

Our second important definition, that of *function*, can now be stated almost as simply as the first. By a **function** we mean a relation with the additional property that different pairs in the relation have different first elements. For example, the set of ordered pairs $C = \{(i, \#),$ $(j, \&), (k, \#)\}$ is a function, while $D = \{(i, \#), (i, \&), (k, \&)\}$ is not a function. Both C and D are relations in $A \times B$ (see above). C is, moreover, a function since no two pairs have the same first element, while D fails to be a function because it contains the pairs $(i, \#)$ and $(i, \&)$ which are distinct pairs but have the same first element.

Several other technical terms may now be described. We consider a function f, which is, by definition, a subset of a set of ordered pairs, call the set of all first elements in the pairs of f the **domain** of f, and call the set of all second elements in the pairs the **range** of f. We also say that a function f is a function **from** its domain **onto** its range. Thus the function C, defined in the preceding paragraph, is a function from A onto B since A is the domain of C and B is the range of C. Consider the further example of the function $E = \{(i, \&), (k, \&)\}$. This function is also a relation in $A \times B$, but it is not a function from A onto B. Rather, it is a function from $\{i, k\}$ onto $\{\&\}$, where $\{i, k\}$ is, of course, a subset of A and $\{\&\}$ is a subset of B. We also say that a function is **into** any set which contains its range as a subset. Hence we would say that E is a function from $\{i, k\}$ into B. Finally, by a **one-to-one** function we mean a function with the additional property that different pairs have different second elements.

The reader will perhaps be familiar with *function* defined as "a function f from A onto B is a correspondence which associates with each element a of A a unique element $b = f(a)$ of B." In this "active" definition of function, the association of b with a corresponds in our "passive" definition to the pair (a, b). We have merely spared ourselves the nuisance of explaining what a "correspondence" is. Note that the symbol f stands for the function itself, so that f is a set of pairs or f is a correspondence, while $f(a)$ denotes a real number which may be thought of as either the second member of the pair $(a, f(a))$ or as the *image* of a under the correspondence f. It is common in much mathematical writing to refer to a certain function as "the function $f(x)$." The reader should understand that this is a brief way of saying "the function whose typical element is the pair $(x, f(x))$." We in no way demand that the reader discard the "active" definition and think only in terms of the "passive" one. On the contrary, both definitions have important connotations for our intuitive understanding of *function* and the reader should be familiar with both.

To illustrate the foregoing, consider the function f first defined as the set of all ordered pairs of the form $(x, 2x + 1)$. We may write this as

$$f = \{(x, f(x)) \mid f(x) = 2x + 1\}.$$

Secondly, the same function f may be described as the function which associates with each real number x the number $2x + 1$; and this we may symbolize as

$$f: x \rightarrow 2x + 1.$$

The phrase "the function $f(x) = 2x + 1$" is then just another way of describing f.

A pictorial representation of a function is helpful in understanding these definitions. If we represent the domain D_f and the range R_f of the function $f = \{(1, 2), (3, 4), (5, 6)\}$ as in Figure 1.2.1, then we may illustrate the correspondence between the individual elements of each pair of the set of ordered pairs.

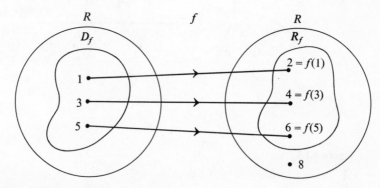

Figure 1.2.1

In this case f is a one-to-one function from D_f onto R_f. Note that f is into R but not onto R, since R contains R_f as a proper subset.

For the function $g = \{(-2, 3), (-1, 2), (0, 2)\}$, we have the representation in Figure 1.2.2. Note in this case that g is not a one-to-one function.

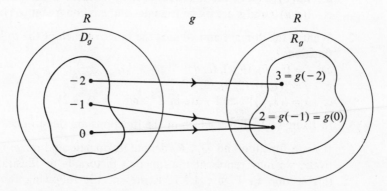

Figure 1.2.2

As an example of a function whose domain is not a subset of the real numbers, consider the function h in $(\mathbb{Z}^+ \times \mathbb{Z}^+) \times \mathbb{Z}^+$ defined as $h = \{((1, 1), 2), ((3, 2), 5)\}$. The function is illustrated in Figure 1.2.3.

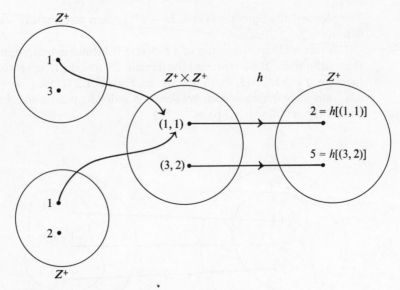

Figure 1.2.3

Exercises 1.2

1. Which of the following relations are functions?
    a. $\{(1, 2), (1, 3), (2, 4)\}$.   b. $\{(x, y), (y, z), (z, w)\}$.
    c. $\{(a, b) \mid a \text{ is in } \mathbb{Z}^+ \text{ and } b = a^2\}$.
    d. $\{(a, b) \mid a \text{ and } b \text{ are in the Jones family and } b \text{ is a daughter of } a\}$.
    e. $\{(t, u) \mid t \text{ and } u \text{ are plane triangles and } u \text{ is congruent to } t\}$.

2. What is the domain and what is the range of each of the following functions?
    a. $f = \{(a, b), (b, c), (c, d)\}$.
    b. $g = \{(1, 4), (2, 5), (3, 4)\}$.
    c. $h = \{(x, y) \mid x \text{ and } y \text{ are in } \mathbb{Z}^+ \text{ and } y = 2x - 2\}$.

3. In Exercise 2, above, which of the functions are one-to-one?

4. If f is a function and D_f, R_f denote its domain and range respectively, we may represent the function pictorially as illustrated in this section in Figure 1.2.1. Represent the following functions pictorially.

    a. $f = \{(1, 2), (2, 3), (3, 4)\}$.
    b. $g = \{(1, 1), (2, 1), (3, 4)\}$.
    c. $h = \{(-1, 3), (2, 4), (4, 4)\}$.
    Which of these functions are one-to-one? How does this show up in pictorial representation?

5. If f and g are functions it is sometimes possible to define a new function $f \circ g = h$ called the *composite* of f and g. For each x in the domain of h, $h(x) = (f \circ g)(x)$ is defined to be the element $f[g(x)]$. The domain of h consists of the subset of the domain of g upon which we can perform the indicated operations. Let $f = \{(1, 2), (3, 5), (4, 6)\}$ and let $g = \{(-1, 3), (2, 7), (4, 1)\}$. Then $h = f \circ g = \{(-1, 5), (4, 2)\}$ (Figure 1.2.4).
    a. Find $g \circ f$.   b. Find $h \circ f$.   c. Find $g \circ h$.

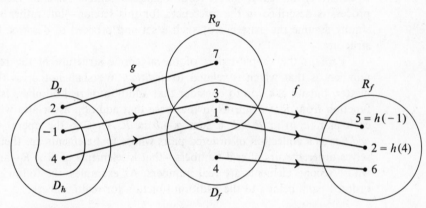

Figure 1.2.4

Suggested reading

R. Crouch & E. Walker, *Introduction to Modern Algebra and Analysis*, Holt, Rinehart & Winston, New York (1962).
L. Mehlenbacher, *Foundations of Modern Mathematics*, Prindle, Weber & Schmidt, Inc., Boston (1966).

New Terms

1.3   The real numbers

In this section, we wish to use the real numbers as an example of a number system (a highly important one), and refresh the reader's memory with respect to several useful properties of that system. To begin, we assume that the reader is in some way familiar with the system R of real numbers. He should be aware that the real numbers contain the set of counting numbers $\mathbb{Z}^+$, that R contains the set of all integers $\mathbb{Z}$ (positive integers, negative integers, and 0), and that R contains the set $\mathbb{Q}$ of rational numbers (quotients of integers). He should know that there do exist some real numbers, such as π, $\sqrt{2}$, $\log_{10} 2$, which are *not* rational numbers; and he should be aware that there is a one-to-one function (correspondence) from the real numbers onto the set of points of a line (the straight line of Euclidean geometry). We do not propose to construct the real numbers from a simpler number system—such a process is described in the references for this section—but rather we simply assume the existence of such a set and proceed to describe its structure.

Perhaps the simplest part of the algebraic structure of the real numbers is that which is related to *addition*. We shall not press the matter, but we ask you to consider that addition of real numbers is a function from $R \times R$ into R in the sense that addition associates with each pair (a, b) in $R \times R$ a sum $a + b$ in R. That is, the operation *addition* is a collection of ordered pairs whose first elements are themselves ordered pairs of real numbers—that is, elements of $R \times R$—and whose second elements are real numbers. As examples, the following ordered pairs belong to the addition function for real numbers:

$$((2, 5), 7), ((1, 0), 1), ((-3, 6), 3), ((2, -2), 0), ((\pi, 3), \pi + 3)$$

and the following pairs do *not* belong to the addition function for real numbers:

$$((2, 5), 10), ((-3, 6), -18), ((1, 2), 2), ((1, 0), 0), ((\pi, 3), 3\pi).$$

Addition of reals, however, is not just *any* function from $R \times R$ into R (such a function is often called a **binary operation**), but one with special properties, the four most basic of which we list below and label A1, A2, A3, A4.

A1.   Addition for real numbers is **associative** in the sense that

$$(a + b) + c = a + (b + c)$$

for every choice of a, b, c in R.

A2.   There is in R an **identity element** 0 (usually called **zero**) for addition in the sense that for each choice of a in R,

$$a + 0 = a = 0 + a.$$

A3.   For each choice of a in R, there is in R an element which we denote by $-a$ such that

$$a + (-a) = 0 = (-a) + a.$$

We call the element $-a$ the **additive inverse** of a.

A4.   Addition for real numbers is **commutative** in the sense that

$$a + b = b + a$$

for each choice of a, b in R.

Let us now consider a few simple consequences of these properties of addition for the real numbers.

(1)   *Uniqueness of the zero.* There is only one identity for addition of real numbers; for if both 0 and $0'$ are identities, then

$$0 = 0 + 0' = 0'.$$

Hence two or more identities cannot exist.

(2)   *Uniqueness of additive inverses.* Let a be any element of R, and consider $-a$ whose existence is postulated in A3. We claim that there is no other element x in R which acts as an additive inverse for a. For if $x + a = 0$, then

$$(x + a) + (-a) = 0 + (-a) = (-a),$$

the last equality being true by virtue of A2. Now associativity (A1) tells us that

$$(x + a) + (-a) = x + [a + (-a)] = x + 0 = x.$$

Thus $(x + a) + (-a)$ is equal to both $-a$ and to x, and hence $x = -a$. Therefore a has only one (a unique) additive inverse.

(3)   *Unique solutions of equations.* Let a and b be real numbers. There is a unique real number x such that

$$x + a = b.$$

The reader will not be surprised if we make the following display

$$x + a = b$$
$$(x + a) + (-a) = b + (-a)$$
$$x + [a + (-a)] = b + (-a)$$
$$x + 0 = b + (-a)$$
$$x = b + (-a)$$

and then announce, "$b + (-a)$ is such an x." Actually, the above display shows that *if* there is a solution x, then the only solution possible is $b + (-a)$. The following argument verifies that $b + (-a)$ actually is a solution:

$$[b + (-a)] + a = b + [(-a) + a]$$
$$= b + 0$$
$$= b.$$

Hence $b + (-a)$ is a number with the required property.

We have proved these properties for real numbers under the assumption that addition for the real numbers satisfies A1, A2, A3, A4, but we call your attention to the fact that these three derived properties are not peculiar to the real numbers, but are true for any "addition" on any set which satisfies the four properties A1–A4. Finally, the reader should note here and elsewhere in the text that $a - b$ is simply a shorthand notation for $a + (-b)$.

Let us now consider a second binary operation for the real numbers —*multiplication*. It, too, is a function from $R \times R$ into R. The reader will recognize that the second display of ordered pairs on page 12 belongs to the multiplication function for real numbers, and moreover should recognize that multiplication has the following properties.

M1.   Multiplication is **associative**; that is,

$$(ab)c = a(bc)$$

for any choice of a, b, c in R.

M2.   There is an **identity element** 1 for multiplication such that for each a in R,

$$1a = a1 = a.$$

M3.   For each a in R, except $a = 0$, there is an element a^{-1} in R such that

$$a^{-1}a = aa^{-1} = 1.$$

The element "a^{-1} is called the **multiplicative inverse** of a.

M4.   Multiplication is **commutative**; that is, for any choice of a, b in R,

$$ab = ba.$$

In the case of real numbers it so happens that the operations of addition and multiplication are linked in an interesting way; namely the following **distributive properties** are valid;

D1. $a(b + c) = ab + ac$, and

D2. $(b + c)a = ba + ca$, for every choice of a, b, c in R.

Some consequences of these further properties of the real numbers are:

1. The multiplicative identity 1 is unique.

2. The multiplicative inverse of an element $a \neq 0$ is unique.

3. The multiplicative inverse of a^{-1} is a; that is, $(a^{-1})^{-1} = a$. The proofs of these three properties are left to the reader as Exercise 9.

4.   If $ab = 0$ then either $a = 0$ or $b = 0$ or both a and b are 0. For if one is not zero, say $a \neq 0$, then $b = 1b = a^{-1}ab = a^{-1}0 = 0$.

5.   For any element $a \neq 0$ and any element b, there is one and only one solution x in R of

$$ax = b.$$

Again, if such a solution x exists, then, since $a \neq 0$, a^{-1} exists by M3 and

$$a^{-1}(ax) = a^{-1}b$$
$$(a^{-1}a)x = a^{-1}b$$
$$1x = a^{-1}b$$
$$x = a^{-1}b$$

and hence there is at most one solution x. Moreover, $a(a^{-1}b) = (aa^{-1})b = 1b = b$, so that $a^{-1}b$ is actually a solution. Notice that here we had to require $a \neq 0$ in order to guarantee the existence of a^{-1}.

6.   If $a \neq 0$ then the "linear equation"

$$ax + b = c$$

has a unique solution x for each choice of b, c in R. In order to verify this, we merely note that the above equation has exactly the same set of solutions as the equation

$$ax = c + (-b)$$

and, as we have seen in 5. above, the latter equation has the unique solution $x = a^{-1}[c + (-b)]$.

The real numbers R, with their usual addition and multiplication, are seen to be an example of a number system which satisfies A1–A4, M1–M4, and D1, D2. Such a system, if it has more than one element, is called a **field**. There are other familiar examples of fields—the rational numbers form one such example, the complex numbers another. And there are some, perhaps unfamiliar, simple examples of fields. See Exercise 6 at the end of this section for one such example.

We are all familiar with the relation $\leqslant$ (read "less than or equal to") defined for the real numbers. We write $2 \leqslant 5$, and $-7 \leqslant -4$, etc. Considering $\leqslant$ as a relation in R, that is, as a set of ordered pairs from $R \times R$, we would say that the pairs $(2, 5)$ and $(-7, -4)$ are elements of $\leqslant$. Thus when we write $a \leqslant b$, we are simply stating that the pair (a, b) is an element of the relation $\leqslant$.

The relation $\leqslant$ is called an *order relation* and, because R is a field with such a relation, we call R an *ordered field*. The rational numbers provide another example of an ordered field, but the complex numbers do *not* form an ordered field. (We would have to decide whether or not $i = \sqrt{-1}$ is less than 1, for example.) For a complete explanation see the reference by N. McCoy.

The property which distinguishes the real numbers from all other ordered fields—the completeness property—will not be described here, but a brief discussion may be found in Appendix A.

Exercises 1.3

1. Consider the set $S = \{a, b, c\}$ and the binary operation "$+$" defined by the table

$+$	a	b	c
a	a	b	c
b	b	c	a
c	c	a	b

To find the sum $b + c$, for example, we look in the b-row, c-column and determine that $b + c = a$. Similarly, $c + a = c$.
   a. Verify that
      1. $a + c = c + a$.
      2. $(a + b) + c = a + (b + c)$.
      3. $(c + c) + b = c + (c + b)$.
      4. $b + a = b$.
   b. Which element of S acts as an identity element for "$+$"?
   c. Is "$+$" a commutative operation? What property of the arrangement of the elements of the table is important for this question?
   d. Find the additive inverse of each of the elements of S.
   e. What would be involved in a proof that the "$+$" operation is associative?

2. In Exercise 1 above, find the unique solution for the equation $x + b = c$.

3. Consider addition for the real numbers. What is
   a. the additive identity?
   b. the additive inverse of 5?
   c. the additive inverse of (-5)?

4. Show in general that in a set with addition satisfying A1–A4, the additive inverse of $(-a)$ is a.

5. Consider the set $S = \{a, b, c\}$, with addition "$+$" and multiplication "$\cdot$" as defined in the tables below:

+	a	b	c		$\cdot$	a	b	c
a	a	b	c		a	a	a	a
b	b	c	a		b	a	b	c
c	c	a	b		c	a	c	b

a. Verify that
   1. $a \cdot c = c \cdot a$.
   2. $a \cdot (b \cdot c) = (a \cdot b) \cdot c$.
   3. $b \cdot (c \cdot a) = (b \cdot c) \cdot a$.
   4. $c \cdot b = b \cdot c$.
   5. $a \cdot b = a$.
b. Show that "$\cdot$" is a commutative operation.
c. What is the identity element for "$\cdot$"?
d. Verify that b is its own multiplicative inverse.
e. Find c^{-1} and a^{-1} if they exist.

6. For the set S and operations defined in Exercise 5, show that
$$(a + b) \cdot c = (a \cdot c) + (b \cdot c)$$
and
$$(b + c) \cdot a = \underline{\hspace{1cm}} + \underline{\hspace{1cm}} = a.$$

These are examples of property _____. Any set $S = \{a, b, c\}$ with two operations satisfying $A_1, \ldots, A_4, M_1, \ldots, M_4, D_1, D_2$, is called a _____.

7. Show that subtraction in the real numbers is neither an associative nor a commutative operation.

8. Show that division (excluding division by 0, of course) is neither associative nor commutative.

9. Prove properties (1), (2), (3) for multiplication of real numbers.

Suggested reading

E. Landau, *Foundations of Analysis*, Chelsea Publishing Co., Bronx, N.Y. (1951).

N. McCoy, *Introduction to Modern Algebra*, 1st Edition, Allyn & Bacon, Boston (1960).

New terms

binary operation, 12
associative, 12
identity element, 13
zero, 13
additive inverse, 13

commutative, 13
multiplicative inverse, 14
distributive properties, 14
field, 15

1.4   Language and logic

Almost all the mathematical theorems which appear in the main text of this book are expressible in one of two types of English sentences:

a.   If ... then ....

b.   There exists ... such that ....

The second type of statement occurs less frequently than the first and is usually proved by the construction of an object which meets the specifications of the statement. The first type of statement is known as an **implication statement** or simply as an **implication**, and is, as we have indicated, of the form

If *A* then *B*.

Here *A* and *B* denote statements which are capable of being assigned one of the "truth values" TRUE or FALSE. For example,

If (7 is less than 14) then (π^2 is equal to 10)

is an implication statement. Statement *A* (7 is less than 14) is called the **hypothesis** of the implication and *B* (π^2 is equal to 10) is called the **conclusion** of the implication.

Since implication statements occur so frequently in our mathematical discussions, it is important to know precisely what an implication statement means; that is, to know when an implication statement is *true*. The meaning intended is this: such a statement is said to be true in all possible situations for *A* and *B* except in the case where *A* is true and B is false. In other words, we consider the implication "if A then B" to be a true implication when: (1) A is true and B is true, or (2) when A is false and B is true, or (3) when A is false and B is false. To repeat, we consider the implication to be false only in the case where A is true and B is false. A "truth table" for this implication is a diagram showing all of the possible situations for A and B, and may be written as follows:

A	B	If A then B
T	T	T
F	F	T
T	F	F
F	T	T

By the **negation** of the statement A, we mean a statement, which we symbolize as (not A), whose truth values are the opposite of those of A; that is, (not A) is false whenever A is true and is true whenever A is false. For example, let A be the statement, "It is raining." Then (not A) is the statement "It is not raining."

The negation statement is used to construct another implication statement which is closely related to "If A then B" and is expressed as "If (not B) then (not A)." The latter implication is called the **contrapositive** of the former one and its importance for us lies in the fact that it has the same truth value as the former; that is, if the implication is true then its contrapositive is true, and if the implication is false, then its contrapositive is false. Thus the two statements are logically equivalent, as may be illustrated by a truth table. We merely extend the above table to include the possible values for (not A) and (not B). In the following table, we note that the only case when the contrapositive is false is the case when its hypothesis (not B) is true and its conclusion (not A) is false. A comparison of the last two columns of this table shows that the two statements are equivalent in the sense that they have the same truth values. Because of this, a proof of either implication constitutes a proof of the other; we shall find this useful here and elsewhere in our development of mathematics, since it is often the case that it is easier to prove one implication than the other.

A	B	not B	not A	If A then B	If (not B) then (not A)
T	T	F	F	T	T
F	F	T	T	T	T
T	F	T	F	F	F
F	T	F	T	T	T

As an example of the contrapositive of an implication, consider "If it is raining then the grass is wet." The contrapositive of this statement is "If the grass is not wet then it is not raining."

It is common in mathematical writing to use the words **necessary** and **sufficient** to relate the hypothesis and conclusion of an implication statement. The meanings of these adjectives are as follows:

$$\text{"}A \text{ is a sufficient condition for } B.\text{"}$$

(or simply, "A is sufficient for B.") means

$$\text{"If } A \text{ then } B.\text{"}$$

The sentence

$$\text{"}A \text{ is a necessary condition for } B.\text{"}$$

(or simply, "A is necessary for B.") means

$$\text{"If } B \text{ then } A.\text{"}$$

Hence the implication "If H then K." may be rephrased either as "K is necessary for H." or as "H is sufficient for K." Finally, the reader will discover that many mathematical theorems are expressed as "H is a necessary and sufficient condition for K." In order to prove such a statement one must prove that "If K then H" (H is necessary for K) is a true implication and also prove that "If H then K" (H is sufficient for K) is a true implication.

Exercises I.4

1. State which of the following implications are true and which are false.
   a. If $1 + 1 = 2$, then $1 + 2 = 3$.
   b. If $1 + 1 = 2$, then $1 + 2 = 4$.
   c. If $1 + 1 = 3$, then $1 + 2 = 3$.
   d. If $1 + 1 = 3$, then $1 + 2 = 4$.

2. Write the contrapositive of each of the following implications.
   a. If the sun rises today, then we will study mathematics.
   b. If we do not study mathematics, then the sun will rise today.
   c. If the sun rises, then we will not study mathematics.
   d. If politicians were philosophers, then all would be right with the world.

3. Rewrite each of the following sentences in the implication form (If ... then ...).
   a. A necessary condition for $1 + 1 = 2$ is that $5 + 7 = 3$.

b. In order to have a winning smile it is necessary to chew Black Twist tobacco.

c. A sufficient condition for eventual bankruptcy is continually overspending one's budget.

d. In order that we have law and order, it is sufficient to have the Gestapo.

4. Rewrite each of the following in the form: "... is a necessary condition for ...."

a. If no one comes to the party, we shall have a surfeit of pink lemonade.

b. A sufficient condition for two triangles to be similar is that they be congruent.

5. Rewrite the following statements in the form: "... is a sufficient condition for ...."

a. A necessary condition for x to be divisible by 36 is that x be divisible by 12.

b. If we put a tourniquet on his neck, then we can stop his nosebleed.

Suggested reading

L. Mehlenbacher, *Foundations of Modern Mathematics*, Prindle, Weber & Schmidt, Boston (1966).

New terms

implication, 18
hypothesis, 18
conclusion, 18

negation, 19
contrapositive, 19

necessary, 20
sufficient, 20

[2] Matrices with Real Elements

In this chapter we introduce the main topic of our discussion—matrices. Here we define the term *matrix* and then develop the algebra of matrices, comparing and contrasting this algebra with that of the real numbers, and close by posing, but not solving, the question of the existence of multiplicative inverses for square matrices.

2.1 What is a matrix?

By a **matrix** we shall mean a rectangular array of real numbers, arranged in horizontal rows and vertical columns. For example

$$\begin{bmatrix} 1 & 2 \\ 2 & 3 \end{bmatrix}, \qquad \begin{bmatrix} -1 & 2 & 3 \\ 0 & 1 & -1 \\ 2 & 1 & 4 \end{bmatrix}, \qquad [2]$$

are matrices. In addition the array

$$\begin{bmatrix} 3 & -2 & 5 & 2\pi \\ 0 & 1/3 & \log_{10} 2 & 17 \\ -1 & e & .007 & 1/4 \end{bmatrix}$$

is a matrix with three rows and four columns. We number the rows from top to bottom in the array and the columns from left to right.

Thus

$$3 \quad -2 \quad 5 \quad 2\pi$$

is the first row of our last example, and

$$5$$
$$\log_{10} 2$$
$$.007$$

is the third column.

We shall denote matrices in several different ways. First, we shall use capital letters to stand for matrices; thus,

$$A = \begin{bmatrix} 3 & -2 & 5 & 2\pi \\ 0 & 1/3 & \log_{10} 2 & 17 \\ -1 & e & .007 & 1/4 \end{bmatrix}$$

means A is a symbol representing this particular array of numbers. We will say that A is a 3×4 matrix when we wish to call attention to the fact that A has 3 rows and 4 columns. Here there should be no real ambiguity in the use of capital letters to designate matrices and their use to denote sets. The context should make clear the distinction.

Second, we may write down an array of lower-case letters

$$\begin{bmatrix} a & b & c & d \\ e & f & g & h \\ i & j & k & m \end{bmatrix}$$

where each letter stands for some, perhaps unspecified, real number. But more frequently we will write down a typical 3×4 matrix A as

$$\begin{bmatrix} a_{11} & a_{12} & a_{13} & a_{14} \\ a_{21} & a_{22} & a_{23} & a_{24} \\ a_{31} & a_{32} & a_{33} & a_{34} \end{bmatrix}.$$

Here the doubly-subscripted letter a_{12} refers to the element of A in the first row, second column; a_{34} refers to the element in the third row, fourth column; and, in general, a_{ij} refers to the element of A in the ith row, jth column. That is, the first subscript always refers to the *row* and the second subscript to the *column* in which the element appears. Hence a third way to denote our matrix A is to refer to the 3×4 matrix

$$A = [a_{ij}]$$

where we have written inside the brackets only one typical element—the one in the i, j position of A. As i and j vary, a_{ij} represents all particular elements of A.

Example 2.1.1

In Winesburg, the Police Department has three precincts. The vehicle requirement matrix for Winesburg is

$$\begin{array}{ccc} & \text{cars} & \text{motorcycles} \\ \text{Precinct 1} & \begin{bmatrix} 3 \\ 2 \\ 4 \end{bmatrix} & \begin{matrix} 6 \\ 3 \\ 8 \end{matrix} \end{array}$$

from which it may be seen, for example, that Precinct 2 requires 3 motorcycles, and Precinct 3 requires 4 cars.

Example 2.1.2

The developer of two housing projects may list his materiel requirements in a matrix as

$$\begin{array}{cccc} & \text{Paint} & \text{Lumber} & \text{Labor} \\ \text{Project 1} & \begin{bmatrix} 1500 \text{ gal.} & 30,000 \text{ bd. ft.} & 10,000 \text{ man hrs.} \\ 2000 \text{ gal.} & 40,000 \text{ bd. ft.} & 15,000 \text{ man hrs.} \end{bmatrix} \end{array}.$$

The reader should note that the row and column headings in the two previous examples are arbitrary, so that there are many different matrices displaying the same information.

We say that two matrices $A = [a_{ij}]$ and $B = [b_{ij}]$ are **equal**, and write $A = B$, provided that they have the same number of rows and the same number of columns and that corresponding elements are equal.

Exercises 2.1

1. Define the term "matrix."

2. A 2×3 matrix has 2 _____ and ____ _____.

3. The symbol a_{23} stands for the element of the matrix A in the _____ _____ and the _____ _____.

4. What do we mean by the symbol a_{ij}? $[a_{ij}]$?

5. Which of the following arrays are not matrices?

a. $\begin{bmatrix} 1 & 2 & 3 \\ 4 & 5 & 6 \end{bmatrix}$ b. $\begin{bmatrix} 1 & 2 & 3 \\ 0 & 2 \\ 1 \end{bmatrix}$ c. $[2]$ d. $\begin{bmatrix} \pi \\ 0 \\ \sqrt{2} \end{bmatrix}$

6. Construct an Age-Height-Weight matrix for the members of your family.

7. How would you describe the shape of the matrix and the pattern of its elements in the following examples?

$$A = \begin{bmatrix} 1 & 2 \\ 3 & 4 \end{bmatrix}, \quad B = \begin{bmatrix} 1 & 2 & 3 \\ 0 & 4 & 5 \\ 0 & 0 & 6 \end{bmatrix}, \quad C = \begin{bmatrix} 1 & 0 & 0 \\ 0 & 2 & 0 \\ 0 & 0 & 3 \end{bmatrix},$$

$$D = \begin{bmatrix} 1 & 0 \\ 0 & 1 \end{bmatrix}, \quad E = \begin{bmatrix} 1 & 2 & 3 \\ 2 & 4 & 5 \\ 3 & 5 & 6 \end{bmatrix}, \quad F = \begin{bmatrix} 1 & 2 & 3 \\ 4 & 5 & 6 \end{bmatrix}.$$

8. Your company has three divisions A, B, C. Division A has 1000 men, 100 women, and produces 5000 units of your product per day. Division B has 650 men, 48 women, and produces 2300 units. Division C, the clerical division, has only 50 men and 40 women. It produces none of the product. Arrange this data in matrix form.

New terms

matrix, 23   equality of matrices, 25

2.2   Matrix Watching—some special types of matrices

In the course of our discussion, and particularly in the next section, we shall have occasion to use matrices of special shapes or matrices whose elements form a definite pattern. We should like to describe these various types of matrices here briefly and then proceed to our development of the algebra of matrices.

First, we shall call a matrix **square** if it has the same number of rows as columns. Thus

$$\begin{bmatrix} 1 & 2 \\ 3 & 4 \end{bmatrix}$$

is a square 2×2 matrix. We see that

$$\begin{bmatrix} 1 & 2 & 3 \\ 4 & 5 & 6 \\ 7 & 8 & 9 \end{bmatrix}$$

is a square 3×3 matrix, and that $[-.27]$ is a square 1×1 matrix. A typical square matrix with n rows and n columns may be denoted by the display

$$\begin{bmatrix} a_{11} & a_{12} & \cdots & a_{1n} \\ a_{21} & a_{22} & \cdots & a_{2n} \\ \cdots\cdots\cdots\cdots\cdots \\ a_{n1} & a_{n2} & \cdots & a_{nn} \end{bmatrix}.$$

A matrix which is not square will be called **rectangular**, and, conversely, when we say "rectangular" we shall mean *not square*.

The elements $a_{11}, a_{22}, a_{33}, \ldots, a_{nn}$ are said to constitute the **main diagonal** of a square matrix. Thus 3, -2, π are the main diagonal elements of the 3×3 matrix

$$\begin{bmatrix} 3 & 1 & 5 \\ 2 & -2 & e \\ .4 & 0 & \pi \end{bmatrix}.$$

If a square matrix is such that all of its elements, except perhaps the main diagonal elements, are zero, then the matrix is called a **diagonal matrix**. Thus, all of the following are diagonal matrices:

$$\begin{bmatrix} 2 & 0 & 0 \\ 0 & -1 & 0 \\ 0 & 0 & e \end{bmatrix}, \quad \begin{bmatrix} 1 & 0 & 0 \\ 0 & 0 & 0 \\ 0 & 0 & 3 \end{bmatrix}, \quad \begin{bmatrix} 0 & 0 & 0 \\ 0 & 0 & 0 \\ 0 & 0 & 0 \end{bmatrix}.$$

As a special case of a diagonal matrix there is the diagonal matrix whose diagonal elements are all equal to each other. For example, all of the following matrices are of this type. Such a matrix is called a **scalar matrix**.

$$\begin{bmatrix} 1 & 0 & 0 \\ 0 & 1 & 0 \\ 0 & 0 & 1 \end{bmatrix}, \quad \begin{bmatrix} 0 & 0 & 0 \\ 0 & 0 & 0 \\ 0 & 0 & 0 \end{bmatrix}, \quad \begin{bmatrix} -.3 & 0 & 0 \\ 0 & -.3 & 0 \\ 0 & 0 & -.3 \end{bmatrix}.$$

Another special type of square matrix is the **upper triangular** matrix, which has the property that all the elements below the main diagonal are zero (regardless of what the diagonal or above-the-diagonal elements are). Thus every diagonal matrix is also upper triangular; and so also are the following examples:

$$\begin{bmatrix} 1 & 2 & 3 \\ 0 & 4 & 5 \\ 0 & 0 & 6 \end{bmatrix}, \quad \begin{bmatrix} 1 & 2 & 0 \\ 0 & 0 & 4 \\ 0 & 0 & 5 \end{bmatrix}, \quad \begin{bmatrix} 0 & 1 & 2 \\ 0 & 0 & 3 \\ 0 & 0 & 4 \end{bmatrix}.$$

Another way of describing in general an upper triangular $n \times n$ matrix $A = [a_{ij}]$ is to require that

$$a_{ij} = 0 \quad \text{for} \quad i > j.$$

Lower triangular matrices are defined in a similar manner, with $a_{ij} = 0$ for $i < j$.

Two useful types of matrices are the **row matrices**, which consist of only one row, and the **column matrices** which consist of only one column; for example the 1×5 matrix

$$[1, 2, 3, 0, -7]$$

is a row matrix; and the 3×1 matrix

$$\begin{bmatrix} 0 \\ -2 \\ 1 \end{bmatrix}$$

is a column matrix. Indeed, we may think of the $m \times n$ matrix $A = [a_{ij}]$ as consisting of m row matrices

$$[a_{11} \quad a_{12} \quad \cdots \quad a_{1n}],$$
$$[a_{21} \quad a_{22} \quad \cdots \quad a_{2n}],$$
$$\cdots\cdots\cdots\cdots\cdots\cdots$$
$$[a_{m1} \quad a_{m2} \quad \cdots \quad a_{mn}]$$

or as consisting of n column matrices

$$\begin{bmatrix} a_{11} \\ a_{21} \\ \vdots \\ a_{m1} \end{bmatrix}, \begin{bmatrix} a_{12} \\ a_{22} \\ \vdots \\ a_{m2} \end{bmatrix}, \ldots, \begin{bmatrix} a_{1n} \\ a_{2n} \\ \vdots \\ a_{mn} \end{bmatrix}.$$

For reasons which we shall see later, it is common to refer to such row matrices or column matrices as **vectors**. We shall also find it convenient in much of what follows to think of matrices as having been partitioned into smaller matrices consisting entirely of either rows or columns as shown above. For example, we may write

$$A = \begin{bmatrix} 1 & -1 & 0 \\ 2 & 2 & 1 \\ 3 & 4 & 2 \end{bmatrix}$$

as a matrix whose elements are column matrices themselves; that is, $A = [A_1, A_2, A_3]$ where

$$A_1 = \begin{bmatrix} 1 \\ 2 \\ 3 \end{bmatrix}, \qquad A_2 = \begin{bmatrix} -1 \\ 2 \\ 4 \end{bmatrix}, \qquad \text{and} \quad A_3 = \begin{bmatrix} 0 \\ 1 \\ 2 \end{bmatrix}.$$

Finally, we define the **transpose** A^T of an $m \times n$ matrix A to be the $n \times m$ matrix whose rows are the columns of A (in order) and whose columns are the rows of A (in order). For example, if

$$A = \begin{bmatrix} 1 & 2 & 3 & 4 \\ 5 & 6 & 7 & 8 \\ 9 & 10 & 11 & 12 \end{bmatrix},$$

then

$$A^T = \begin{bmatrix} 1 & 5 & 9 \\ 2 & 6 & 10 \\ 3 & 7 & 11 \\ 4 & 8 & 12 \end{bmatrix}.$$

For a square matrix, the transpose A^T of A is simply the matrix obtained by the reflection of the elements in the main diagonal. And, of course, the transpose of a row matrix is a column matrix, the transpose of an upper triangular matrix is lower triangular, and the transpose of a diagonal matrix is itself. We may use the transpose to define a special subset of matrices which are very important in applications. The square matrix A is said to be a **symmetric** matrix provided that $A = A^T$. This definition is equivalent to saying that $a_{ij} = a_{ji}$ for each i and j. The following matrices are symmetric:

$$\begin{bmatrix} 1 & 2 \\ 2 & 0 \end{bmatrix}, \quad \begin{bmatrix} -1 & 0 & -2 \\ 0 & 3 & 7 \\ -2 & 7 & 5 \end{bmatrix}, \quad \begin{bmatrix} 0 & 1 & 2 & 3 \\ 1 & 0 & -1 & 4 \\ 2 & -1 & 0 & 5 \\ 3 & 4 & 5 & 0 \end{bmatrix}.$$

Exercises 2.2

Consider the following special categories of matrices:
a. square b. rectangular c. diagonal d. scalar e. upper triangular
f. lower triangular g. row matrix h. column matrix i. symmetric.
After each of the following examples of matrices, write the letters corresponding to the categories in which the matrix belongs.

1. $\begin{bmatrix} 1 & 0 & 0 \\ 0 & 0 & 0 \end{bmatrix}$

2. $\begin{bmatrix} 0 & 0 & 0 \\ 0 & 1 & 0 \\ 0 & 0 & 1 \end{bmatrix}$

3. $[1]$

4. $[1 \quad 2 \quad 0 \quad 0 \quad 0 \quad 6]$

5. $\begin{bmatrix} 1 & 0 & 0 & 0 & 0 & 0 \\ 0 & 0 & 0 & 0 & 0 & 1 \\ 0 & 0 & 1 & 0 & 0 & 0 \\ 0 & 0 & 0 & 0 & 0 & 0 \\ 0 & 0 & 0 & 0 & 0 & 0 \\ 1 & 0 & 0 & 0 & 0 & 1 \end{bmatrix}$

6. $\begin{bmatrix} 3 & 0 & 1 \\ 0 & 2 & 1 \\ 0 & 0 & 1 \end{bmatrix}$

7. $\begin{bmatrix} 2 \\ 1 \\ 3 \\ 5 \end{bmatrix}$

8. $\begin{bmatrix} 3 & 4 \\ 4 & -1 \end{bmatrix}$

9. $\begin{bmatrix} 5 & 0 & 0 & 0 \\ 2 & 1 & 0 & 0 \\ 3 & 1 & 6 & 0 \\ 6 & 4 & 3 & 2 \end{bmatrix}$

10. $\begin{bmatrix} 1 & 2 & 3 & 4 & 5 \\ 0 & 6 & 7 & 8 & 9 \\ 0 & 0 & 10 & 11 & 12 \\ 0 & 0 & 0 & 13 & 14 \end{bmatrix}$

11. Write down an example of a 2×2 matrix (if one exists) which is
   a. upper triangular and not diagonal.
   b. lower triangular, diagonal, and not scalar.
   c. symmetric, scalar, and not diagonal.
   d. symmetric.

12. Find the transposes of the matrices in Exercises 1, 7, 8, 9. Which are symmetric?

13. a. For $A = \begin{bmatrix} 1 & -1 \\ 3 & 2 \end{bmatrix}$, find $(A^T)^T$.

   b. Form a conjecture about $(A^T)^T$ for any 2×2 matrix.

New terms

square matrix, 26	scalar matrix, 27	column matrix, 27
rectangular matrix, 27	upper triangular, 27	vectors, 28
main diagonal, 27	lower triangular, 27	transpose, 28
diagonal matrix, 27	row matrix, 27	symmetric matrix, 29

2.3   Addition of matrices

We now begin our development of the algebra of matrices with the definition of the first of three operations, namely, *addition*. We consider two $m \times n$ matrices $A = [a_{ij}]$ and $B = [b_{ij}]$ and define the **sum** of A and B, written as $A + B$, as follows:

$$A + B = [a_{ij} + b_{ij}];$$

that is, $A + B$ is the $m \times n$ matrix obtained by simply adding corresponding elements of A and B. For example,

$$\begin{bmatrix} 1 & 2 & 3 \\ 0 & -2 & 4 \end{bmatrix} + \begin{bmatrix} -3 & 1 & 5 \\ 2 & 1 & 3 \end{bmatrix}$$

$$= \begin{bmatrix} 1 + (-3) & 2 + 1 & 3 + 5 \\ 0 + 2 & -2 + 1 & 4 + 3 \end{bmatrix} = \begin{bmatrix} -2 & 3 & 8 \\ 2 & -1 & 7 \end{bmatrix}.$$

We ask the reader to note carefully that addition is defined for two matrices A and B which have the same number of rows and the same number of columns—we say in this case that A and B are **conformable for addition**. It should thus be clear that

$$A = \begin{bmatrix} 1 & 2 & 3 \\ 0 & -2 & 4 \end{bmatrix} \quad \text{and} \quad B = \begin{bmatrix} 3 & 2 \\ 1 & 1 \\ 5 & 3 \end{bmatrix}$$

are *not* conformable for addition, so that a sum for A and B is not defined.

Let us now select two positive integers m and n and restrict our attention for the moment to the set of all $m \times n$ matrices with real elements. We denote this set of matrices by $\mathcal{M}_{m,n}$ and proceed to show that addition in $\mathcal{M}_{m,n}$ satisfies the properties A1–A4 of Section 1.3. We will thus have shown that each of these additive real number properties has a direct analogue in the set of $m \times n$ matrices.

A1.   Addition in $\mathcal{M}_{m,n}$ is *associative*.

Proof

If A, B, C are in $\mathcal{M}_{m,n}$ with $A = [a_{ij}]$, $B = [b_{ij}]$, and $C = [c_{ij}]$, then

$$
\begin{aligned}
(A + B) + C &= ([a_{ij}] + [b_{ij}]) + [c_{ij}] \\
&= [a_{ij} + b_{ij}] + [c_{ij}] \\
*\left\{ &= [(a_{ij} + b_{ij}) + c_{ij}] \right. \\
&= [a_{ij} + (b_{ij} + c_{ij})] \\
&= [a_{ij}] + [b_{ij} + c_{ij}] \\
&= A + (B + C).
\end{aligned}
$$

The step in the above display marked * follows from the associativity of addition in R.   □

Example 2.3.1

$$
\left(\begin{bmatrix} 1 & 2 & 3 \\ 4 & 5 & 6 \end{bmatrix} + \begin{bmatrix} -1 & 1 & 4 \\ 2 & 1 & 1 \end{bmatrix} \right) + \begin{bmatrix} 0 & 1 & 5 \\ 2 & 2 & 2 \end{bmatrix}
$$

$$
= \begin{bmatrix} 0 & 3 & 7 \\ 6 & 6 & 7 \end{bmatrix} + \begin{bmatrix} 0 & 1 & 5 \\ 2 & 2 & 2 \end{bmatrix} = \begin{bmatrix} 0 & 4 & 12 \\ 8 & 8 & 9 \end{bmatrix}.
$$

$$
\begin{bmatrix} 1 & 2 & 3 \\ 4 & 5 & 6 \end{bmatrix} + \left(\begin{bmatrix} -1 & 1 & 4 \\ 2 & 1 & 1 \end{bmatrix} + \begin{bmatrix} 0 & 1 & 5 \\ 2 & 2 & 2 \end{bmatrix} \right)
$$

$$
= \begin{bmatrix} 1 & 2 & 3 \\ 4 & 5 & 6 \end{bmatrix} + \begin{bmatrix} -1 & 2 & 9 \\ 4 & 3 & 3 \end{bmatrix} = \begin{bmatrix} 0 & 4 & 12 \\ 8 & 8 & 9 \end{bmatrix}.
$$

A2.   There is an *additive identity* element $0 = [0]$ (usually called the **zero matrix**) in $\mathcal{M}_{m,n}$ whose entries are zero in each position and such that for each $A = [a_{ij}]$ in $\mathcal{M}_{m,n}$

$$
A + 0 = A = 0 + A.
$$

Proof

$$
\begin{aligned}
A + 0 &= [a_{ij}] + [0] = [a_{ij} + 0] = [a_{ij}] \\
&= A = [0 + a_{ij}] = [0] + [a_{ij}] = 0 + A. \quad □
\end{aligned}
$$

(*Note.* The reader should observe that the symbol 0 is used in the above proof in two different senses. In the left-hand side of the equation

$A + 0$, it means the $m \times n$ matrix of zeros. In $[a_{ij} + 0]$ it means the zero scalar. The context however, makes it clear which is meant, since we cannot add a scalar to a matrix.)

Example 2.3.2

$$\begin{bmatrix} 1 & 2 & 3 \\ 4 & 5 & 6 \end{bmatrix} + \begin{bmatrix} 0 & 0 & 0 \\ 0 & 0 & 0 \end{bmatrix} = \begin{bmatrix} 1 & 2 & 3 \\ 4 & 5 & 6 \end{bmatrix} = \begin{bmatrix} 0 & 0 & 0 \\ 0 & 0 & 0 \end{bmatrix} + \begin{bmatrix} 1 & 2 & 3 \\ 4 & 5 & 6 \end{bmatrix}.$$

A3.   For each choice of $A = [a_{ij}]$ in $\mathcal{M}_{m,n}$ there is a matrix

$$-A = [-a_{ij}] \text{ such that } A + (-A) = 0 = (-A) + A.$$

Proof:

$$A + (-A) = [a_{ij}] + [-a_{ij}] = [a_{ij} + (-a_{ij})] = [0] = 0$$
$$= [-a_{ij} + a_{ij}] = [-a_{ij}] + [a_{ij}] = -A + A. \quad \square$$

Example 2.3.3

$$\begin{bmatrix} 1 & 2 & 3 \\ 4 & 5 & 6 \end{bmatrix} + \begin{bmatrix} -1 & -2 & -3 \\ -4 & -5 & -6 \end{bmatrix} = \begin{bmatrix} 0 & 0 & 0 \\ 0 & 0 & 0 \end{bmatrix}.$$

We shall find it convenient henceforth to write $B - A$ when we mean $B + (-A)$.

A4.   Addition in $\mathcal{M}_{m,n}$ is *commutative*.

Proof:

For each $A = [a_{ij}]$ and $B = [b_{ij}]$ in $\mathcal{M}_{m,n}$, $A + B = [a_{ij}] + [b_{ij}] = [a_{ij} + b_{ij}] = [b_{ij} + a_{ij}] = [b_{ij}] + [a_{ij}] = B + A. \quad \square$

Example 2.3.4

$$\begin{bmatrix} 1 & 2 & 3 \\ 4 & 5 & 6 \end{bmatrix} + \begin{bmatrix} -1 & 1 & 4 \\ 2 & 1 & 1 \end{bmatrix} = \begin{bmatrix} 0 & 3 & 7 \\ 6 & 6 & 7 \end{bmatrix} = \begin{bmatrix} -1 & 1 & 4 \\ 2 & 1 & 1 \end{bmatrix} + \begin{bmatrix} 1 & 2 & 3 \\ 4 & 5 & 6 \end{bmatrix}.$$

Thus $\mathcal{M}_{m,n}$ enjoys properties A1–A4 just as the real numbers do. Since we used only A1–A4 to establish Property (1), *Uniqueness of the zero*, Property (2), *Uniqueness of additive inverses*, and Property (3), *Unique solution of equations* for addition of real numbers, then there must exist direct analogues of these properties for addition in $\mathcal{M}_{m,n}$. The proofs of these properties for matrix addition are left to the reader in Exercises 14, 15, and 17.

Exercises 2.3

In Exercises 1–8, find the indicated matrix sum (if it is defined).

1. $\begin{bmatrix} 1 & 2 & 3 \\ 4 & 5 & 6 \end{bmatrix} + \begin{bmatrix} -2 & -4 & -6 \\ -8 & -10 & -12 \end{bmatrix}$

2. $[1 \quad 2 \quad 3 \quad 4] + \begin{bmatrix} 5 & 2 & 1 & 3 \\ 1 & 2 & 3 & 4 \end{bmatrix}$

3. $[1 \quad 2 \quad 3 \quad 4] + [5 \quad 2 \quad 1 \quad 3]$

4. $\begin{bmatrix} 1 \\ 2 \\ -5 \\ .3 \end{bmatrix} + \begin{bmatrix} .3 \\ -.2 \\ .4 \\ -.1 \end{bmatrix}$ 5. $\begin{bmatrix} 1 & 5 \\ 2 & 6 \\ 3 & 7 \\ 4 & 8 \end{bmatrix} + \begin{bmatrix} 1 \\ 1 \\ 2 \\ -3 \end{bmatrix}$

6. $\begin{bmatrix} 1 & 2 & 3 \\ 4 & 5 & 6 \end{bmatrix} + \begin{bmatrix} 0 & 0 & 0 \\ 0 & 0 & 0 \end{bmatrix}$ 7. $\begin{bmatrix} 0 & 0 \\ 0 & 0 \\ 0 & 0 \end{bmatrix} + \begin{bmatrix} 1 & -1 \\ 2 & -3 \\ 3 & -4 \end{bmatrix}$

8. $\begin{bmatrix} 1 & 2 & 3 \\ 4 & 5 & 6 \end{bmatrix} + \begin{bmatrix} -1 & -2 & -3 \\ -4 & -5 & -6 \end{bmatrix}$

9. Let $A = \begin{bmatrix} 1 & -1 & 2 \\ -2 & 3 & 1 \end{bmatrix}$ and $B = \begin{bmatrix} 2 & 1 & 3 \\ 5 & 6 & -1 \end{bmatrix}$. Is there a matrix X such that

$$X + A = B?$$

10. Is the sum of two lower triangular $n \times n$ matrices also lower triangular? What about the sum of two diagonal matrices?

11. a. Find the transpose of each of the matrices A, B in Exercise 1.
    b. Compare $(A + B)^T$ with $A^T + B^T$.
    c. Verify for any 2×2 matrices A, B, that $(A + B)^T = A^T + B^T$.

12. Find the additive inverses of the following matrices.

    a. $[1 \quad 2 \quad 3 \quad 4]$ b. $\begin{bmatrix} -1 \\ 2 \\ -3 \\ 4 \end{bmatrix}$ c. $\begin{bmatrix} -2.5 & -3.1 \\ 4.6 & 7.4 \end{bmatrix}$

13. What is the additive identity for $\mathcal{M}_{1,3}$? For $\mathcal{M}_{4,1}$? For $\mathcal{M}_{3,6}$?

14. Prove that for fixed positive integers m, n the matrix 0 (additive identity) for $\mathcal{M}_{m,n}$ is unique.

15.   Prove that for fixed positive integers m, n the additive inverse $-A$ of $A = [a_{ij}]$ is unique.

16.   For Exercise 9, show that there is one and only one (a unique) solution.

17.   Show in general that if A, B are in the set $\mathscr{M}_{m,n}$ then there is a unique solution X for the equation

$$X + A = B.$$

Does this solution belong to $\mathscr{M}_{m,n}$?

New Terms

sum (of matrices), 30   conformable for addition, 30   zero matrix, 31

2.4   Matrix multiplication

In this section we define the operation of multiplication for certain matrices and develop some elementary properties of this multiplication. Several more elaborate properties are stated and illustrated by example, but the proofs of these latter properties are relegated to Appendix B, "Sigma Notation and More Matrix Algebra."

We first define multiplication of a $1 \times n$ row matrix A by an $n \times 1$ column matrix B as follows:

$$AB = [a_1, a_2, \ldots, a_n] \begin{bmatrix} b_1 \\ b_2 \\ \vdots \\ b_n \end{bmatrix} = [a_1 b_1 + a_2 b_2 + \cdots + a_n b_n].$$

Here a $\mathbf{1} \times n$ matrix multiplied on the right by an $n \times \mathbf{1}$ matrix yields a 1×1 matrix product (the dimensions in boldface give us the dimensions of the product). The reader should note carefully that this definition only makes sense when the two matrices involved have the same number of elements. For example,

$$[2 \quad 3 \quad 4] \begin{bmatrix} 5 \\ 6 \\ 7 \end{bmatrix} = [2 \cdot 5 + 3 \cdot 6 + 4 \cdot 7] = [56],$$

and

$$[-1, 0.2, 2.1]\begin{bmatrix} 0.2 \\ -3 \\ 1 \end{bmatrix} = [-0.2 - 0.6 + 2.1] = [1.3],$$

but $[1 \quad 2 \quad 3 \quad 4]\begin{bmatrix} 1 \\ 2 \\ 3 \end{bmatrix}$ is simply not defined.

Since it turns out that the set of 1×1 matrices have exactly the same algebraic structure as the real numbers, we will usually not distinguish between them. Thus we will consider the matrix [5] and the real number 5 to be algebraically interchangeable.

Exercises 2.4

In the following exercises, find the indicated matrix product (if it is defined).

1. $[1 \quad 2 \quad 3]\begin{bmatrix} 4 \\ 5 \\ 6 \end{bmatrix}$ 2. $[1 \quad 2 \quad 3]\begin{bmatrix} 4 \\ 5 \end{bmatrix}$ 3. $[1 \quad 2 \quad 3 \quad 4]\begin{bmatrix} 5 \\ 6 \\ 7 \end{bmatrix}$

4. $[-2.1 \quad 3.7]\begin{bmatrix} 2.2 \\ -1.5 \end{bmatrix}$ 5. $[a \quad b \quad c]\begin{bmatrix} 2 \\ 3 \\ 4 \end{bmatrix}$

6. $[-x \quad 2y \quad -z]\begin{bmatrix} h \\ k \\ -3p \end{bmatrix}$

7. $[-1 \quad 2 \quad 3 \quad -4 \quad 5]\begin{bmatrix} -2j \\ 3k \\ -4k \\ 6j \\ -k \end{bmatrix}$

8. $[a \quad b \quad c]\begin{bmatrix} a \\ b \\ c \end{bmatrix}$ 9. $[0 \quad 1 \quad 0]\begin{bmatrix} a \\ b \\ c \end{bmatrix}$

10. $[0 \quad 0 \quad 0]\begin{bmatrix} 1 \\ 3 \\ -2 \end{bmatrix}$ 11. $[a \quad b \quad c]\begin{bmatrix} 0 \\ 0 \\ 1 \end{bmatrix}$ 12. $[1 \quad 0 \quad 1]\begin{bmatrix} a \\ b \\ c \end{bmatrix}$

With our first type of multiplication clearly in mind, we now proceed to a slightly more elaborate type; namely, we define the multiplication of a $1 \times n$ row matrix A by an $n \times k$ matrix B as

$$\overbrace{}^{k \text{ columns}}$$

$$AB = [a_1, a_2, \ldots, a_n] \begin{bmatrix} b_1 & c_1 & \cdots & e_1 \\ b_2 & c_2 & \cdots & e_2 \\ \cdot & \cdot & \cdots & \cdot \\ b_n & c_n & \cdots & e_n \end{bmatrix} = [p_1, p_2, \ldots, p_k],$$

where, as in the simpler case when B consisted of just one column,

$$p_1 = a_1 b_1 + a_2 b_2 + \cdots + a_n b_n$$
$$p_2 = a_1 c_1 + a_2 c_2 + \cdots + a_n c_n$$
$$\cdots\cdots\cdots\cdots\cdots\cdots\cdots\cdots\cdots\cdots\cdots\cdots$$
$$p_k = a_1 e_1 + a_2 e_2 + \cdots + a_n e_n.$$

That is, we simply think of the $n \times k$ matrix B as consisting of k column matrices (each $n \times 1$) and form the individual products as we did earlier. For example,

$$[1 \quad 2 \quad 3] \begin{bmatrix} 2 & -1 & 0 \\ 1 & 2 & 1 \\ 3 & 1 & 2 \end{bmatrix} = [2+2+9, \, -1+4+3, \, 0+2+6]$$

$$= [13 \quad 6 \quad 8].$$

We draw your attention to the following feature of this more general type of multiplication; namely, that a $\mathbf{1} \times n$ matrix multiplied on the right by an $n \times \mathbf{k}$ matrix yields a $1 \times k$ product, and that each element of the product matrix is a sum of n terms.

Exercises 2.4 (continued)

Find the indicated product (if it is defined).

13. $[1 \quad 2] \begin{bmatrix} 3 & 6 \\ 4 & 7 \\ 5 & 8 \end{bmatrix}$

14. $[1 \quad 2] \begin{bmatrix} 2 & 3 \\ 1 & 4 \end{bmatrix}$

15. $[a \quad b \quad c] \begin{bmatrix} 1 & 0 & 0 \\ 0 & 1 & 0 \\ 0 & 0 & 1 \end{bmatrix}$

16. $[1 \quad 2 \quad 3 \quad 4] \begin{bmatrix} 2 & 1 & 2 & 1 \\ 1 & 3 & 1 & 1 \\ 3 & 2 & 3 & 0 \end{bmatrix}$

17. $[1 \quad 2 \quad 3 \quad 4] \begin{bmatrix} 5 & -1 & 0 & 1 & 1 \\ 6 & -3 & 1 & 4 & 1 \\ 7 & 2 & 3 & 3 & 2 \\ 8 & 1 & 2 & -2 & -3 \end{bmatrix}$

18. $[1 \quad 2 \quad 3 \quad 4]\begin{bmatrix} 1 & 2 \\ 2 & 1 \\ 3 & 3 \\ 6 & 7 \\ 8 & 9 \end{bmatrix}$

We are now able to define general matrix multiplication in terms of the special multiplication previously explained. To illustrate the procedure, we let

$$A = \begin{bmatrix} 1 & 2 & 3 \\ 5 & 6 & 7 \end{bmatrix} \quad \text{and} \quad B = \begin{bmatrix} 1 & 3 & 1 \\ 2 & 2 & 1 \\ 3 & 1 & 1 \end{bmatrix}$$

and partition A into two row matrices A_1 and A_2 as illustrated below:

$$\begin{bmatrix} A_1 \\ \hline A_2 \end{bmatrix} = \begin{bmatrix} [1 \quad 2 \quad 3] \\ \hline [5 \quad 6 \quad 7] \end{bmatrix}.$$

The product AB may now be easily described as the matrix whose rows are the row matrices $A_1 B$ and $A_2 B$; that is,

$$AB = \begin{bmatrix} A_1 B \\ \hline A_2 B \end{bmatrix}$$

where

$$A_1 B = [1 \quad 2 \quad 3]\begin{bmatrix} 1 & 3 & 1 \\ 2 & 2 & 1 \\ 3 & 1 & 1 \end{bmatrix} = [14, 10, 6]$$

and

$$A_2 B = [5 \quad 6 \quad 7]\begin{bmatrix} 1 & 3 & 1 \\ 2 & 2 & 1 \\ 3 & 1 & 1 \end{bmatrix} = [38, 34, 18].$$

Thus

$$\begin{bmatrix} 1 & 2 & 3 \\ \hline 5 & 6 & 7 \end{bmatrix}\begin{bmatrix} 1 & 3 & 1 \\ 2 & 2 & 1 \\ 3 & 1 & 1 \end{bmatrix} = \begin{bmatrix} 14 & 10 & 6 \\ \hline 38 & 34 & 18 \end{bmatrix}.$$

Here A is a **2** $\times$ 3 matrix, B is a 3 $\times$ **3** matrix and the product AB is a 2 $\times$ 3 matrix.

In our most general situation, then, if A is an **m** $\times$ p matrix

$$A = \begin{bmatrix} a_{11} & \cdots & a_{1p} \\ a_{21} & \cdots & a_{2p} \\ \cdot & \cdots & \cdot \\ a_{m1} & \cdots & a_{mp} \end{bmatrix}$$

and B is a $p \times \mathbf{n}$ matrix

$$B = \begin{bmatrix} b_{11} & \cdots & b_{1n} \\ b_{21} & \cdots & b_{2n} \\ \cdot & \cdots & \cdot \\ b_{p1} & \cdots & b_{pn} \end{bmatrix}$$

then the product AB is defined as follows. We first partition A as before into m row matrices $A_1, A_2, \ldots, A_m$ each of which is a $1 \times p$ matrix; thus

$$A = \begin{bmatrix} A_1 \\ \hline A_2 \\ \hline \cdots \\ \hline A_m \end{bmatrix} = \begin{bmatrix} a_{11} & \cdots & a_{1p} \\ \hline a_{21} & \cdots & a_{2p} \\ \cdot & \cdots & \cdot \\ \hline a_{m1} & \cdots & a_{mp} \end{bmatrix}.$$

The product AB is the $m \times n$ matrix whose rows are $A_1 B, A_2 B, \ldots, A_m B$; that is,

$$AB = \begin{bmatrix} A_1 B \\ \hline A_2 B \\ \hline \cdots \\ \hline A_m B \end{bmatrix},$$

where, for example,

$$A_1 B = \begin{bmatrix} a_{11} & a_{12} & \cdots & a_{1p} \end{bmatrix} \begin{bmatrix} b_{11} & \cdots & b_{1n} \\ b_{21} & \cdots & b_{2n} \\ \cdot & \cdots & \cdot \\ b_{p1} & \cdots & b_{pn} \end{bmatrix},$$

and in general

$$A_i B = \begin{bmatrix} a_{i1} & a_{i2} & \cdots & a_{ip} \end{bmatrix} \begin{bmatrix} b_{11} & \cdots & b_{1n} \\ b_{21} & \cdots & b_{2n} \\ \cdot & \cdots & \cdot \\ b_{p1} & \cdots & b_{pn} \end{bmatrix}$$

for each $i = 1, 2, \ldots, m$.

Another way of thinking of the product $C = AB$ of two matrices A and B is to think of a typical element c_{ij} (lying in the ith row, jth column of C) as being the product $A_i B_j$, where A_i is the ith row of A and B_j is the jth column of B. For example, the element c_{23} in the second row, third column of the product

$$C = \begin{bmatrix} 1 & 2 & 3 \\ 4 & 5 & 6 \end{bmatrix} \begin{bmatrix} 1 & 2 & 2 \\ 0 & 1 & -2 \\ -2 & 3 & 1 \end{bmatrix}$$

is

$$c_{23} = A_2 B_3 = \begin{bmatrix} 4 & 5 & 6 \end{bmatrix} \begin{bmatrix} 2 \\ -2 \\ 1 \end{bmatrix} = 4.$$

We call your attention to the fact that in the general description above, A is $\mathbf{m} \times p$, B is $p \times \mathbf{n}$, and the product AB is $m \times n$, with each element of the product consisting of a sum of p terms. Moreover, the matrix product AB is defined only when the *column* dimension of the left factor A is the same as the *row* dimension of the right factor B. Such matrices are said to be **conformable for multiplication in the order** AB.

The following examples should be studied carefully. They not only provide practice in computation, but also provide some instances which illustrate that matrix multiplication is not completely analogous to multiplication of real numbers.

Example 2.4.1

Let $A = \begin{bmatrix} 1 & 1 & 2 \\ 0 & 1 & 3 \end{bmatrix}$ and $B = \begin{bmatrix} 1 & 0 & 2 \\ 2 & 1 & 0 \\ 1 & 2 & 1 \end{bmatrix}$. Then the product AB is defined and

$$AB = \begin{bmatrix} 1 & 1 & 2 \\ 0 & 1 & 3 \end{bmatrix} \begin{bmatrix} 1 & 0 & 2 \\ 2 & 1 & 0 \\ 1 & 2 & 1 \end{bmatrix}$$

$$= \begin{bmatrix} 1 \cdot 1 + 1 \cdot 2 + 2 \cdot 1 & 1 \cdot 0 + 1 \cdot 1 + 2 \cdot 2 & 1 \cdot 2 + 1 \cdot 0 + 2 \cdot 1 \\ 0 \cdot 1 + 1 \cdot 2 + 3 \cdot 1 & 0 \cdot 0 + 1 \cdot 1 + 3 \cdot 2 & 0 \cdot 2 + 1 \cdot 0 + 3 \cdot 1 \end{bmatrix}$$

$$= \begin{bmatrix} 5 & 5 & 4 \\ 5 & 7 & 3 \end{bmatrix}.$$

Note that while the product AB *is* defined, the product BA is not defined. Since the column dimension of B is not the same as the row dimension of A, our original row matrix by column matrix multiplication could not be performed.

Example 2.4.2

Let

$$C = \begin{bmatrix} 1 & 1 & 2 \\ 0 & 1 & 3 \end{bmatrix} \text{ and } D = \begin{bmatrix} 1 & 0 \\ 2 & 1 \\ 1 & 2 \end{bmatrix}.$$

Then

$$CD = \begin{bmatrix} 1 & 1 & 2 \\ 0 & 1 & 3 \end{bmatrix} \begin{bmatrix} 1 & 0 \\ 2 & 1 \\ 1 & 2 \end{bmatrix} = \begin{bmatrix} 5 & 5 \\ 5 & 7 \end{bmatrix}.$$

In this instance the product DC is also defined and

$$DC = \begin{bmatrix} 1 & 0 \\ 2 & 1 \\ 1 & 2 \end{bmatrix} \begin{bmatrix} 1 & 1 & 2 \\ 0 & 1 & 3 \end{bmatrix} = \begin{bmatrix} 1 & 1 & 2 \\ 2 & 3 & 7 \\ 1 & 3 & 8 \end{bmatrix}.$$

Here the products CD and DC are each defined but are certainly not equal; they are both square (as must be the case when products are defined in both orders) but here CD is 2×2 while DC is 3×3.

Example 2.4.3

Let

$$A = \begin{bmatrix} 1 & 2 \\ 3 & 4 \end{bmatrix} \quad \text{and} \quad B = \begin{bmatrix} 1 & 2 \\ 0 & -1 \end{bmatrix}.$$

Then, using the fact that $c_{ij} = A_i B_j$,

$$AB = [A_i B_j] = \begin{bmatrix} A_1 \\ A_2 \end{bmatrix} [B_1 \quad B_2] = \begin{bmatrix} 1 & 2 \\ 3 & 4 \end{bmatrix} \begin{bmatrix} 1 & 2 \\ 0 & -1 \end{bmatrix} = \begin{bmatrix} 1 & 0 \\ 3 & 2 \end{bmatrix},$$

and

$$BA = \begin{bmatrix} 1 & 2 \\ 0 & -1 \end{bmatrix} \begin{bmatrix} 1 & 2 \\ 3 & 4 \end{bmatrix} = \begin{bmatrix} 7 & 10 \\ -3 & -4 \end{bmatrix}.$$

Here both products are defined, and each is 2×2, but $AB \neq BA$. We shall discover by experience that it is only in very special situations that matrix products commute; that is, that $AB = BA$.

Example 2.4.4

Let

$$A = [1 \quad 2 \quad 3] \quad \text{and} \quad B = \begin{bmatrix} 3 \\ 2 \\ 1 \end{bmatrix}.$$

Then

$$AB = [1 \quad 2 \quad 3] \begin{bmatrix} 3 \\ 2 \\ 1 \end{bmatrix} = [10],$$

while

$$BA = \begin{bmatrix} B_1 A \\ B_2 A \\ B_3 A \end{bmatrix} = \begin{bmatrix} 3 \\ 2 \\ 1 \end{bmatrix} [1 \quad 2 \quad 3] = \begin{bmatrix} 3 & 6 & 9 \\ 2 & 4 & 6 \\ 1 & 2 & 3 \end{bmatrix}.$$

Example 2.4.5

Consider the two products

$$\begin{bmatrix} 1 & 0 & 0 \\ 0 & 1 & 0 \\ 0 & 0 & 1 \end{bmatrix} \begin{bmatrix} a_{11} & a_{12} & a_{13} \\ a_{21} & a_{22} & a_{23} \\ a_{31} & a_{32} & a_{33} \end{bmatrix} = \begin{bmatrix} a_{11} & a_{12} & a_{13} \\ a_{21} & a_{22} & a_{23} \\ a_{31} & a_{32} & a_{33} \end{bmatrix},$$

and

$$\begin{bmatrix} a_{11} & a_{12} & a_{13} \\ a_{21} & a_{22} & a_{23} \\ a_{31} & a_{32} & a_{33} \end{bmatrix} \begin{bmatrix} 1 & 0 & 0 \\ 0 & 1 & 0 \\ 0 & 0 & 1 \end{bmatrix} = \begin{bmatrix} a_{11} & a_{12} & a_{13} \\ a_{21} & a_{22} & a_{23} \\ a_{31} & a_{32} & a_{33} \end{bmatrix}.$$

It is easy to verify that the products above are as stated (you should do this) and hence that

$$I_3 = \begin{bmatrix} 1 & 0 & 0 \\ 0 & 1 & 0 \\ 0 & 0 & 1 \end{bmatrix}$$

acts as a multiplicative identity for 3×3 matrices, in the sense that, as above, for any A in $\mathcal{M}_{3,3}$,

$$AI_3 = A = I_3 A.$$

We will have more to say about this situation in a later section, and will in general use the symbol I_n to denote the $n \times n$ multiplicative identity.

In Section 2.2 we defined what is meant by the *transpose* of a matrix A; to repeat, it is the matrix whose rows (in order) are the columns of A and whose columns are the rows of A. As a final remark in this section on matrix multiplication, we present a result concerning matrix products and transposes; namely:

If A and B are matrices conformable for multiplication in the order AB, then

$$(AB)^T = B^T A^T.$$

That is, the transpose of a product is the product of the transposes of the factors *in reverse order*. After giving two examples, we shall prove this result in the case in which both A and B are 2×2 matrices, placing the general argument in Appendix B.

Example 2.4.6

Let

$$A = \begin{bmatrix} 1 & 2 & 3 \\ 4 & 5 & 6 \end{bmatrix} \quad \text{and} \quad B = \begin{bmatrix} 2 & 1 & 0 \\ -1 & 2 & 1 \\ 0 & -1 & 1 \end{bmatrix}.$$

Then

$$AB = \begin{bmatrix} 1 & 2 & 3 \\ 4 & 5 & 6 \end{bmatrix} \begin{bmatrix} 2 & 1 & 0 \\ -1 & 2 & 1 \\ 0 & -1 & 1 \end{bmatrix} = \begin{bmatrix} 0 & 2 & 5 \\ 3 & 8 & 11 \end{bmatrix};$$

thus

$$(AB)^T = \begin{bmatrix} 0 & 3 \\ 2 & 8 \\ 5 & 11 \end{bmatrix}$$

while

$$B^T A^T = \begin{bmatrix} 2 & -1 & 0 \\ 1 & 2 & -1 \\ 0 & 1 & 1 \end{bmatrix} \begin{bmatrix} 1 & 4 \\ 2 & 5 \\ 3 & 6 \end{bmatrix} = \begin{bmatrix} 0 & 3 \\ 2 & 8 \\ 5 & 11 \end{bmatrix},$$

so that $(AB)^T = B^T A^T$.

Example 2.4.7

Let $C = [1 \quad 2 \quad 3]$ and $D = \begin{bmatrix} 4 \\ 5 \\ 6 \end{bmatrix}$. Then $CD = [1 \quad 2 \quad 3] \begin{bmatrix} 4 \\ 5 \\ 6 \end{bmatrix} = [32]$,

so that $(CD)^T = [32]$ also. $D^T C^T = [4 \quad 5 \quad 6] \begin{bmatrix} 1 \\ 2 \\ 3 \end{bmatrix} = [32]$, so that in this

case, as above, $(CD)^T = D^T C^T$.

Now, if A and B are arbitrary 2×2 matrices with

$$A = \begin{bmatrix} a_{11} & a_{12} \\ a_{21} & a_{22} \end{bmatrix} \quad \text{and} \quad B = \begin{bmatrix} b_{11} & b_{12} \\ b_{21} & b_{22} \end{bmatrix},$$

then

$$AB = \begin{bmatrix} a_{11}b_{11} + a_{12}b_{21} & a_{11}b_{12} + a_{12}b_{22} \\ a_{21}b_{11} + a_{22}b_{21} & a_{21}b_{12} + a_{22}b_{22} \end{bmatrix},$$

so that

$$(AB)^T = \begin{bmatrix} a_{11}b_{11} + a_{12}b_{21} & a_{21}b_{11} + a_{22}b_{21} \\ a_{11}b_{12} + a_{12}b_{22} & a_{21}b_{12} + a_{22}b_{22} \end{bmatrix},$$

while

$$B^T A^T = \begin{bmatrix} b_{11} & b_{21} \\ b_{12} & b_{22} \end{bmatrix} \begin{bmatrix} a_{11} & a_{21} \\ a_{12} & a_{22} \end{bmatrix} = \begin{bmatrix} b_{11}a_{11} + b_{21}a_{12} & b_{11}a_{21} + b_{21}a_{22} \\ b_{12}a_{11} + b_{22}a_{12} & b_{12}a_{21} + b_{22}a_{22} \end{bmatrix}$$

$$= \begin{bmatrix} a_{11}b_{11} + a_{12}b_{21} & a_{21}b_{11} + a_{22}b_{21} \\ a_{11}b_{12} + a_{12}b_{22} & a_{21}b_{12} + a_{22}b_{22} \end{bmatrix},$$

where the last step follows from the commutativity of multiplication of the real numbers. Thus we have shown for 2×2 matrices that $B^T A^T = (AB)^T$.

Exercises 2.4 (continued)

In Exercises 19–26, calculate the indicated matrix product.

19. $\begin{bmatrix} 1 & 0 & 0 \\ 0 & 0 & 0 \\ 0 & 0 & 0 \end{bmatrix} \begin{bmatrix} a & b & c \\ d & e & f \\ g & h & i \end{bmatrix}$

20. $\begin{bmatrix} 0 & 0 & 0 \\ 0 & 1 & 0 \\ 0 & 0 & 0 \end{bmatrix} \begin{bmatrix} a & b & c \\ d & e & f \\ g & h & i \end{bmatrix}$

21. $\begin{bmatrix} 0 & 0 & 0 \\ 0 & 0 & 0 \\ 0 & 0 & 1 \end{bmatrix} \begin{bmatrix} a & b & c \\ d & e & f \\ g & h & i \end{bmatrix}$

22. $\begin{bmatrix} a & b & c \\ d & e & f \\ g & h & i \end{bmatrix} \begin{bmatrix} 1 & 0 & 0 \\ 0 & 0 & 0 \\ 0 & 0 & 0 \end{bmatrix}$

23. $\begin{bmatrix} a & b & c \\ d & e & f \\ g & h & i \end{bmatrix} \begin{bmatrix} 0 & 0 & 0 \\ 0 & 1 & 0 \\ 0 & 0 & 0 \end{bmatrix}$

24. $\begin{bmatrix} a & b & c \\ d & e & f \\ g & h & i \end{bmatrix} \begin{bmatrix} 0 & 0 & 0 \\ 0 & 0 & 0 \\ 0 & 0 & 1 \end{bmatrix}$

25. $\begin{bmatrix} 1 & 1 & 0 \\ 0 & 1 & 0 \\ 0 & 0 & 1 \end{bmatrix} \begin{bmatrix} a & b & c \\ d & e & f \\ g & h & i \end{bmatrix}$

26. $\begin{bmatrix} 2 & 3 & 0 \\ 0 & 1 & 0 \\ 0 & 0 & 1 \end{bmatrix} \begin{bmatrix} a & b & c \\ d & e & f \\ g & h & i \end{bmatrix}$

27. Describe in words the matrix product

$$\begin{bmatrix} x & y & 0 \\ 0 & 1 & 0 \\ 0 & 0 & 1 \end{bmatrix} \begin{bmatrix} a & b & c \\ d & e & f \\ g & h & i \end{bmatrix}.$$

28. Find

$$\begin{bmatrix} a & b & c \\ d & e & f \\ g & h & i \end{bmatrix} \begin{bmatrix} x & y & 0 \\ 0 & 1 & 0 \\ 0 & 0 & 1 \end{bmatrix}.$$

In Exercises 29–32, calculate the indicated matrix product.

29. $\begin{bmatrix} 1 & 2 & 1 \\ 0 & 1 & 3 \end{bmatrix} \begin{bmatrix} 1 & 2 & 1 & 1 \\ 0 & 1 & 1 & 4 \\ 1 & 0 & 3 & 2 \end{bmatrix}$

30. $\begin{bmatrix} 1.3 & 2.1 \\ 4.3 & -1.2 \end{bmatrix} \begin{bmatrix} -1.1 & 2.1 & -.1 \\ -0.3 & 3.1 & -1.1 \end{bmatrix}$

31. $\begin{bmatrix} 5 & 1 & 2 & 3 \\ 2 & 1 & 4 & 1 \\ -1 & -1 & 1 & 1 \\ 0 & 1 & 0 & 1 \end{bmatrix} \begin{bmatrix} 2 & 1 \\ 1 & 0 \\ 3 & 0 \\ 1 & 2 \end{bmatrix}$

32. $\begin{bmatrix} 1 & 2 \\ 0 & 1 \\ 1 & 1 \end{bmatrix} \begin{bmatrix} 1 & 2 & 0 & 1 & 3 & 4 & 6 \\ -1 & -1 & 1 & 0 & 1 & -2 & 1 \end{bmatrix}$

33. Let $A = \begin{bmatrix} 1 & 2 \\ 3 & 4 \end{bmatrix}$, $B = \begin{bmatrix} 1 & 2 \\ -1 & 1 \end{bmatrix}$, and $C = \begin{bmatrix} 1 & 0 \\ 3 & -2 \end{bmatrix}$.

Is $(A + B)C = AC + BC$?

New Terms

conformable for multiplication, 39

2.5   Distributive properties

In Exercise 33 of the preceding set, it was seen in a numerical example that the property illustrated by the statement

$$(A + B)C = AC + BC$$

is analogous to the distributive property D2 for real numbers (see Section 1.3) and is an example of

D2.   *Right Distributive Property.* If A and B are conformable for addition and are also conformable for multiplication with C on the right then

$$(A + B)C = AC + BC.$$

Similarly, we also have

D1.   *Left Distributive Property.*

$$A(B + C) = AB + AC,$$

providing the individual sums and products are defined.

We have placed the general proofs of these important properties in Appendix B for the interested reader to study separately. Here we merely illustrate these properties by further example and give the proof of the right distributive property in the simple case where A, B, and C are each 2×2 matrices.

Example 2.5.1

$(A + B)C$

$$= \left(\begin{bmatrix} 2 & 1 & 3 & 1 \\ -1 & 0 & 2 & -1 \end{bmatrix} + \begin{bmatrix} -1 & 1 & -2 & 0 \\ 1 & 1 & -1 & 2 \end{bmatrix} \right) \begin{bmatrix} 1 & -1 & 0 \\ 1 & 1 & 1 \\ 2 & -1 & 1 \\ 1 & 1 & 0 \end{bmatrix}$$

$$= \begin{bmatrix} 1 & 2 & 1 & 1 \\ 0 & 1 & 1 & 1 \end{bmatrix} \begin{bmatrix} 1 & -1 & 0 \\ 1 & 1 & 1 \\ 2 & -1 & 1 \\ 1 & 1 & 0 \end{bmatrix} = \begin{bmatrix} 6 & 1 & 3 \\ 4 & 1 & 2 \end{bmatrix},$$

while

$$AC = \begin{bmatrix} 2 & 1 & 3 & 1 \\ -1 & 0 & 2 & -1 \end{bmatrix} \begin{bmatrix} 1 & -1 & 0 \\ 1 & 1 & 1 \\ 2 & -1 & 1 \\ 1 & 1 & 0 \end{bmatrix} = \begin{bmatrix} 10 & -3 & 4 \\ 2 & -2 & 2 \end{bmatrix}$$

and

$$BC = \begin{bmatrix} -1 & 1 & -2 & 0 \\ 1 & 1 & -1 & 2 \end{bmatrix} \begin{bmatrix} 1 & -1 & 0 \\ 1 & 1 & 1 \\ 2 & -1 & 1 \\ 1 & 1 & 0 \end{bmatrix} = \begin{bmatrix} -4 & 4 & -1 \\ 2 & 3 & 0 \end{bmatrix}$$

so that

$$AC + BC = \begin{bmatrix} 10 & -3 & 4 \\ 2 & -2 & 2 \end{bmatrix} + \begin{bmatrix} -4 & 4 & -1 \\ 2 & 3 & 0 \end{bmatrix}$$

$$= \begin{bmatrix} 6 & 1 & 3 \\ 4 & 1 & 2 \end{bmatrix} = (A + B)C.$$

Example 2.5.2

$D(E + F)$

$$= \begin{bmatrix} 1 & 2 & 3 \end{bmatrix} \left(\begin{bmatrix} 1 & 2 & 1 & 2 \\ -1 & 1 & 4 & -1 \\ 0 & -3 & 2 & 3 \end{bmatrix} + \begin{bmatrix} 2 & -1 & 1 & -1 \\ 0 & 1 & -2 & 3 \\ 1 & 2 & 0 & -1 \end{bmatrix} \right)$$

$$= \begin{bmatrix} 1 & 2 & 3 \end{bmatrix} \begin{bmatrix} 3 & 1 & 2 & 1 \\ -1 & 2 & 2 & 2 \\ 1 & -1 & 2 & 2 \end{bmatrix} = \begin{bmatrix} 4 & 2 & 12 & 11 \end{bmatrix}.$$

$$DE + DF = \begin{bmatrix} 1 & 2 & 3 \end{bmatrix} \begin{bmatrix} 1 & 2 & 1 & 2 \\ -1 & 1 & 4 & -1 \\ 0 & -3 & 2 & 3 \end{bmatrix}$$

$$+ \begin{bmatrix} 1 & 2 & 3 \end{bmatrix} \begin{bmatrix} 2 & -1 & 1 & -1 \\ 0 & 1 & -2 & 3 \\ 1 & 2 & 0 & -1 \end{bmatrix}$$

$$= \begin{bmatrix} -1 & -5 & 15 & 9 \end{bmatrix} + \begin{bmatrix} 5 & 7 & -3 & 2 \end{bmatrix}$$

$$= \begin{bmatrix} 4 & 2 & 12 & 11 \end{bmatrix}.$$

Thus

$$D(E + F) = DE + DF.$$

Now let us prove the right distributive property in the case where A, B, and C are general 2×2 matrices. Let

$$A = \begin{bmatrix} a_{11} & a_{12} \\ a_{21} & a_{22} \end{bmatrix}, \qquad B = \begin{bmatrix} b_{11} & b_{12} \\ b_{21} & b_{22} \end{bmatrix}, \qquad \text{and} \quad C = \begin{bmatrix} c_{11} & c_{12} \\ c_{21} & c_{22} \end{bmatrix}.$$

Then

$$(A + B)C = \begin{bmatrix} a_{11} + b_{11} & a_{12} + b_{12} \\ a_{21} + b_{21} & a_{22} + b_{22} \end{bmatrix} \begin{bmatrix} c_{11} & c_{12} \\ c_{21} & c_{22} \end{bmatrix}$$

$$= \begin{bmatrix} (a_{11} + b_{11})c_{11} & (a_{11} + b_{11})c_{12} \\ + (a_{12} + b_{12})c_{21} & + (a_{12} + b_{12})c_{22} \\ (a_{21} + b_{21})c_{11} & (a_{21} + b_{21})c_{12} \\ + (a_{22} + b_{22})c_{21} & + (a_{22} + b_{22})c_{22} \end{bmatrix}$$

$$= \begin{bmatrix} (a_{11}c_{11} + a_{12}c_{21}) & (a_{11}c_{12} + a_{12}c_{22}) \\ + (b_{11}c_{11} + b_{12}c_{21}) & + (b_{11}c_{12} + b_{12}c_{22}) \\ (a_{21}c_{11} + a_{22}c_{21}) & (a_{21}c_{12} + a_{22}c_{22}) \\ + (b_{21}c_{11} + b_{22}c_{21}) & + (b_{21}c_{12} + b_{22}c_{22}) \end{bmatrix}$$

$$= \begin{bmatrix} a_{11}c_{11} + a_{12}c_{21} & a_{11}c_{12} + a_{12}c_{22} \\ a_{21}c_{11} + a_{22}c_{21} & a_{21}c_{12} + a_{22}c_{22} \end{bmatrix}$$

$$+ \begin{bmatrix} b_{11}c_{11} + b_{12}c_{21} & b_{11}c_{12} + b_{12}c_{22} \\ b_{21}c_{11} + b_{22}c_{21} & b_{21}c_{12} + b_{22}c_{22} \end{bmatrix}$$

$$= AC + BC.$$

Exercises 2.5

Verify the left or right distributive property in the following exercises.

1. $[2 \quad 1 \quad 5 \quad 3]\left(\begin{bmatrix} 1 \\ -1 \\ -1 \\ 2 \end{bmatrix} + \begin{bmatrix} 1 \\ 1 \\ 1 \\ -1 \end{bmatrix}\right)$

2. $\begin{bmatrix} 2 & 1 & 2 \\ 1 & 3 & 1 \\ 4 & 1 & 4 \end{bmatrix}\left(\begin{bmatrix} -1 & 1 & -1 \\ 0 & -1 & 1 \\ -2 & 1 & 2 \end{bmatrix} + \begin{bmatrix} 1 & 2 & 1 \\ 3 & 1 & 5 \\ 4 & 2 & 0 \end{bmatrix}\right)$

3. $([-1 \quad 2 \quad 1] + [1 \quad -1 \quad 2])\begin{bmatrix} 1 \\ 2 \\ 1 \end{bmatrix}$

4. $\left(\begin{bmatrix} 2 & 0 & 2 \\ 1 & 4 & 3 \end{bmatrix} + \begin{bmatrix} 3 & 1 & -2 \\ 1 & 0 & 2 \end{bmatrix}\right)\begin{bmatrix} 1 & 0 & 1 & 0 & 0 \\ 1 & 1 & 0 & 1 & 0 \\ 2 & 1 & 0 & 0 & 1 \end{bmatrix}$

5. $\begin{bmatrix} 3 & 1 & 2 \\ 1 & 1 & 1 \end{bmatrix}\left(\begin{bmatrix} 2 & 1 \\ -1 & 2 \\ 1 & 1 \end{bmatrix} + \begin{bmatrix} -1 & -1 \\ 1 & -1 \\ 0 & 1 \end{bmatrix}\right)$

6. $\left(\begin{bmatrix} 1 & 2 \\ 3 & 4 \\ 5 & 6 \end{bmatrix} + \begin{bmatrix} -1 & -1 \\ 1 & -2 \\ -3 & 2 \end{bmatrix}\right)\begin{bmatrix} 1 & 2 & 3 & 4 \\ -1 & 1 & -2 & 3 \end{bmatrix}$

7. $\left(\begin{bmatrix} 1 \\ -1 \\ -1 \\ 2 \end{bmatrix} + \begin{bmatrix} 1 \\ 1 \\ 1 \\ -1 \end{bmatrix}\right)[2 \quad 1 \quad 5 \quad 3]$ (Compare with Exercise 1 above.)

8. $\begin{bmatrix} 1 & 0 & 1 & 0 & 0 \\ 1 & 1 & 0 & 1 & 0 \\ 2 & 1 & 0 & 0 & 1 \end{bmatrix}\left(\begin{bmatrix} 1 & 3 & 1 \\ 2 & 0 & 2 \\ 1 & 1 & 1 \\ 1 & 4 & 3 \\ 0 & 0 & 1 \end{bmatrix} + \begin{bmatrix} 2 & 1 & -4 \\ 3 & 1 & -2 \\ 1 & 2 & 3 \\ 1 & 0 & 2 \\ 1 & 1 & 0 \end{bmatrix}\right)$

2.6 Some algebraic properties of square matrices

We have already seen in Section 2.3 of this chapter that the set $\mathcal{M}_{m,n}$ of all $m \times n$ real matrices satisfies the matrix analogues of properties A1–A4 of addition for real numbers. In this section we shall discover that certain matrices satisfy further properties with analogues in the real number system. We shall see also that while there are striking similarities, there are also significant differences between these two algebraic structures.

We now wish to explore further multiplicative properties of matrices, and thus develop further analogies with the real numbers. In order to do this we consider a set of matrices in which any two matrices are conformable for addition and for multiplication. Thus we must restrict our attention to the set $\mathscr{M}_{n,n}$ of all real $n \times n$ (square) matrices. As in the earlier sections of this chapter, we have placed the more difficult proofs in Appendix B. We shall illustrate our properties with examples from $\mathscr{M}_{2,2}$ and $\mathscr{M}_{3,3}$.

For convenience of reference, we re-list the properties for real numbers whose analogues will be discussed in this section:

M1.   Associativity of Multiplication
M2.   Multiplicative Identity
M3.   Multiplicative Inverses
M4.   Commutativity of Multiplication
Property 1.   Uniqueness of Identity
Property 2.   Uniqueness of Multiplicative Inverse
Property 3. $(a^{-1})^{-1} = a$.
Property 4.   If $ab = 0$ then $a = 0$ or $b = 0$.
Property 5.   Solution of $ax = b$.
Property 6.   Solution of $ax + b = c$.

Our first matrix analogue of real number multiplication is

M1.   *Matrix multiplication is associative.* That is, if A, B, C are in $\mathscr{M}_{n,n}$, then

$$A(BC) = (AB)C.$$

In other words, the product BC multiplied on the left by A is precisely the same as AB multiplied on the right by C. The reader should note here and in Exercises 3 and 4 of the next set, that this property is not peculiar simply to square matrices, but is valid whenever the matrices are conformable for multiplication in the order indicated. We consider an example from $\mathscr{M}_{2,2}$ and let

$$A = \begin{bmatrix} 1 & -1 \\ 2 & 3 \end{bmatrix}, \quad B = \begin{bmatrix} 2 & 1 \\ -1 & 0 \end{bmatrix}, \quad \text{and} \quad C = \begin{bmatrix} 1 & 1 \\ -1 & 2 \end{bmatrix}.$$

Then

$$AB = \begin{bmatrix} 1 & -1 \\ 2 & 3 \end{bmatrix} \begin{bmatrix} 2 & 1 \\ -1 & 0 \end{bmatrix} = \begin{bmatrix} 3 & 1 \\ 1 & 2 \end{bmatrix},$$

so that

$$(AB)C = \begin{bmatrix} 3 & 1 \\ 1 & 2 \end{bmatrix}\begin{bmatrix} 1 & 1 \\ -1 & 2 \end{bmatrix} = \begin{bmatrix} 2 & 5 \\ -1 & 5 \end{bmatrix}.$$

On the other hand,

$$BC = \begin{bmatrix} 2 & 1 \\ -1 & 0 \end{bmatrix}\begin{bmatrix} 1 & 1 \\ -1 & 2 \end{bmatrix} = \begin{bmatrix} 1 & 4 \\ -1 & -1 \end{bmatrix},$$

and hence

$$A(BC) = \begin{bmatrix} 1 & -1 \\ 2 & 3 \end{bmatrix}\begin{bmatrix} 1 & 4 \\ -1 & -1 \end{bmatrix} = \begin{bmatrix} 2 & 5 \\ -1 & 5 \end{bmatrix}.$$

Thus $(AB)C = A(BC)$.

Exercises 2.6

1. Verify the associative property for matrix multiplication in the case that

  a. $A = \begin{bmatrix} 1 & 2 \\ 3 & 4 \end{bmatrix}$, $B = \begin{bmatrix} -2 & 1 \\ -1 & 0 \end{bmatrix}$, $C = \begin{bmatrix} 1 & 3 \\ 0 & 2 \end{bmatrix}$.

  b. $A = \begin{bmatrix} 3 & 1 & -2 \\ 2 & 1 & 3 \\ 1 & 0 & 1 \end{bmatrix}$, $B = \begin{bmatrix} -1 & 2 & -1 \\ 0 & 1 & 2 \\ 1 & -1 & 0 \end{bmatrix}$,

  $C = \begin{bmatrix} 1 & 1 & 1 \\ 2 & 0 & 1 \\ 0 & -1 & 0 \end{bmatrix}$.

2. Prove the associative property in the case of 2×2 matrices; that is, let

$$A = \begin{bmatrix} a_{11} & a_{12} \\ a_{21} & a_{22} \end{bmatrix}, \quad B = \begin{bmatrix} b_{11} & b_{12} \\ b_{21} & b_{22} \end{bmatrix}, \quad C = \begin{bmatrix} c_{11} & c_{12} \\ c_{21} & c_{22} \end{bmatrix};$$

  compute $A(BC)$ and $(AB)C$ separately and compare the results.

3. Let $A = \begin{bmatrix} 2 \\ 1 \end{bmatrix}$, $B = [1 \quad -1 \quad 2]$,

$$C = \begin{bmatrix} 1 & 0 & 1 & -1 \\ -1 & 1 & 2 & 0 \\ 2 & -1 & -1 & 1 \end{bmatrix},$$

  and show that $A(BC) = (AB)C$, even in this case of non-square matrices.

4. Verify that, with $A = [1 \quad 2 \quad 1]$, $B = \begin{bmatrix} 3 & 1 \\ -1 & 0 \\ 2 & 1 \end{bmatrix}$, $C = \begin{bmatrix} 1 \\ -1 \end{bmatrix}$, we again have $A(BC) = (AB)C$.

5. Let $A = \begin{bmatrix} 1 & 2 \\ 3 & 4 \end{bmatrix}$ and $B = \begin{bmatrix} -1 & 6 \\ 2 & 8 \end{bmatrix}$. Verify that

   a. $(A^T)^T = A$.
   b. $(AB)^T = B^T A^T$.
   c. $(A + B)^T = A^T + B^T$.

6. Verify the statement of Exercise 5 for arbitrary 2×2 matrices.

7. Show that if each of A and B is a 2×2 symmetric matrix, then their sum $A + B$ is symmetric.

8. Is the product AB in Exercise 7 symmetric?

Our next property is

M2. *There is a multiplicative identity* I_n *in* $\mathcal{M}_{n,n}$ *such that for each* A *in* $\mathcal{M}_{n,n}$

$$I_n A = AI_n = A.$$

Indeed, such a matrix I_n is obtained by setting

$$I_n = \begin{bmatrix} 1 & 0 & 0 & \cdots & 0 & 0 \\ 0 & 1 & 0 & \cdots & 0 & 0 \\ 0 & 0 & 1 & \cdots & 0 & 0 \\ \cdot & \cdot & \cdot & \cdots & \cdot & \cdot \\ 0 & 0 & 0 & \cdots & 1 & 0 \\ 0 & 0 & 0 & \cdots & 0 & 1 \end{bmatrix}.$$

That is, I_n is the $n \times n$ diagonal matrix whose main diagonal elements are all 1's. That I_n as defined above acts as an identity may be verified by inspection. It is readily computed in the following example from $\mathcal{M}_{2,2}$.

$$\begin{bmatrix} 1 & 0 \\ 0 & 1 \end{bmatrix}\begin{bmatrix} a_{11} & a_{12} \\ a_{21} & a_{22} \end{bmatrix} = \begin{bmatrix} a_{11} & a_{12} \\ a_{21} & a_{22} \end{bmatrix} = \begin{bmatrix} a_{11} & a_{12} \\ a_{21} & a_{22} \end{bmatrix}\begin{bmatrix} 1 & 0 \\ 0 & 1 \end{bmatrix}.$$

Exercises 2.6 (continued)

9. Calculate the product $\begin{bmatrix} 1 & 0 \\ 0 & 1 \end{bmatrix}\begin{bmatrix} a_{11} & a_{12} & a_{13} & a_{14} \\ a_{21} & a_{22} & a_{23} & a_{24} \end{bmatrix}$.

Here I_2 acts as a left identity for all 2×4 matrices (indeed for all $2 \times n$ matrices, where n is any positive integer).

10.   Is there a right identity for $\mathcal{M}_{2,4}$, and, if so, what is it?

Now that we have established the existence of a multiplicative identity I_n for $\mathcal{M}_{n,n}$, it is reasonable to ask whether or not the matrix analogue of M3 is true in $\mathcal{M}_{n,n}$. That is, does each non-zero matrix A in $\mathcal{M}_{n,n}$ have a multiplicative inverse (denoted by A^{-1}) such that

$$AA^{-1} = A^{-1}A = I_n?$$

The answer to this question is: No; *some square matrices do have inverses and some do not*. (Those matrices which have inverses will be called **non-singular** and those which do not have inverses will be called **singular**.) The question "How can one determine whether or not a given matrix has an inverse?" and some other closely related questions will only be mentioned briefly in this section and will be dealt with more fully in our next chapter.

Let us note that at least one non-zero member of $\mathcal{M}_{n,n}$ has a multiplicative inverse—namely, I_n, which is its own inverse, since

$$I_n I_n = I_n.$$

Our old familiar matrix $A = \begin{bmatrix} 1 & 2 \\ 3 & 4 \end{bmatrix}$ in $\mathcal{M}_{n,n}$ also has a multiplicative inverse—namely,

$$A^{-1} = \begin{bmatrix} 1 & 2 \\ 3 & 4 \end{bmatrix}^{-1} = \begin{bmatrix} -2 & 1 \\ 3/2 & -1/2 \end{bmatrix}.$$

(You should verify this by direct calculation of the products AA^{-1} and $A^{-1}A$.)

In order to see that some non-zero matrices do not have inverses, consider the non-zero matrix

$$A = \begin{bmatrix} 1 & 0 \\ 0 & 0 \end{bmatrix}.$$

Were there an inverse A^{-1} for A with, say

$$A^{-1} = \begin{bmatrix} x & y \\ z & w \end{bmatrix},$$

then $I_2 = AA^{-1}$, which means that

$$I_2 = \begin{bmatrix} 1 & 0 \\ 0 & 1 \end{bmatrix} = \begin{bmatrix} 1 & 0 \\ 0 & 0 \end{bmatrix}\begin{bmatrix} x & y \\ z & w \end{bmatrix} = \begin{bmatrix} x & y \\ 0 & 0 \end{bmatrix}.$$

Since this equality is impossible (compare the elements in the 2,2 position) A cannot have an inverse.

It is not purely the number of zero elements in a matrix, however, that causes it to have no inverse. Consider the matrix

$$B = \begin{bmatrix} 1 & 2 \\ 2 & 4 \end{bmatrix}$$

which has no zero elements at all. B also has no inverse. Suppose B did have an inverse

$$B^{-1} = \begin{bmatrix} x & y \\ z & w \end{bmatrix}.$$

Then, in particular, $I_2 = BB^{-1}$, so that

$$\begin{bmatrix} 1 & 0 \\ 0 & 1 \end{bmatrix} = \begin{bmatrix} 1 & 2 \\ 2 & 4 \end{bmatrix}\begin{bmatrix} x & y \\ z & w \end{bmatrix} = \begin{bmatrix} x + 2z & y + 2w \\ 2x + 4z & 2y + 4w \end{bmatrix}.$$

By equating elements in the 1,1 position we find that we must have

$$1 = x + 2z, \cdot$$

while if we equate elements in the 2,1 position we find that at the same time we must have

$$0 = 2x + 4z.$$

That such numbers x and z cannot exist is easily seen by subtracting twice the first equation from the second to obtain the absurd result that

$$-2 = 0.$$

From these examples, then, we see that a direct analogue of M3 (multiplicative inverses) does not hold in $\mathscr{M}_{n,n}$.

The matrix analogue of M4 (commutativity of multiplication) does not hold in $\mathscr{M}_{n,n}$ either, as we have seen in Example 2.4.3. We have seen, however, that *some* matrices do commute (a matrix and its inverse, for instance). We shall not probe the question of commutativity in our discussions here, but let the reader be warned that he should assume that products are not guilty of commuting until they are proven otherwise.

Of course, a member A of $\mathscr{M}_{n,n}$ does commute with itself, and we are able to define through associativity the positive integral powers of A inductively; thus

$$A^1 = A, \qquad A^2 = AA, \qquad A^3 = AA^2, \ldots, \qquad A^{k+1} = AA^k.$$

In the special case that A has an inverse, we remain consistent if we define, for positive integers k,

$$A^{-k} = (A^{-1})^k \qquad \text{and} \qquad A^0 = I_n.$$

For example, $A^{-2} = (A^{-1})^2 = (A^{-1})(A^{-1})$. Thus,

$$\begin{aligned}
A^{-2}(A^2) &= (A^{-1}A^{-1})(AA) \\
&= A^{-1}(A^{-1}A)A \\
&= A^{-1}I_n A \\
&= A^{-1}A \\
&= I_n.
\end{aligned}$$

Exercises 2.6 (continued)

In Exercises 11–16, discover whether or not the given matrix has a multiplicative inverse, and find the inverse if it exists.

11. $\begin{bmatrix} 3 & 0 & 0 \\ 0 & 3 & 0 \\ 0 & 0 & 3 \end{bmatrix}$ 12. $\begin{bmatrix} 2 & 0 \\ 0 & 3 \end{bmatrix}$ 13. $\begin{bmatrix} 0 & 2 \\ 3 & 0 \end{bmatrix}$

14. $\begin{bmatrix} 3 & 0 & 0 \\ 0 & 0 & 0 \\ 0 & 0 & 3 \end{bmatrix}$ 15. $\begin{bmatrix} 2 & 1 \\ -4 & -2 \end{bmatrix}$ 16. $\begin{bmatrix} 1 & 0 & 1 \\ 0 & 1 & 0 \\ 0 & 0 & 1 \end{bmatrix}$

17. Let A and B belong to $\mathcal{M}_{n,n}$. Is $(A + B)^2 = A^2 + 2AB + B^2$? Is $(A + B)(A - B) = A^2 - B^2$? (Hint: Consider an example from $\mathcal{M}_{2,2}$.)

18. Expand $(A + I_n)^2$. What is $(A + I_n)(A - I_n)$?

19. Let

$$A = \begin{bmatrix} 0 & 1 & 1 \\ 0 & 0 & 1 \\ 0 & 0 & 0 \end{bmatrix}.$$

Calculate A^2 and A^3. Notice that A satisfies the equation $X^3 = 0$ but does not satisfy $X^2 = 0$.

20. Use the fact that $(AB)^T = B^T A^T$ to prove that $(A^T)^{-1} = (A^{-1})^T$. Verify this statement in Exercises 13 and 16 above.

Let us now examine which of Properties 1.–6. for the real numbers have analogues in $\mathcal{M}_{n,n}$.

Property 1.   Uniqueness of I_n. As with real numbers, if there were an identity E other than I_n, then, necessarily,

$$I_n = I_n E = E.$$

Hence there is only one identity for multiplication in $\mathcal{M}_{n,n}$.

Property 2.   Uniqueness of Inverses. Not every non-zero member of $\mathcal{M}_{n,n}$ has an inverse. However, if a certain member A does have an inverse, then the inverse is unique; for if both A^{-1} and X are multiplicative inverses of A, then $AX = I_n$. Multiplying both sides of this equation on the left by A^{-1} we have

$$A^{-1}(AX) = A^{-1}I_n$$
$$(A^{-1}A)X = A^{-1}$$
$$I_n X = A^{-1}$$
$$X = A^{-1}.$$

Thus there can be only one multiplicative inverse for A.

Property 3. If A^{-1} exists, then $(A^{-1})^{-1} = A$. This property is true because A does act as an inverse for A^{-1} in the sense that $AA^{-1} = A^{-1}A = I_n$. Since inverses are unique by Property 2, it follows that $(A^{-1})^{-1} = A$.

Thus Property 1 has a direct analogue for matrices while Properties 2 and 3, although not valid for every non-zero matrix, are valid for those matrices which possess inverses.

Property 4. ($ab = 0$ implies $a = 0$ or $b = 0$). The situation degenerates further when we calculate the product

$$AB = \begin{bmatrix} 1 & 2 \\ 2 & 4 \end{bmatrix} \begin{bmatrix} 2 & 4 \\ -1 & -2 \end{bmatrix}$$

and find that it is

$$\begin{bmatrix} 0 & 0 \\ 0 & 0 \end{bmatrix} = 0.$$

Thus $AB = 0$ and yet neither factor is zero, in direct contradiction to the matrix analogue of Property 4. We shall not explore the question of *divisors of zero* in this book, but let the reader be warned again that the familiar argument

$$ax = ay \quad \text{implies} \quad x = y \text{ (or } a = 0),$$

which is so frequently employed in solving equations involving real numbers can *not* be used with matrices. For if, with A, X, Y members of $\mathcal{M}_{n,n}$ we have

$$AX = AY,$$

then it *is* true that

$$A(X - Y) = 0.$$

But, at this point, we cannot conclude that either $X - Y$ is zero or that A is zero. Hence we cannot further conclude that $X = Y$ or $A = 0$.

Property 5. "$ax = b$ has the unique solution $a^{-1}b$ for $a \neq 0$" does have a matrix analogue for matrices to the following extent. For each member A of $\mathcal{M}_{n,n}$ which has an inverse (is non-singular) and each member B of $\mathcal{M}_{n,n}$, there is one and only one solution X in $\mathcal{M}_{n,n}$ of the matrix equation

$$AX = B.$$

To verify this, we note that $A^{-1}B$ is one solution, since $A(A^{-1}B) = (AA^{-1})B = I_n B = B$. Now, if X is any solution whatever, so that $AX = B$, then, multiplying on the left by A^{-1} (which we assume exists) we obtain

$$A^{-1}(AX) = A^{-1}B$$
$$(A^{-1}A)X = A^{-1}B$$
$$I_n X = A^{-1}B$$
$$X = A^{-1}B.$$

Thus, the only solution is $A^{-1}B$.

Property 6. We have a similar matrix analogue for Property 6 in that if A has an inverse and B and C are any members of $\mathcal{M}_{n,n}$, then the equation

$$AX + B = C$$

has the unique solution

$$X = A^{-1}(C - B).$$

The restricted analogue of Property 5 gives us valuable information about the equation $AX = B$ when A is non-singular, but says nothing about the situation when A is singular; nor does it touch on the question of solutions of

$$AX = B$$

when A is not square. These and the related question, "How do we find the inverse of a non-singular matrix?" will be answered in the next chapter.

In summary, then, the set $\mathcal{M}_{n,n}$ satisfies A1–A4, M1, and D1, D2. Such an algebraic structure is called a *ring*. Moreover $\mathcal{M}_{n,n}$ satisfies M2 (identity) and does not satisfy M4 (commutativity) so that $\mathcal{M}_{n,n}$ may properly be termed a *non-commutative ring with identity*.

Exercises 2.6 (continued)

21. Show for $A = \begin{bmatrix} 2 & -1 \\ 4 & -2 \end{bmatrix}$, $X = \begin{bmatrix} 0 & 1 \\ 3 & 2 \end{bmatrix}$, $Y = \begin{bmatrix} -1 & -1 \\ 1 & -2 \end{bmatrix}$ that

$AX = AY$, even though $X \neq Y$.

22. Solve the matrix equation $AX = B$, where

$$A = \begin{bmatrix} 1 & 2 \\ 3 & 4 \end{bmatrix}, \quad B = \begin{bmatrix} 1 & -2 \\ 1 & 3 \end{bmatrix}.$$

23. Can you solve the matrix equation $AX = B$ with

$$A = \begin{bmatrix} 1 & 2 \\ 2 & 4 \end{bmatrix}, \quad B = \begin{bmatrix} 3 & 1 \\ 6 & 2 \end{bmatrix}?$$

New terms

non-singular matrix, 51   singular matrix, 51

2.7 Scalar product

In this section we define the multiplication of a matrix A by a scalar (real number) s, and develop a few elementary properties of this "mixed" multiplication.

Thus if s is a scalar and $A = [a_{ij}]$ is any $m \times n$ matrix, we define the product of A by s, as

$$sA = [sa_{ij}].$$

That is, to multiply the matrix A by the scalar s, we simply multiply each element of A by s. Thus

$$2\begin{bmatrix} 1 & 2 \\ 3 & 4 \end{bmatrix} = \begin{bmatrix} 2 \cdot 1 & 2 \cdot 2 \\ 2 \cdot 3 & 2 \cdot 4 \end{bmatrix} = \begin{bmatrix} 2 & 4 \\ 6 & 8 \end{bmatrix}.$$

You should now verify that the additive inverse $-A$ of A is simply $(-1)A$. Moreover, our *scalar matrices*, which we defined in Section 2.2 are now seen to be simply scalar multiples of the identity matrix I_n. Thus

$$\begin{bmatrix} 3 & 0 & 0 \\ 0 & 3 & 0 \\ 0 & 0 & 3 \end{bmatrix} = 3\begin{bmatrix} 1 & 0 & 0 \\ 0 & 1 & 0 \\ 0 & 0 & 1 \end{bmatrix} = 3I_3.$$

The following three properties of this scalar multiplication are easily proved. Further numerical examples illustrating their use are found in the exercises.

S1. $1A = A$ for each A in $\mathcal{M}_{m,n}$.

Proof:

$$1A = [1a_{ij}] = [a_{ij}] = A. \ \square$$

Example 2.7.1

$$1\begin{bmatrix} 2 & 3 \\ 4 & 5 \end{bmatrix} = \begin{bmatrix} 1 \cdot 2 & 1 \cdot 3 \\ 1 \cdot 4 & 1 \cdot 5 \end{bmatrix} = \begin{bmatrix} 2 & 3 \\ 4 & 5 \end{bmatrix}.$$

S2. For each pair of scalars s, t in R, $(s + t)A = sA + tA$. (a distributive property)

Proof:

$$(s + t)A = (s + t)[a_{ij}] = [(s + t)a_{ij}]$$
$$= [sa_{ij} + ta_{ij}] = [sa_{ij}] + [ta_{ij}] = sA + tA. \ \square$$

Example 2.7.2

$$(2 + 3)\begin{bmatrix} 2 & 3 \\ 4 & 5 \end{bmatrix} = \begin{bmatrix} (2 + 3)2 & (2 + 3)3 \\ (2 + 3)4 & (2 + 3)5 \end{bmatrix} = \begin{bmatrix} 2 \cdot 2 + 3 \cdot 2 & 2 \cdot 3 + 3 \cdot 3 \\ 2 \cdot 4 + 3 \cdot 4 & 2 \cdot 5 + 3 \cdot 5 \end{bmatrix}$$

$$= \begin{bmatrix} 2 \cdot 2 & 2 \cdot 3 \\ 2 \cdot 4 & 2 \cdot 5 \end{bmatrix} + \begin{bmatrix} 3 \cdot 2 & 3 \cdot 3 \\ 3 \cdot 4 & 3 \cdot 5 \end{bmatrix}$$

$$= 2\begin{bmatrix} 2 & 3 \\ 4 & 5 \end{bmatrix} + 3\begin{bmatrix} 2 & 3 \\ 4 & 5 \end{bmatrix}.$$

S3. For each pair of scalars s, t in R, $(st)A = s(tA)$. (an associative property)

Proof:

$$(st)A = (st)[a_{ij}] = [(st)a_{ij}] = [s(ta_{ij})] = s[ta_{ij}] = s(tA). \ \square$$

Example 2.7.3

$$(2 \cdot 3)\begin{bmatrix} 4 & 5 \\ 6 & 7 \end{bmatrix} = \begin{bmatrix} (2 \cdot 3)4 & (2 \cdot 3)5 \\ (2 \cdot 3)6 & (2 \cdot 3)7 \end{bmatrix} = \begin{bmatrix} 2(3 \cdot 4) & 2(3 \cdot 5) \\ 2(3 \cdot 6) & 2(3 \cdot 7) \end{bmatrix}$$

$$= 2\begin{bmatrix} 3 \cdot 4 & 3 \cdot 5 \\ 3 \cdot 6 & 3 \cdot 7 \end{bmatrix} = 2\left(3\begin{bmatrix} 4 & 5 \\ 6 & 7 \end{bmatrix}\right).$$

Exercises 2.7

1. Show that $(-2)\begin{bmatrix} -1 & 2 & 1 \\ 3 & 1 & 5 \end{bmatrix} = 3\begin{bmatrix} -1 & 2 & 1 \\ 3 & 1 & 5 \end{bmatrix} - 5\begin{bmatrix} -1 & 2 & 1 \\ 3 & 1 & 5 \end{bmatrix}.$

2. Show that

$$(-12)\begin{bmatrix} 1 & 1 & -1 & 6 \\ 2 & 1 & 3 & 1 \end{bmatrix} = (-4)\left(3\begin{bmatrix} 1 & 1 & -1 & 6 \\ 2 & 1 & 3 & 1 \end{bmatrix}\right).$$

3. Show that for $A = \begin{bmatrix} 1 & -2 \\ 3 & 4 \end{bmatrix}$, $B = \begin{bmatrix} 4 & 6 \\ 5 & 8 \end{bmatrix}$, $a = 2$,

$$a(A + B) = aA + aB.$$

4. Prove that for any 2×2 matrices A, B and the scalar a,
    a. $a(A + B) = aA + aB$.
    b. $a(AB) = (aA)B = A(aB)$.

5. Verify that $(aA)^T = aA^T$ for a and A as in Exercise 3.

6. Prove the statement in Exercise 5 for 2×2 matrices.

[3] Systems of linear equations and Gauss-Jordan reduction

3.1 Matrix representation of systems of linear equations

One of the most important uses of matrices and matrix notation occurs in the study of systems of linear equations. Such equations arise in many different contexts, some of which we shall see later. In this chapter we shall observe how matrices can be used to represent such systems. We shall learn how to solve systems geometrically, when possible, and then proceed to develop a method, known as Gauss-Jordan reduction, for solving any system of linear equations. In order to introduce some terminology and to familiarize the reader with two equivalent matrix formulations we shall now consider two small systems of linear equations.

Example 3.1.1

$$2x_1 + 3x_2 = 0$$
$$4x_1 + 2x_2 = 0.$$

In the equations of Example 3.1.1 we say that we have two homogeneous linear equations in the two unknowns x_1 and x_2. Each equation is said to be a **homogeneous equation** because its right-hand side is zero. If each of a set of equations is homogeneous then the set of equations is called **homogeneous**. It is possible to express the set of equations of Example 3.1.1 very compactly in matrix notation. If we let

$$A = \begin{bmatrix} 2 & 3 \\ 4 & 2 \end{bmatrix}, \qquad X = \begin{bmatrix} x_1 \\ x_2 \end{bmatrix}, \qquad \text{and} \qquad 0 = \begin{bmatrix} 0 \\ 0 \end{bmatrix},$$

then we see that the matrix equation $AX = 0$, where

$$AX = \begin{bmatrix} 2 & 3 \\ 4 & 2 \end{bmatrix} \begin{bmatrix} x_1 \\ x_2 \end{bmatrix} = \begin{bmatrix} 2x_1 + 3x_2 \\ 4x_1 + 2x_2 \end{bmatrix} = \begin{bmatrix} 0 \\ 0 \end{bmatrix} = 0$$

must be satisfied by a pair x_1, x_2 that happens to satisfy the original set of equations. On the other hand, any $X = \begin{bmatrix} x_1 \\ x_2 \end{bmatrix}$ that satisfies the matrix equation $AX = 0$ also provides values for x_1, x_2 that satisfy the original set of equations. Thus we say that $AX = 0$ is an equivalent representation of the original set of equations in the sense that a solution of either problem provides a solution to the other. We wish now to find a matrix X, if one exists, which will satisfy the matrix equation. Such a matrix X is called a **solution** of the matrix equation, and the set of all such matrices is called the **complete** or **general solution set** for the matrix equation.

There is an alternative matrix representation of this set of linear equations which will be of considerable assistance in our later work. If we let $A_1 = \begin{bmatrix} 2 \\ 4 \end{bmatrix}$ denote the first column of A and let $A_2 = \begin{bmatrix} 3 \\ 2 \end{bmatrix}$ denote the second column, then we could say that our problem is to find x_1, x_2, if they exist, such that

$$x_1 \begin{bmatrix} 2 \\ 4 \end{bmatrix} + x_2 \begin{bmatrix} 3 \\ 2 \end{bmatrix} = \begin{bmatrix} 0 \\ 0 \end{bmatrix},$$

or such that

$$x_1 A_1 + x_2 A_2 = 0.$$

We shall now consider a similar set of equations in which the right-hand constants are not all zeros. Such a set of equations is said to be **non-homogeneous**.

Example 3.1.2

$$2x_1 + 3x_2 = 5$$
$$4x_1 + 2x_2 = 6.$$

In the example, if we let $A = \begin{bmatrix} 2 & 3 \\ 4 & 2 \end{bmatrix}$ and $X = \begin{bmatrix} x_1 \\ x_2 \end{bmatrix}$ as before, and denote $\begin{bmatrix} 5 \\ 6 \end{bmatrix}$ by B, then we have the equivalent matrix equation $AX = B$. In the second matrix format, we wish to find numbers x_1 and x_2 such that

$$x_1 \begin{bmatrix} 2 \\ 4 \end{bmatrix} + x_2 \begin{bmatrix} 3 \\ 2 \end{bmatrix} = \begin{bmatrix} 5 \\ 6 \end{bmatrix},$$

or such that

$$x_1 A_1 + x_2 A_2 = B.$$

Exercises 3.1

1. Consider the set of equations

$$x_1 - 4x_2 = -5$$
$$-2x_1 + 2x_2 = 4.$$

   a. Find A, B, X which represent this system as $AX = B$.

   b. Find A_1, A_2, and B such that $x_1 A_1 + x_2 A_2 = B$. We say that B is a **linear combination** of A_1 and A_2.

   c. Is the system a homogeneous system?

   d. Verify that $X = \begin{bmatrix} -1 \\ 1 \end{bmatrix}$ is a solution for the system.

2. a. Write the system of equations corresponding to the matrix equation $AX = B$, if

$$A = \begin{bmatrix} 1 & 2 & 3 \\ -1 & 4 & 5 \end{bmatrix}, \quad X = \begin{bmatrix} x_1 \\ x_2 \\ x_3 \end{bmatrix}, \quad B = \begin{bmatrix} 0 \\ -1 \end{bmatrix}.$$

   b. Express the set of equations in a. in the alternative matrix format.

   c. Verify that $X = [1/3, (-1/6), 0]^T$ is a solution.

3. Consider the system of equations

$$x_1 + 2x_2 - x_3 = 0$$
$$2x_1 - x_2 + 3x_3 = 0.$$

   a. Find A, X, B such that $AX = B$.

   b. Is the system homogeneous?

   c. Can you think of any solution matrix X that will satisfy the equation?

   d. Verify that $[-1, 1, 1]^T$ is a solution.

4. a. Describe verbally the following set of points in the x, y-plane:

$$S = \{(x, y) \mid y = 2x + 1\}$$

   b. Represent S geometrically by drawing its graph.

   c. Consider $T = \{(x, y) \mid y = -x + 1\}$. Draw the graph of T on the same set of axes as you did S.

   d. Geometrically, what is $S \cap T$?

   e. What is the relationship between your solution in d. and the solution of the set of equations

$$y - 2x = 1$$
$$y + x = 1 \ ?$$

5. Let X_1 and X_2 be solutions of a homogeneous equation $AX = 0$. Use the properties of matrix addition and multiplication to show that:

   a. $X_1 + X_2$ is a solution to $AX = 0$.
   b. cX_1 is a solution to $AX = 0$, for any scalar c (you need to use the properties of scalar multiplication here).
   c. For any scalars c_1, c_2,

   $$Y = c_1 X_1 + c_2 X_2 \text{ is a solution to } AX = 0.$$

6. Verify the statements of Exercise 5 above for the case where

   $$A = \begin{bmatrix} 1 & -1 \\ 2 & -2 \end{bmatrix}, \text{ and } X_1 = \begin{bmatrix} 1 \\ 1 \end{bmatrix}, X_2 = \begin{bmatrix} -3 \\ -3 \end{bmatrix}.$$

New terms

homogeneous equation, 59
homogeneous set of equations, 59
solution of a matrix equation, 60

complete or general solution set, 60
non-homogeneous set of equations, 60
linear combination, 61

3.2 Geometrical solutions

It is possible to find solutions of each of the sets of equations in the previous section geometrically, since the graph of each equation is a straight line in the x_1, x_2-plane.

Example 3.2.1

$$2x_1 + 3x_2 = 0$$
$$4x_1 + 2x_2 = 0.$$

By setting one of the variables equal to some constant we can solve for the value of the remaining variable and obtain a point on the graph of the straight line represented by the equation. For example, letting $x_2 = 2$ in the first equation we find that $x_1 = (-3/2)x_2 = (-3/2)(2) = -3$, so that $(x_1, x_2) = (-3, 2)$ is on the first line. If we let $x_2 = -2$ we find that $x_1 = (-3/2)(-2) = 3$, so that $(3, -2)$ is also on the line. Drawing an x_1, x_2-axis system as shown in Figure 3.2.1, we can then plot the points $(-3, 2)$ and $(3, -2)$ and use them to obtain the graph of the straight line. For equation 2, we find that $x_1 = (-1/2)x_2$. If $x_2 = 2$, then $x_1 = -1$ so that $(-1, 2)$ is on the second line. When $x_2 = -2$, then $x_1 = 1$, and $(1, -2)$ is also on the line. We plot and connect these two points to obtain the graph of the second line as shown in Figure 3.2.1.

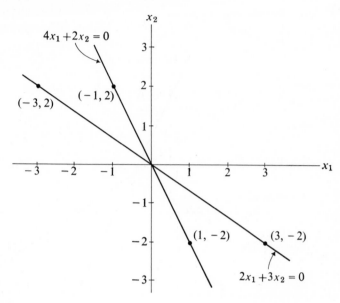

Figure 3.2.1

In Example 3.2.1, the two straight lines, whose equations are given above, intersect only at the point (0, 0) in the plane. We would thus say that $0 = \begin{bmatrix} 0 \\ 0 \end{bmatrix}$ is the *unique* (only) solution. For such a homogeneous set of equations we say that 0 is the **trivial solution**, since it is always true that a homogeneous set of linear equations will be satisfied if we set all of the x_i equal to zero. Therefore we will be concerned with finding non-trivial solutions for such a set of equations.

The geometrical solution for the second example is shown in Figure 3.2.2.

Example 3.2.2

$$2x_1 + 3x_2 = 5$$
$$4x_1 + 2x_2 = 6.$$

We see from the graphical solution of Example 3.2.2 that we again have a unique point of intersection, namely the point (1, 1). Thus again, the matrix $X = \begin{bmatrix} 1 \\ 1 \end{bmatrix}$ is our desired solution matrix for the matrix equation $AX = B$. We can verify this by substitution in the original set of linear equations or by checking to see that

$$AX = \begin{bmatrix} 2 & 3 \\ 4 & 2 \end{bmatrix} \begin{bmatrix} 1 \\ 1 \end{bmatrix}$$

is indeed equal to the matrix $\begin{bmatrix} 5 \\ 6 \end{bmatrix} = B$.

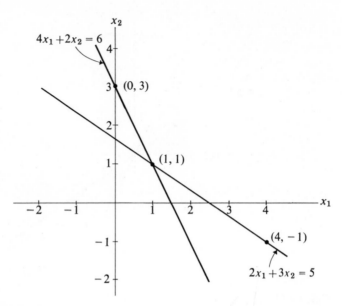

Figure 3.2.2

Unfortunately, this geometrical approach fails us when we have more than three unknowns or variables, and we must defer to a strictly algebraic procedure for our solutions. It will be very helpful, however, even when we are dealing with larger systems, for the reader to refer to the geometry of two or three dimensions and to reflect upon the problems of intersecting lines or of intersecting planes, and the possible solutions that result.

Example 3.2.3

The set of points (x_1, x_2, x_3) which satisfy the equation

$$x_1 + x_2 + x_3 = 1$$

all lie on a plane (a surface of two dimensions) in 3-dimensional space. Letting two of the variables, say x_1 and x_2, be 0, we find that $x_3 = 1$, or that the point $(0, 0, 1)$ lies on the plane in question. Letting $x_2 = x_3 = 0$, we have $x_1 = 1$, so that $(1, 0, 0)$ is on the plane. Similarly, $(0, 1, 0)$ is also on the plane. Connecting these points as shown in Figure 3.2.3, we have a pictorial representation of part of the plane.

In general, two such planes which intersect will intersect in a line as shown in Figure 3.2.4. The reader should now consider the various intersection possibilities which arise when a third plane is introduced.

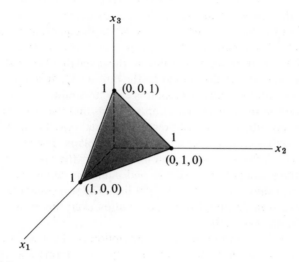

Figure 3.2.3

There is yet another geometrical way of looking at sets of equations and their solutions. Consider the equations of Example 3.2.1 and refer to Figure 3.2.1.

$$2x_1 + 3x_2 = 0$$
$$4x_1 + 2x_2 = 0.$$

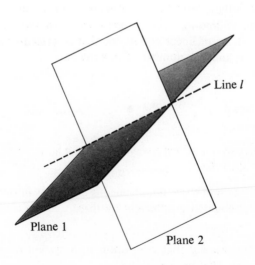

Figure 3.2.4

Let A be the set of points in the plane which satisfy the first equation (the points of A form a straight line) and let B denote the set of points in the plane which satisfy the second equation (also a straight line). Then the set of points which satisfy both equations is the set of points that are common to both A and B; that is, $A \cap B$. In this case, $A \cap B = \{(0,0)\}$. If there were no points in the plane that satisfied both equations then the intersection would be the null set $\emptyset$. When one thinks of a set of equations in this fashion, it is easy to comprehend that we start with a certain set of potential solution points and then successively eliminate certain subsets as we add restrictive equations. Thus, in Example 3.2.1, we start with the set of all points in the plane. The first equation, alone, removes from consideration all points of the plane except those on a certain straight line. The second equation, alone, removes all points except those on another straight line. The two equations, together, thus succeed in deleting from consideration every point in the plane except one, namely $(0, 0)$.

Before we proceed to a description of the general problem, let us pause to reiterate some of the important terms and methods so far discussed in this chapter.

At this point you should be able to recognize given sets of equations as being *homogeneous* or *non-homogeneous*. You should know what we mean by a *solution* to such a set of equations. You should be able to express a set of equations in either of the two matrix formats covered, and also be able to solve small sets of equations graphically. We recall that a homogeneous set of equations always has at least the *trivial* solution. Can you think of any small homogeneous set of equations which has more than this one solution?

With these introductory ideas in mind, we now turn to the general problem of finding solution matrices X (if any exist) for arbitrarily large systems of linear equations, that is, systems with any number of equations and any number of unknowns.

Exercises 3.2

1. The solution which always exists for a homogeneous set of equations is called the _____ solution.

2. A system of three homogeneous equations in two unknowns x_1, x_2 is represented graphically by three _____ which intersect at _____.

3. When we say that a solution to a system of linear equations is *unique*, what do we mean?

4. Solve the following systems of equations graphically:

a. $x_1 - x_2 = 0$
     $2x_1 + x_2 = 0$

b. $x_1 + 2x_2 = 3$
     $-3x_1 + x_2 = -2$

c. $2x_1 - x_2 = 3$
     $x_1 + 4x_2 = 6$
     $4x_1 + 7x_2 = 15$

d. $x_1 + x_2 = 4$
     $-x_1 - x_2 = -4.$

5. Describe the geometric counterpart of the following:
    a. One linear equation in two unknowns
    b. Two linear equations in two unknowns
    c. One homogeneous linear equation in three unknowns
    d. Two linear equations in three unknowns
    e. Three homogeneous linear equations in three unknowns

6. Use your intuitive knowledge of geometry in 2 and 3 dimensions to answer the following:
    a. In which of the cases of Exercise 5 above must solutions exist?
    b. In which of the cases of Exercise 5 above must more than one solution exist?

7. In Exercise 4a. above, what set of points is excluded by the first equation? By the second equation? What set of points is excluded by the pair of equations?

New terms

trivial solution, 63

3.3   The general problem

If we let m and n be any positive integers, then we can formulate our general problem as that of finding values for the unknowns $x_1, x_2, \ldots,$ x_n such that

$$a_{11}x_1 + a_{12}x_2 + \cdots + a_{1n}x_n = b_1$$
$$a_{21}x_1 + a_{22}x_2 + \cdots + a_{2n}x_n = b_2$$
$$\cdots$$
$$a_{m1}x_1 + a_{m2}x_2 + \cdots + a_{mn}x_n = b_m,$$

where we assume that the constants a_{ij} and b_i are known real numbers for all i and j. To express this problem in the first matrix format, we merely let

$$A = [a_{ij}] = \begin{bmatrix} a_{11} & a_{12} & \cdots & a_{1n} \\ a_{21} & a_{22} & \cdots & a_{2n} \\ & & \cdots & \\ a_{m1} & a_{m2} & \cdots & a_{mn} \end{bmatrix}, \quad X = \begin{bmatrix} x_1 \\ x_2 \\ \vdots \\ x_n \end{bmatrix}, \quad B = \begin{bmatrix} b_1 \\ b_2 \\ \vdots \\ b_m \end{bmatrix},$$

from which we obtain the matrix representation

$$AX = B$$

as before. In this general case, as in our previous examples, we will say that the set of equations is **homogeneous** if $B = 0$. Otherwise, the set will be called **non-homogeneous**.

To obtain the second matrix formulation we let A_i denote column i of A, so that

$$A_1 = \begin{bmatrix} a_{11} \\ a_{21} \\ \vdots \\ a_{m1} \end{bmatrix}, A_2 = \begin{bmatrix} a_{12} \\ a_{22} \\ \vdots \\ a_{m2} \end{bmatrix}, \ldots, A_n = \begin{bmatrix} a_{1n} \\ a_{2n} \\ \vdots \\ a_{mn} \end{bmatrix}.$$

We then wish to find constants $x_1, x_2, \ldots, x_n$ such that

$$x_1 A_1 + x_2 A_2 + \cdots + x_n A_n = B.$$

Example 3.3.1

$$x_1 + 2x_2 + 3x_3 + x_4 = 7$$
$$2x_1 + x_2 + x_3 + 2x_4 = 6$$
$$-x_1 + x_2 + 2x_3 - x_4 = 1.$$

In this non-homogeneous set of three equations in four unknowns we see that $m = 3$ and $n = 4$, while

$$A = \begin{bmatrix} 1 & 2 & 3 & 1 \\ 2 & 1 & 1 & 2 \\ -1 & 1 & 2 & -1 \end{bmatrix}, \quad X = \begin{bmatrix} x_1 \\ x_2 \\ x_3 \\ x_4 \end{bmatrix}, \quad B = \begin{bmatrix} 7 \\ 6 \\ 1 \end{bmatrix}.$$

The reader may have observed that, in reality, all of the known information is contained in the **augmented matrix** denoted by $[A \mid B]$, in which we merely write the column of constants, B, as an additional column to obtain a slightly larger matrix. In the general case the augmented matrix is the partitioned matrix

$$[A \mid B] = \begin{bmatrix} a_{11} & a_{12} & \cdots & a_{1n} & b_1 \\ a_{21} & a_{22} & \cdots & a_{2n} & b_2 \\ \cdot & \cdot & \cdots & \cdot & \vdots \\ a_{m1} & a_{m2} & \cdots & a_{mn} & b_m \end{bmatrix},$$

while in Example 3.3.1 the augmented matrix is

$$[A \mid B] = \begin{bmatrix} 1 & 2 & 3 & 1 & \bigm| & 7 \\ 2 & 1 & 1 & 2 & \bigm| & 6 \\ -1 & 1 & 2 & -1 & \bigm| & 1 \end{bmatrix}.$$

We observe that in both cases we have essentially removed the unknowns from the sets of equations to obtain the augmented matrices.

It may prove helpful to the reader to consider the general problem in the same manner that we considered the two-dimensional example earlier. When we have m equations in n unknowns we are looking for the set of elements in n-dimensional space (a concept which may be rather vague at the moment—you may think of these elements as merely column matrices with n elements just as we may think of 2-space as consisting of column matrices with two elements) which satisfy each of the m equations. Letting S_1 denote the subset of n-space which satisfies equation 1, and S_2 the subset which satisfies equation 2, etc., then the solution set for the system of m equations may be considered to be the intersection of the m sets $S_1, S_2, \ldots, S_m$; that is,

$$S_1 \cap S_2 \cap \cdots \cap S_m.$$

If there are no points in the intersection then there are no solutions to the set of equations. If it should be the case that equation 3, for example, excludes no points from consideration not already excluded by equation 1 and equation 2, then we say that equation 3 is a **redundant equation**, with respect to equation 1 and equation 2. Equivalently, we may say that equation 3 is redundant if

$$S_1 \cap S_2 = S_1 \cap S_2 \cap S_3.$$

For example, if we were to add a third equation to the two of Example 3.2.1, say

$$x_1 - x_2 = 0$$

whose solution points also form a straight line through the origin as shown in Figure 3.3.1, then it is seen that the new equation has really excluded no new points, and is thus redundant. It could just as well have been omitted as far as its effect upon the ultimate solution is concerned.

Several questions arise about the existence and number of solutions to our general problem. All of these questions have geometrical counterparts in two- and three-dimensional problems concerning the existence and number of points of intersection of lines and planes. Thus, for a given set of equations with matrix format $AX = B$, one may ask:

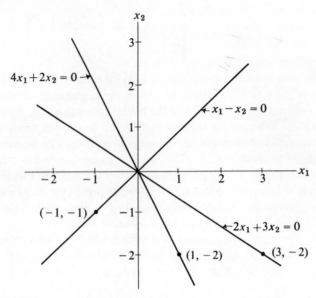

Figure 3.3.1

1. Are there any solutions? (Do the lines or planes intersect?)
2. If so, is the solution unique?
3. If there is at least one solution and it is not unique, how many solutions are there?
4. What is the complete set of solutions?

These are the types of questions to which we will develop answers in the following sections. After a slight diversion we shall develop a simple but systematic and easily-computerized technique for solving the general problem when A is square and nonsingular. We will thus gain experience with the essential ideas involved so that the extension of our technique to the singular and non-square cases will not be difficult.

Exercises 3.3

1. Let

$$A = \begin{bmatrix} 1 & -1 & 2 & 4 \\ 0 & 2 & 3 & 7 \\ 6 & 3 & 4 & 5 \end{bmatrix}, B = \begin{bmatrix} 2 & 1 \\ 3 & 3 \\ 4 & 7 \end{bmatrix}, C = \begin{bmatrix} 1 & 2 \\ 3 & 4 \end{bmatrix},$$

$$D = \begin{bmatrix} 1 \\ 2 \\ 3 \end{bmatrix}, E = \begin{bmatrix} 3 \\ 7 \end{bmatrix}.$$

Write down the augmented matrices for the following equations for which the multiplication makes sense, and suppose that X, Y, Z are column matrices of appropriate length.

   a. $AX = D$ b. $AY = E$ c. $BZ = D$ d. $CX = E$.

2. Consider the system of equations:

$$x_1 - 2x_2 = -1$$
$$2x_1 + 3x_2 = 5$$
$$-x_1 + 5x_2 = 4$$

   a. Describe S_1, S_2, S_3 as they apply to this problem.

   b. Find $S_1 \cap S_2$ and $S_2 \cap S_3$.

   c. In order that any solution exist, it is necessary that $S_1 \cap S_2 =$ _____.

   d. Here we observe that when we have two unknowns we can have no more than two non-redundant equations. If we have n unknowns, how many non-redundant equations do you think we can have and still have a solution?

3. Let A be any 2×2 matrix, $B = \begin{bmatrix} 1 \\ 0 \end{bmatrix}$, $C = \begin{bmatrix} 0 \\ 1 \end{bmatrix}$. Suppose that we solve the equations $AX = B$ and $AY = C$ for X and Y, and solutions exist.

   a. Consider $A[X | Y] = [AX | AY] = \begin{bmatrix} 1 & 0 \\ 0 & 1 \end{bmatrix}$. What can you conclude about A^{-1}?

   b. Let $A = \begin{bmatrix} 0 & -1 \\ -1 & 0 \end{bmatrix}$. Use the technique described above to find A^{-1}.

New terms

augmented matrix, 68   redundant equation, 69

3.4 A special case—solution by analogy

Because it fits with our philosophy of presenting new ideas by analogy with previously well-understood concepts, we shall digress from our general solution procedure and first investigate the solution of certain problems in which A is a square matrix, implying that the number of equations is the same as the number of unknowns. Examples 3.2.1 and 3.2.2 are of this type. There is a special solution technique which is sometimes available for the solution of equations of this form.

The method which we wish to illustrate arises as an analogue of the solution of the single equation

$$ax = b,$$

when a, x, and b are each real numbers and a is not zero. To be specific, suppose that we wish to find a number x such that

$$2x = 3.$$

As we indicated in Section 1.3, we merely multiply both sides of the equation by $\frac{1}{2}$ to obtain

$$(\tfrac{1}{2})(2x) = (\tfrac{1}{2} \cdot 2)x = 1x = x$$

and

$$\tfrac{1}{2}(3) = \tfrac{3}{2}$$

so that

$$x = \tfrac{3}{2}.$$

Thus the only possible solution is 3/2. The solution above depends upon our being able to find the multiplicative inverse of the real number $a = 2$; that is, we found a number a^{-1} such that $a^{-1}a = 1$. In general, we can always find the multiplicative inverse of a non-zero real number a (namely, $a^{-1} = 1/a$), and hence we can always solve such an equation by multiplying both sides of the equation by a^{-1}. Thus to solve $ax = b$, we multiply both sides by $1/a$ to obtain

$$\left(\frac{1}{a}\right)(ax) = \left(\frac{1}{a} \cdot a\right)x = 1x = x$$

and

$$\left(\frac{1}{a}\right)b = a^{-1}b,$$

so that

$$x = a^{-1}b,$$

from which we note that $x = a^{-1}b$ is the only possible solution.

Let us now recall Example 3.2.2 in its matrix formulation $AX = B$, where

$$A = \begin{bmatrix} 2 & 3 \\ 4 & 2 \end{bmatrix}, \quad X = \begin{bmatrix} x_1 \\ x_2 \end{bmatrix}, \quad \text{and} \quad B = \begin{bmatrix} 5 \\ 6 \end{bmatrix},$$

and describe the analogy which exists with the above procedure. We suppose that we know a matrix which we have called A^{-1} such that $AA^{-1} = A^{-1}A = I_2$. Then $A(A^{-1}B) = (AA^{-1})B = I_2 B = B$ so that $A^{-1}B$ is a solution. Moreover, multiplying each side of the equation

$AX = B$ by A^{-1} on the left, we obtain

$$A^{-1}(AX) = (A^{-1}A)X = I_2 X = X = A^{-1}B$$

implying that $X = A^{-1}B$ is the unique solution. The same argument, of course, is valid for any size non-singular matrix A. In the specific example above, A^{-1} does exist and we check that

$$A^{-1} = \begin{bmatrix} -2/8 & 3/8 \\ 4/8 & -2/8 \end{bmatrix}$$

by multiplication. Thus

$$A^{-1}A = \begin{bmatrix} -2/8 & 3/8 \\ 4/8 & -2/8 \end{bmatrix}\begin{bmatrix} 2 & 3 \\ 4 & 2 \end{bmatrix} = \begin{bmatrix} 1 & 0 \\ 0 & 1 \end{bmatrix}$$

$$= AA^{-1} = \begin{bmatrix} 2 & 3 \\ 4 & 2 \end{bmatrix}\begin{bmatrix} -2/8 & 3/8 \\ 4/8 & -2/8 \end{bmatrix}.$$

We now calculate $X = A^{-1}B$ as

$$X = A^{-1}B = \begin{bmatrix} -2/8 & 3/8 \\ 4/8 & -2/8 \end{bmatrix}\begin{bmatrix} 5 \\ 6 \end{bmatrix} = \begin{bmatrix} 1 \\ 1 \end{bmatrix},$$

the same solution which we found earlier by geometrical considerations.

To further illustrate this method, recall Example 3.2.1 in which A is the same as above, but $B = 0$. Since the same inverse suffices, we have

$$X = A^{-1}B = A^{-1}0 = \begin{bmatrix} 0 \\ 0 \end{bmatrix},$$

which is the same solution we obtained earlier. Although this method appears very easy at first glance, we must point out two important drawbacks as far as our present situation is concerned. First, even if the method were applicable, we do not at present know how to calculate A^{-1}. Secondly, the method does not work for all square matrices A because, as was shown in the previous chapter, not all square matrices have a multiplicative inverse.

We thus observe that this method does have limitations, but in those cases in which A^{-1} does exist and you happen to know what it is (for example, if we tell you), you should be able to find the solution X very easily.

In the next section we shall begin to describe a solution technique which will always work, in the sense that if there are any solutions, we will find all of them, and if there are none, then we will discover that fact also. The procedure is called *Gauss-Jordan reduction* after the men who received credit for its discovery. As we indicated earlier, we shall first consider the case where A is a non-singular square matrix and then proceed to the more general case in which A may not even be square.

Exercises 3.4

1. Consider the set of equations $AX = B$ where $A = \begin{bmatrix} 1 & -1 \\ -1 & 2 \end{bmatrix}$,
    $X = \begin{bmatrix} x_1 \\ x_2 \end{bmatrix}$, $B = \begin{bmatrix} -1 \\ 4 \end{bmatrix}$.
    a. Verify that $A^{-1} = \begin{bmatrix} 2 & 1 \\ 1 & 1 \end{bmatrix}$.
    b. Use A^{-1} to find X. Verify that X is a solution.
    c. Solve the equation $A^{-1}Y = 0$, where $Y = \begin{bmatrix} y_1 \\ y_2 \end{bmatrix}$:

2. Let $A = \begin{bmatrix} 1 & 0 & 1 \\ -1 & 1 & 0 \\ 0 & 1 & 2 \end{bmatrix}$, $X = \begin{bmatrix} x_1 \\ x_2 \\ x_3 \end{bmatrix}$, $B = \begin{bmatrix} -2 \\ 0 \\ -1 \end{bmatrix}$, and consider
    $AX = B$.
    a. Verify that $A^{-1} = \begin{bmatrix} 2 & 1 & -1 \\ 2 & 2 & -1 \\ -1 & -1 & 1 \end{bmatrix}$.
    b. Use A^{-1} to find X. Verify that X is a solution.
    c. Solve the equation $A^{-1}Y = \begin{bmatrix} -1 \\ 1 \\ -1 \end{bmatrix}$.

3. Let $A = \begin{bmatrix} 1 & -1 \\ 0 & 1 \end{bmatrix}$, $X = \begin{bmatrix} x_1 \\ x_2 \end{bmatrix}$, and $B = \begin{bmatrix} 0 \\ 1 \end{bmatrix}$.
    a. Verify that $A^{-1} = \begin{bmatrix} 1 & 1 \\ 0 & 1 \end{bmatrix}$, and
    b. Solve the equation $AX = B$. Verify that X is a solution.
    c. Solve the equation $A^{-1}Y = B$.

3.5   Gauss-Jordan reduction for non-singular square matrices

The basic principle underlying the algorithm (computational procedure) known as **Gauss-Jordan reduction** is the following:

One may exchange the augmented matrix representation $[A \mid B]$ of the original set of equations for a new but equivalent augmented matrix representation, in the sense that any solution matrix for either represented problem is also a solution for the other.

We wish to systematically exchange augmented matrix representations until we obtain a form so simple that the solution matrix X is obvious. For example, from the augmented matrix representation

$$\left[\begin{array}{cc|c} 1 & 0 & 5 \\ 0 & 1 & -3 \end{array}\right]$$

for the set of equations

$$1x_1 + 0x_2 = 5$$
$$0x_1 + 1x_2 = -3$$

we readily observe that $X = \begin{bmatrix} 5 \\ -3 \end{bmatrix}$ is the desired solution. Our goal, then, is to be able to start with augmented matrices of a more complicated form, and to systematically "reduce" them to equivalent augmented matrices in successively simpler form, terminating when we have reached the simplest possible augmented matrix representation. Using $A^{(1)}$ to denote A and $B^{(1)}$ to denote B at the start of our problem, and then exchanging $A^{(1)}$ for $A^{(2)}$ and $B^{(1)}$ for $B^{(2)}$, we will generate a sequence $[A \mid B] = [A^{(1)} \mid B^{(1)}]$, $[A^{(2)} \mid B^{(2)}]$, $[A^{(3)} \mid B^{(3)}]$, $\ldots$, $[A^{(s)} \mid B^{(s)}]$ of augmented matrix representations of s different sets of linear equations —all equivalent in that they have exactly the same solutions.

A problem that immediately arises is the following one. What reduction operations may we perform on a given augmented matrix and insure that the set of solution matrices does not change? The allowable operations are simply the analogues of the operations that one may perform on a set of equations without changing the solution set. Namely, one may perform operations of the following three types without affecting the solutions:

Type 1: Multiply any equation by a non-zero constant.

Example 3.5.1

$$x_1 + x_2 = 2 \quad \text{and} \quad 2x_1 + 2x_2 = 4$$

have exactly the same solution set.

Type 2: Interchange any two equations.

Example 3.5.2

$$\begin{array}{l} x_1 + x_2 = 2 \\ x_1 - x_2 = 4 \end{array} \quad \text{and} \quad \begin{array}{l} x_1 - x_2 = 4 \\ x_1 + x_2 = 2 \end{array}$$

have exactly the same solution set.

Type 3: Replace any equation by the *new* equation obtained by multiplying any other equation by a constant and adding the result to the original equation.

Example 3.5.3

$$x_1 + x_2 = 2 \qquad \text{and} \qquad x_1 + x_2 = 2$$
$$x_1 - x_2 = 4 \qquad\qquad\qquad 3x_1 + x_2 = 8$$

have the same solution set; namely $X = \begin{bmatrix} x_1 \\ x_2 \end{bmatrix} = \begin{bmatrix} 3 \\ -1 \end{bmatrix}$.

The original second equation has been replaced by a new equation obtained by multiplying equation 1 by the constant 2 and adding the resulting equation to equation 2. If the constant of multiplication in the operation of Type 3 happens to be 1, then we have merely added equations; while if the constant is (-1) then we have subtracted.

In order to obtain the allowable operations on the augmented matrix, we merely replace the word "equation(s)" by "row(s)" in the above description of Type 1, Type 2, and Type 3 operations.

Let us now consider the following set of equations from Example 3.1.2 and its equivalent augmented matrix form. We will systematically exchange the sets of equations and their respective augmented matrix forms, using operations of the three types just described, until we reach sets from which the solution is obvious.

Equations   *Augmented Matrix Form*

$$2x_1 + 3x_2 = 5 \qquad\qquad \begin{bmatrix} 2 & 3 & | & 5 \\ 4 & 2 & | & 6 \end{bmatrix}$$
$$4x_1 + 2x_2 = 6$$

We replace the first set of equations with an equivalent set in which the coefficient of x_1 in equation 1 is a 1 (In some sets of equations this will require an interchange of equations. Why?). We accomplish this by multiplying the original equation 1 by 1/2, an operation of Type 1.

$$1 \cdot x_1 + (3/2)x_2 = 5/2 \qquad \begin{bmatrix} 1 & 3/2 & | & 5/2 \\ 4 & 2 & | & 6 \end{bmatrix}$$
$$4x_1 + \quad 2x_2 = 6$$

We proceed now to eliminate x_1 from all of the equations except equation 1 (namely, equation 2 in this case) by means of operations of Type 3. To do so, we replace the present second equation by the new equation obtained by multiplying equation 1 by (-4) and adding it to equation 2 to obtain

$$1 \cdot x_1 + (3/2)x_2 = 5/2 \qquad \begin{bmatrix} 1 & 3/2 & | & 5/2 \\ 0 & -4 & | & -4 \end{bmatrix}.$$
$$0 \cdot x_1 - 4x_2 \quad = -4$$

We now replace the last set of equations by a set in which the coefficient of x_2 in equation 2 is the constant 1, by multiplying equation 2 by $(-1/4)$, another operation of Type 1.

$$1 \cdot x_1 + (3/2)x_2 = 5/2 \qquad \begin{bmatrix} 1 & 3/2 & | & 5/2 \\ 0 & 1 & | & 1 \end{bmatrix}.$$
$$0 \cdot x_1 + \quad 1 \cdot x_2 = 1$$

We conclude by eliminating x_2 from equation 1 by another Type 3 operation in which we replace equation 1 by the new equation obtained from multiplying equation 2 by $(-3/2)$ and adding the result to equation 1. Thus we have

$$
\begin{aligned}
1 \cdot x_1 + 0 \cdot x_2 &= 1 \\
0 \cdot x_1 + 1 \cdot x_2 &= 1
\end{aligned}
\qquad
\left[\begin{array}{cc|c}
1 & 0 & 1 \\
0 & 1 & 1
\end{array}\right].
$$

We see that in this case we have been able, by means of operations of Type 1 and Type 3 to obtain an equivalent augmented matrix representation from which we can readily find the solution to the original set of equations. What is it?

Although not used in the foregoing example, operations of Type 2 are sometimes required. For instance, if the original set of equations had been

$$
\begin{aligned}
0 \cdot x_1 + 3x_2 &= 1 \\
2x_1 - x_2 &= 3
\end{aligned}
$$

then our algorithm fails at the first step (since the coefficient of x_1 in equation 1 is 0, and hence has no multiplicative inverse). At this point we merely interchange the two equations and proceed as before. The reader should note that this situation might occur at later steps in the algorithm, and, if so, that we remedy the situation by interchanging the faulty equation with any following equation which has a non-zero coefficient for the unknown in question. (In the non-singular case there will always be such an equation.) We shall illustrate this further after the next example.

Example 3.5.4

$$
\begin{aligned}
x_1 - x_2 + x_3 &= 3 \\
4x_1 - 3x_2 - x_3 &= 6 \\
3x_1 + x_2 + 2x_3 &= 4
\end{aligned}
$$

In this case the original augmented matrix representation is

$$
\left[\begin{array}{ccc|c}
1 & -1 & 1 & 3 \\
4 & -3 & -1 & 6 \\
3 & 1 & 2 & 4
\end{array}\right].
$$

In order to proceed to an equivalent augmented matrix representation in a simpler form, we wish to find one in which the only non-zero element in column 1 is the constant 1 in row 1. In other words, we are exchanging the original set of equations for a new set of equations with the same solution set, but with the helpful property that x_1 has been eliminated from all of the equations except equation 1. In order to accomplish this, we merely perform two operations of Type 3, replacing row 2 and row 3 as follows:

For row 2, we multiply row one by (-4) and add the result to the original row 2 to obtain the equivalent augmented matrix

$$\left[\begin{array}{ccc|c} 1 & -1 & 1 & 3 \\ 0 & 1 & -5 & -6 \\ 3 & 1 & 2 & 4 \end{array}\right];$$

and we denote this change by writing $R_2 \leftarrow -4R_1 + R_2$, which means that the contents of row 2 have been replaced as indicated. For row 3, we multiply row 1 by (-3) and add the result to the original row 3 to obtain

$$\left[\begin{array}{ccc|c} 1 & -1 & 1 & 3 \\ 0 & 1 & -5 & -6 \\ 0 & 4 & -1 & -5 \end{array}\right],$$

and note that $R_3 \leftarrow -3R_1 + R_3$.

We now proceed to essentially eliminate x_2 from all equations except the second, obtaining an equivalent augmented matrix representation in which the only non-zero element in column 2 is the number 1 in row 2. We first obtain

$$\left[\begin{array}{ccc|c} 1 & 0 & -4 & -3 \\ 0 & 1 & -5 & -6 \\ 0 & 4 & -1 & -5 \end{array}\right],$$

in which $R_1 \leftarrow R_2 + R_1$, in order to have the desired zero in the 1, 2 position, and then let $R_3 \leftarrow -4R_2 + R_3$ to arrive at

$$\left[\begin{array}{ccc|c} 1 & 0 & -4 & -3 \\ 0 & 1 & -5 & -6 \\ 0 & 0 & 19 & 19 \end{array}\right],$$

with the desired zero in the 3, 2 position.

To achieve an even simpler form, we perform an operation of Type 1, multiplying row 3 (equation 3) by $1/19$ to obtain

$$\left[\begin{array}{ccc|c} 1 & 0 & -4 & -3 \\ 0 & 1 & -5 & -6 \\ 0 & 0 & 1 & 1 \end{array}\right],$$

where $R_3 \leftarrow (1/19)R_3$, and then obtain zeros in positions 1, 3 and 2, 3 by essentially eliminating x_3 from all of the corresponding equations except for equation 3. First, we change row 2 to get

$$\left[\begin{array}{ccc|c} 1 & 0 & -4 & -3 \\ 0 & 1 & 0 & -1 \\ 0 & 0 & 1 & 1 \end{array}\right],$$

in which we let $R_2 \leftarrow 5R_3 + R_2$, and then change row 1 to finally arrive at

$$\begin{bmatrix} 1 & 0 & 0 & | & 1 \\ 0 & 1 & 0 & | & -1 \\ 0 & 0 & 1 & | & 1 \end{bmatrix},$$

by letting $R_1 \leftarrow 4R_3 + R_1$. We can then see immediately that our solution is

$$X = \begin{bmatrix} x_1 \\ x_2 \\ x_3 \end{bmatrix} = \begin{bmatrix} 1 \\ -1 \\ 1 \end{bmatrix},$$

as we may verify by direct substitution in the original set of equations.

The technique illustrated above is a straightforward method of solution that is sufficient to solve systems of linear equations in which the coefficient matrix A is square and non-singular. The procedure may be very easily programmed for use on a digital computer. *By the use of certain allowable row operations which do not affect the solution set, we have merely exchanged $[A \mid B]$ for a sequence of equivalent representations—first eliminating x_1 from all equations except the first, then eliminating x_2 from all equations except the second, and proceeding, in general, until x_n has been removed from all equations except the nth.* We should re-emphasize here that we refer to the final numbering of the equations after they have been juggled (perhaps more than once) to insure that the (perhaps revised) coefficient of x_i is not 0 in equation i. The following example illustrates the procedure in a case where such juggling is required.

Example 3.5.5

$$\begin{aligned} x_1 + x_2 + x_3 &= 3 \\ 2x_1 + 2x_2 + x_3 &= 5 \\ x_1 + 2x_2 + 3x_3 &= 6. \end{aligned}$$

We shall use the symbol $\sim$ to mean "is equivalent to." Proceeding as before, we find that

$$\begin{bmatrix} 1 & 1 & 1 & | & 3 \\ 2 & 2 & 1 & | & 5 \\ 1 & 2 & 3 & | & 6 \end{bmatrix} \sim \begin{bmatrix} 1 & 1 & 1 & | & 3 \\ 0 & 0 & -1 & | & -1 \\ 0 & 1 & 2 & | & 3 \end{bmatrix}.$$

$$R_2 \leftarrow -2R_1 + R_2$$
$$R_3 \leftarrow -1R_1 + R_3$$

At this point we notice that the 2, 2 element is 0. Since the 3, 2 element is non-zero, namely 1, we interchange the last two rows (indicated by $R_2 \leftrightarrow R_3$) to obtain

$$\begin{bmatrix} 1 & 1 & 1 & | & 3 \\ 0 & 1 & 2 & | & 3 \\ 0 & 0 & -1 & | & -1 \end{bmatrix},$$

$$R_2 \leftrightarrow R_3$$

from which we would proceed as before:

$$\begin{bmatrix} 1 & 1 & 1 & | & 3 \\ 0 & 1 & 2 & | & 3 \\ 0 & 0 & -1 & | & -1 \end{bmatrix} \sim \begin{bmatrix} 1 & 0 & -1 & | & 0 \\ 0 & 1 & 2 & | & 3 \\ 0 & 0 & -1 & | & -1 \end{bmatrix}$$

$$R_1 \leftarrow -R_2 + R_1$$

$$\sim \begin{bmatrix} 1 & 0 & -1 & | & 0 \\ 0 & 1 & 2 & | & 3 \\ 0 & 0 & 1 & | & 1 \end{bmatrix}$$

$$R_3 \leftarrow -R_3$$

$$\sim \begin{bmatrix} 1 & 0 & 0 & | & 1 \\ 0 & 1 & 0 & | & 1 \\ 0 & 0 & 1 & | & 1 \end{bmatrix}.$$

$$R_1 \leftarrow \quad R_3 + R_1$$
$$R_2 \leftarrow -2R_3 + R_2$$

The unique solution is the matrix $X = \begin{bmatrix} 1 \\ 1 \\ 1 \end{bmatrix}$.

We thus have a system for solving $AX = B$ when A is square and non-singular. We will first use this procedure to develop a method to find A^{-1} and then extend the Gauss-Jordan algorithm to cover the case when A is singular. Perhaps you can design the method for computing $A^{-1} = \begin{bmatrix} a & b \\ c & d \end{bmatrix}$ yourself. Consider, in the 2×2 case, the problem of finding A^{-1} when $A = \begin{bmatrix} 4 & 1 \\ 3 & 2 \end{bmatrix}$. What two matrix equations are to be solved? Could they be solved concurrently?

Exercises 3.5

1. What are the operations which one may perform on a system of equations without changing the solution set?

2. Consider the set of equations

$$2x_1 - x_2 = 3$$
$$4x_1 + x_2 = 7.$$

a. Find $[A^{(1)} | B^{(1)}] = [A | B]$.
b. Let $R_1 \leftarrow (1/2)R_1$, and find $[A^{(2)} | B^{(2)}]$.

3. Consider the equation $AX = B$ with $A = \begin{bmatrix} 1 & 1 \\ -1 & 2 \end{bmatrix}$, $B = \begin{bmatrix} -1 \\ 4 \end{bmatrix}$.

a. Find $[A^{(1)} | B^{(1)}]$.
b. Let $R_2 \leftarrow R_1 + R_2$ and find $[A^{(2)} | B^{(2)}]$.
c. Let $R_2 \leftarrow (1/3)R_2$ and find $[A^{(3)} | B^{(3)}]$.
d. Let $R_1 \leftarrow -R_2 + R_1$ and find $[A^{(4)} | B^{(4)}]$.
e. What is X?

4. Use the technique of this section to solve the following sets of equations.

a. $x_1 + 2x_2 = 1$ b. $2x_1 - 3x_2 = -2$
    $2x_1 + 5x_2 = 3.$ $-x_1 + 4x_2 = \quad 6.$

c. $x_1 + x_2 = 1$ d. $x_1 + x_2 = 0$
    $-x_1 + x_2 = 0.$ $-x_1 + x_2 = 1.$

5. Use the results of Exercise 4c. and 4d. above to find the inverse of the matrix $A = \begin{bmatrix} 1 & 1 \\ -1 & 1 \end{bmatrix}$.

6. Solve the equation $AX = B$ with

a. $A = \begin{bmatrix} 2 & -1 & 2 \\ 4 & -1 & 3 \\ 1 & 2 & 1 \end{bmatrix}$, $B = \begin{bmatrix} 2 \\ 5 \\ 4 \end{bmatrix}$.

b. $A = \begin{bmatrix} 2 & -1 & 3 \\ 3 & 1 & -1 \\ 1 & 2 & 3 \end{bmatrix}$, $B = \begin{bmatrix} 1 \\ 2 \\ -6 \end{bmatrix}$.

c. $A = \begin{bmatrix} 1 & 1 & 1 \\ 2 & 3 & 5 \\ -1 & 2 & 2 \end{bmatrix}$, $B = \begin{bmatrix} 0 \\ -4 \\ -6 \end{bmatrix}$.

7. Solve the equation $AX = B$, with

$$A = \begin{bmatrix} 1 & -1 & 1 & -1 \\ 0 & 1 & 0 & 1 \\ 1 & 0 & -1 & 0 \\ 0 & 1 & 0 & -1 \end{bmatrix}, B = \begin{bmatrix} -2 \\ 4 \\ 0 \\ 0 \end{bmatrix}.$$

8. Solve the equation $AX = B$, with

$$A = \begin{bmatrix} 1 & 0 & 1 & -1 & 1 \\ 2 & 1 & 1 & -1 & 3 \\ 0 & 0 & 1 & -1 & 2 \\ 3 & 1 & 4 & -4 & 4 \\ 0 & -1 & 2 & 3 & 0 \end{bmatrix}, \quad B = \begin{bmatrix} -3 \\ -2 \\ -3 \\ -11 \\ 3 \end{bmatrix}$$

New terms

Gauss-Jordan reduction, 74

3.6 The use of Gauss-Jordan reduction to find A^{-1}

We have noted previously that if we knew A^{-1} then we could find the unique X which satisfies

$$AX = B$$

by multiplication of both sides of the equation on the left by A^{-1} to obtain

$$X = A^{-1}B.$$

In Example 3.5.5 we started with an augmented matrix of the form $[A \,|\, B]$ and obtained an equivalent augmented matrix of the form $[I_3 \,|\, X]$. The matrix $[A \,|\, B]$ is an example of a **partitioned matrix**. If B_1 and B_2 are matrices with the same number of rows then the matrix $[B_1 \,|\, B_2]$ can always be formed. If A is a matrix that is conformable with each of B_1 and B_2, then the product $A[B_1 \,|\, B_2]$ is defined and

$$A[B_1 \,|\, B_2] = [AB_1 \,|\, AB_2].$$

For example,

$$\begin{bmatrix} 1 & 2 \\ 3 & 4 \end{bmatrix} \begin{bmatrix} 1 & 2 & | & 1 & 2 \\ 1 & 2 & | & 2 & 1 \end{bmatrix} = \begin{bmatrix} 3 & 6 & | & 5 & 4 \\ 7 & 14 & | & 11 & 10 \end{bmatrix}.$$

We use this type of product in the following examination of the partitioned matrix $[I_3 \,|\, X]$. We see that

$$[I_3 \,|\, X] = [I_3 \,|\, A^{-1}B]$$

and note that the same result would have been obtained by multiplying the augmented matrix $[A \,|\, B]$ on the left by A^{-1} to obtain

$$A^{-1}[A \,|\, B] = [A^{-1}A \,|\, A^{-1}B] = [I_3 \,|\, A^{-1}B] = [I_3 \,|\, X].$$

Thus we observe that the sequence of row operations which we performed on $[A \,|\, B]$ to reduce it to $[I_3 \,|\, X]$ had the same effect as if we had multiplied $[A \,|\, B]$ on the left by A^{-1}.

What if we had further augmented A with the appropriate identity matrix I_3 to form the matrix $[A \mid B \mid I_3]$? It can be proved that the effect on I_3 would then have been as if I_3 were multiplied by A^{-1} to obtain

$$A^{-1}[A \mid B \mid I_3] = [A^{-1}A \mid A^{-1}B \mid A^{-1}I_3] = [I_3 \mid X \mid A^{-1}]$$

at the completion of our sequence of row operations. *By performing the same operations on the rows of I_3 that we perform on the rows of A, we obtain A^{-1} as a by-product of our solution process.* Let us verify this in the case of Example 3.1.2, where we had the following system of equations:

$$2x_1 + 3x_2 = 5$$
$$4x_1 + 2x_2 = 6.$$

$$[A \mid B \mid I_2] = \begin{bmatrix} 2 & 3 & 5 & 1 & 0 \\ 4 & 2 & 6 & 0 & 1 \end{bmatrix} \sim \begin{bmatrix} 1 & 3/2 & 5/2 & 1/2 & 0 \\ 4 & 2 & 6 & 0 & 1 \end{bmatrix}$$

$$R_1 \leftarrow (1/2)R_1$$

$$\sim \begin{bmatrix} 1 & 3/2 & 5/2 & 1/2 & 0 \\ 0 & -4 & -4 & -2 & 1 \end{bmatrix}$$

$$R_2 \leftarrow -4R_1 + R_2$$

$$\sim \begin{bmatrix} 1 & 3/2 & 5/2 & 1/2 & 0 \\ 0 & 1 & 1 & 1/2 & -1/4 \end{bmatrix}$$

$$R_2 \leftarrow (-1/4)R_2$$

$$\sim \begin{bmatrix} 1 & 0 & 1 & -1/4 & 3/8 \\ 0 & 1 & 1 & 1/2 & -1/4 \end{bmatrix}.$$

$$R_1 \leftarrow (-3/2)R_2 + R_1$$

We verify by direct multiplication that

$$\begin{bmatrix} 2 & 3 \\ 4 & 2 \end{bmatrix} \begin{bmatrix} -1/4 & 3/8 \\ 1/2 & -1/4 \end{bmatrix} = \begin{bmatrix} 1 & 0 \\ 0 & 1 \end{bmatrix} = \begin{bmatrix} -1/4 & 3/8 \\ 1/2 & -1/4 \end{bmatrix} \begin{bmatrix} 2 & 3 \\ 4 & 2 \end{bmatrix},$$

and thus that we have found A^{-1} in this case. It should be clear that there is no need to carry the B matrix through the above manipulations if A^{-1} is the only output desired.

Exercises 3.6

1. Find A^{-1} if A is

a. $\begin{bmatrix} 1 & 2 \\ 2 & 1 \end{bmatrix}$ b. $\begin{bmatrix} 1 & -1 \\ 0 & 1 \end{bmatrix}$ c. $\begin{bmatrix} 2 & 3 \\ 4 & 5 \end{bmatrix}$

2. Use the inverses found in Exercise 1 above to solve the equations
$AX = B$ where $B = \begin{bmatrix} 1 \\ 1 \end{bmatrix}$.

3. Find A^{-1} if A is

a. $\begin{bmatrix} 1 & 1 & 1 \\ 0 & 1 & 0 \\ 0 & 0 & 1 \end{bmatrix}$

   b. $\begin{bmatrix} 1 & -1 & 1 \\ -1 & 1 & 0 \\ 0 & -1 & 1 \end{bmatrix}$

c. $\begin{bmatrix} 2 & -1 & 3 \\ 1 & 0 & 2 \\ -1 & 2 & 1 \end{bmatrix}$

4. Find A^{-1} if

$$A = \begin{bmatrix} 1 & -1 & 1 & -1 \\ 0 & 1 & 0 & 1 \\ 1 & 0 & -1 & 0 \\ 0 & 1 & 0 & -1 \end{bmatrix}.$$

New terms

partitioned matrix, 82

3.7 Gauss-Jordan reduction. The general case—redundant equations

Now that we have a reasonably good idea of how we can work with row operations and understand that we are really only eliminating the variables in a systematic fashion, we shall study the situations that arise when A is singular, or indeed when A is rectangular rather than square. In either case the previously described procedure needs some revision because of the new circumstances which will arise. One of those situations occurs when one or more of the original equations is redundant (with respect to those preceding it).

Consider the singular matrix $A = \begin{bmatrix} 1 & 2 \\ 2 & 4 \end{bmatrix}$ that we have seen before (p. 51). Suppose that we attempted to use our technique to solve a set of equations, say

$$x_1 + 2x_2 = 3$$
$$2x_1 + 4x_2 = 6$$

which has A for its coefficient matrix. Proceeding as before,

$$\begin{bmatrix} 1 & 2 & | & 3 \\ 2 & 4 & | & 6 \end{bmatrix} \sim \begin{bmatrix} 1 & 2 & | & 3 \\ 0 & 0 & | & 0 \end{bmatrix}.$$
$$R_2 \leftarrow -2R_1 + R_2$$

We now observe that it is impossible to eliminate x_2 from equation 1 by any row operation because the element in the 2, 2 position of the last matrix is 0.

It will be worthwhile to consider the geometry of the situation in an attempt to describe what has taken place. We first note that the original equation 2 is merely a multiple of equation 1 and that in reality we started with only one independent equation, namely

$$x_1 + 2x_2 = 3,$$

in that no new points were excluded from the potential solution set by the additional equation. Geometrically, the set of points in the x_1, x_2-plane which satisfy the first equation form a straight line, and there are an infinite number of them. The set of points which satisfy the second equation also form a straight line and it has turned out that the two straight lines are really the same line. *Whenever, in the course of our application of the Gauss-Jordan reduction technique, we create an entire row of zeros, we shall have discovered the fact that the original equation, whose coefficients appeared in that row, was really redundant and that its presence excluded no points as solutions which were not excluded by the previous equations.* In this particular case, we may find all of the possible solutions by letting x_2 take on some arbitrary value, say a, and then solving for x_1 to find that

$$x_1 = 3 - 2a.$$

A solution matrix X is thus any matrix of the form

$$X = \begin{bmatrix} 3 - 2a \\ a \end{bmatrix},$$

where a may be any real number whatsoever. For example, if $a = 0$, we have $X_1 = \begin{bmatrix} 3 \\ 0 \end{bmatrix}$; or if $a = 1$, we have $X_2 = \begin{bmatrix} 1 \\ 1 \end{bmatrix}$, each of which is a solution to the original set of equations. *We shall use this technique of arbitrary assignment of values to a particular subset of the variables a great deal.* We note that X as used above really denotes a set of matrices —a different one for each value of a.

Let us now investigate what would have happened if we had tried to use our standard technique to find A^{-1}. We would have proceeded to obtain

$$\begin{bmatrix} 1 & 2 & 3 & 1 & 0 \\ 2 & 4 & 6 & 0 & 1 \end{bmatrix} \sim \begin{bmatrix} 1 & 2 & 3 & 1 & 0 \\ 0 & 0 & 0 & -2 & 1 \end{bmatrix}.$$

Since there are no non-zero elements remaining in row 2 of the final left-hand submatrix we can proceed no further in our reduction to I_2 and may legitimately conclude that A^{-1} does not exist. If you happen to be familiar with 2×2 determinants, you will observe that the determinant of A, namely $\begin{bmatrix} 1 & 2 \\ 2 & 4 \end{bmatrix}$, is zero. *This is always a sure sign that* A^{-1} *does not exist.* We shall discuss determinants of square matrices of all sizes in Chapter 5.

Example 3.7.1

$$x_1 + x_2 + x_3 = 3$$
$$2x_1 - x_2 + 2x_3 = 3$$
$$4x_1 + x_2 + 4x_3 = 9.$$

$$\begin{bmatrix} 1 & 1 & 1 & | & 3 \\ 2 & -1 & 2 & | & 3 \\ 4 & 1 & 4 & | & 9 \end{bmatrix} \sim \begin{bmatrix} 1 & 1 & 1 & | & 3 \\ 0 & -3 & 0 & | & -3 \\ 0 & -3 & 0 & | & -3 \end{bmatrix}$$
$$R_2 \leftarrow -2R_1 + R_2$$
$$R_3 \leftarrow -4R_1 + R_3$$

$$\sim \begin{bmatrix} 1 & 1 & 1 & | & 3 \\ 0 & 1 & 0 & | & 1 \\ 0 & -3 & 0 & | & -3 \end{bmatrix} \sim \begin{bmatrix} 1 & 0 & 1 & | & 2 \\ 0 & 1 & 0 & | & 1 \\ 0 & 0 & 0 & | & 0 \end{bmatrix}$$
$$R_2 \leftarrow (-1/3)R_2 \qquad R_1 \leftarrow -R_2 + R_1$$
$$R_3 \leftarrow 3R_2 + R_3$$

We see that the original equation 3 was redundant. Geometrically, the plane represented by the third equation passes through the line of intersection of the first two planes, a situation illustrated in Figure 3.7.1.

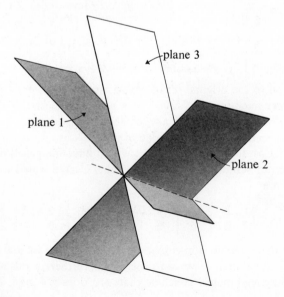

plane 3

plane 1

plane 2

Figure 3.7.1

Observing the final matrix of Example 3.7.1, namely,

$$\begin{bmatrix} 1 & 0 & 1 & | & 2 \\ 0 & 1 & 0 & | & 1 \\ 0 & 0 & 0 & | & 0 \end{bmatrix},$$

we note that the value of x_3 is not fixed by the third equation (the element in the 3, 3 position is 0). Thus we are permitted to arbitrarily assign any value, say a, to x_3. We call such a variable a **free variable**. (We shall discuss free variables more fully in the next section.) However, x_2 is fixed by equation 2, and is clearly equal to 1. Also, x_1 is fixed by equation 1, but only in terms of the parameter a. For any a that we have assigned to x_3, we have $x_1 = 2 - a$. Thus the general solution set consists of matrices X of the form

$$X = \begin{bmatrix} 2 - a \\ 1 \\ a \end{bmatrix},$$

for any value of a. We could have split the solution matrix into two parts and written

$$X = \begin{bmatrix} 2 \\ 1 \\ 0 \end{bmatrix} + a \begin{bmatrix} -1 \\ 0 \\ 1 \end{bmatrix} = X_P + X_H.$$

We use the notation X_P to denote a **particular solution** to our equation $AX = B$—that is, a single matrix X_P such that $AX_P = B$. You can verify that X_P is a particular solution to the original set of equations and that X_H is a solution to the homogeneous set of equations obtained when we let 0 replace the original constants on the right-hand side. (This will have more meaning to those of you who have studied differential equations. We shall discuss it in more detail later.)

Although we started with a square coefficient matrix in both of our examples, the phenomenon of redundancy could also have occurred had A been rectangular rather than square.

Example 3.7.2

$$2x_1 + 3x_2 = 5$$
$$4x_1 + 2x_2 = 6$$
$$2x_1 - x_2 = 1.$$

$$\begin{bmatrix} 2 & 3 & | & 5 \\ 4 & 2 & | & 6 \\ 2 & -1 & | & 1 \end{bmatrix} \sim \begin{bmatrix} 1 & 3/2 & | & 5/2 \\ 0 & -4 & | & -4 \\ 0 & -4 & | & -4 \end{bmatrix} \sim \begin{bmatrix} 1 & 0 & | & 1 \\ 0 & 1 & | & 1 \\ 0 & 0 & | & 0 \end{bmatrix}.$$

$$R_1 \leftarrow (1/2)R_1 \qquad R_2 \leftarrow (-1/4)R_2$$
$$R_2 \leftarrow -4R_1 + R_2 \quad R_1 \leftarrow (-3/2)R_2 + R_1$$
$$R_3 \leftarrow -2R_1 + R_3 \quad R_3 \leftarrow 4R_2 + R_3$$

Thus $X = \begin{bmatrix} 1 \\ 1 \end{bmatrix}$ is the unique solution.

The reader may have noticed a startling similarity between Examples 3.2.2 and 3.7.2. Geometrically, we merely added another straight line and it just happened to go through the point of intersection of the original two straight lines. If it had not, then there would have been no solution at all. We shall point out a valid general conclusion from this particular example in which we had more equations (3) than variables (2). *If, in our general problem, with m equations in n unknowns,*

$$m > n$$

then there will be no solution unless at least

$$m - n$$

of the equations are redundant. Geometrically, we may illustrate this statement by pointing out that two intersecting straight lines in the plane (not three or more) determine a point, as do three properly intersecting planes in 3-space (not four or more). In general, n non-redundant equations is the maximum number that we may have in n-space if a solution is to exist. We shall suppose henceforth that $m \leqslant n$ since any other problem for which a solution exists can be reduced to this case by using Gauss-Jordan reduction to determine the non-redundant equations.

Exercises 3.7

1. Use Gauss-Jordan reduction to solve the following systems of linear equations:

    a. $\begin{aligned} x_1 + x_2 &= 2 \\ -2x_1 - 2x_2 &= -4 \end{aligned}$ b. $\begin{aligned} x_1 - x_2 + 2x_3 &= 3 \\ 2x_1 - x_2 + x_3 &= 3 \\ -3x_1 + 2x_2 - 3x_3 &= -6 \end{aligned}$

    c. $x_1 + x_2 = 0$ d. $\begin{aligned} x_1 + x_2 + x_3 - x_4 &= 1 \\ -x_1 \qquad + 3x_3 + x_4 &= -1 \\ x_1 + 2x_2 + 5x_3 - x_4 &= 1 \\ x_1 - x_2 - 4x_3 + 2x_4 &= 1 \end{aligned}$

2. There is a method shown in the text of G. Hadley (see Suggested Reading) of controlling arithmetic errors during the Gauss-Jordan reduction process. It consists of merely adjoining an additional column to the right of the augmented matrix and *performing the same operations on it* that we do on the B column. If we call this new column S, then, to start with, the element in row i of S is merely the sum of the elements of row i of the augmented matrix; that is,

$$s_i = a_{i1} + a_{i2} + \cdots + a_{in} + b_i.$$

As we perform the row operations on *all* the columns and go from augmented matrix to augmented matrix, this *new* column should always record the present sum of the elements in each row. If not, an arithmetic mistake has been made and we should correct it before proceeding. We verify that this procedure is valid for

$$A = \begin{bmatrix} 1 & 2 \\ 3 & 4 \end{bmatrix}, B = \begin{bmatrix} -1 \\ -1 \end{bmatrix}.$$

$$\begin{bmatrix} 1 & 2 & | -1 & | & 2 \\ 3 & 4 & | -1 & | & 6 \end{bmatrix} \sim \begin{bmatrix} 1 & 2 & | -1 & | & 2 \\ 0 & -2 & | & 2 & | & 0 \end{bmatrix}$$

$$R_2 \leftarrow -3R_1 + R_2$$

$$\sim \begin{bmatrix} 1 & 0 & | & 1 & | & 2 \\ 0 & 1 & | -1 & | & 0 \end{bmatrix}.$$

$$R_2 \leftarrow (-1/2)R_2$$
$$R_1 \leftarrow -2R_2 + R_1$$

Use the extra column and solve $AX = B$ where

a. $A = \begin{bmatrix} 3 & 6 \\ -1 & 2 \end{bmatrix}, B = \begin{bmatrix} -6 \\ 2 \end{bmatrix}$

b. $A = \begin{bmatrix} 1 & 1 & 0 \\ 3 & 4 & 1 \\ -1 & 2 & 3 \end{bmatrix}, B = \begin{bmatrix} 4 \\ 15 \\ 5 \end{bmatrix}.$

3. a. Solve the equation $AX = 0$ where

$$A = \begin{bmatrix} -1 & 2 & 3 \\ 3 & -5 & 2 \\ 5 & -8 & 7 \end{bmatrix}.$$

b. If we let the free variable $x_3 = a$, say, what particular solution do you get when $a = 1, -2, 3$?

c. Verify by direct multiplication by A that your solution for $a = 1$ is valid.

4. Let

$$\left\{ X \mid X = \begin{bmatrix} 1 - 2a + 3b \\ 2 + 4a - b \end{bmatrix} \right\}$$

be the set of all solutions of the matrix equation $AX = B$.

a. Show that X may be expressed as a sum of two matrices, one a constant matrix X_P and the other a matrix X_H with the parameters (arbitrary constants) a and b.

b. Show that X_H may be further decomposed as a sum of two matrices, one containing a's only, and the other containing only b's.

5. Suppose that the following augmented matrices are the result of the Gauss-Jordan reduction algorithm. In each case find the number of redundant original equations and the solution. Break the solution matrix up into its constant part X_P and the remainder X_H. Find the particular solution obtained when each of the free variables is set equal to 1 simultaneously.

a.
$$\left[\begin{array}{cccc|c} 1 & 0 & -1 & 2 & 3 \\ 0 & 1 & 2 & 3 & 4 \\ 0 & 0 & 0 & 0 & 0 \\ 0 & 0 & 0 & 0 & 0 \end{array}\right].$$

b.
$$\left[\begin{array}{ccc|c} 1 & 0 & 0 & 4 \\ 0 & 1 & 0 & -1 \\ 0 & 0 & 1 & 0 \\ 0 & 0 & 0 & 0 \\ 0 & 0 & 0 & 0 \end{array}\right].$$

c.
$$\left[\begin{array}{ccc|c} 1 & 0 & 2 & -1 \\ 0 & 1 & 0 & 3 \\ 0 & 0 & 0 & 0 \\ 0 & 0 & 0 & 0 \end{array}\right].$$

d.
$$\left[\begin{array}{cccccc|c} 1 & 0 & 0 & 0 & 5 & -1 & 2 \\ 0 & 1 & 0 & 1 & 4 & 3 & 3 \\ 0 & 0 & 1 & 0 & 0 & 1 & -1 \\ 0 & 0 & 0 & 0 & 0 & 0 & 0 \end{array}\right].$$

Suggested reading

G. Hadley, *Linear Programming*, Addison-Wesley, Reading, Mass. (1962).

New terms

free variable, 87   particular solution of a matrix equation, 87

3.8 Gauss-Jordan reduction. The general case—free variables

Consider the following example in which we have fewer non-redundant equations than unknowns.

Example 3.8.1

$$x_1 + x_2 + x_3 = 3$$
$$2x_1 - x_2 + 2x_3 = 3.$$

The Gauss-Jordan reduction process can be used to solve this system much as it was used in the square non-singular case. The discriminating student may have already noticed that these are merely the non-redundant equations from Example 3.7.1. The iterative procedure for this system is exactly the same as it was for the first two rows of that example.

$$\begin{bmatrix} 1 & 1 & 1 & | & 3 \\ 2 & -1 & 2 & | & 3 \end{bmatrix} \sim \begin{bmatrix} 1 & 1 & 1 & | & 3 \\ 0 & -3 & 0 & | & -3 \end{bmatrix} \sim \begin{bmatrix} 1 & 1 & 1 & | & 3 \\ 0 & 1 & 0 & | & 1 \end{bmatrix}$$

$$R_2 \leftarrow -2R_1 + R_2 \qquad\qquad R_2 \leftarrow (-1/3)R_2$$

$$\sim \begin{bmatrix} 1 & 0 & 1 & | & 2 \\ 0 & 1 & 0 & | & 1 \end{bmatrix}.$$

$$R_1 \leftarrow -R_2 + R_1$$

The solution is then obtained in the same manner as previously. Nothing of an extraordinary nature has arisen. The *last* $n - m = 3 - 2 = 1$ variable(s) could be arbitrarily assigned to obtain the solution. Let us illustrate that such is not always the case by the following example.

Example 3.8.2

$$\begin{aligned} x_1 + x_2 + x_3 + x_4 &= 4 \\ x_1 + x_2 + 2x_3 + 3x_4 &= 7 \\ 3x_1 + 3x_2 + 5x_3 + 4x_4 &= 15. \end{aligned}$$

At the first step in the Gauss-Jordan reduction to obtain a solution to Example 3.8.2 we obtain

$$\begin{bmatrix} 1 & 1 & 1 & 1 & | & 4 \\ 1 & 1 & 2 & 3 & | & 7 \\ 3 & 3 & 5 & 4 & | & 15 \end{bmatrix} \sim \begin{bmatrix} 1 & 1 & 1 & 1 & | & 4 \\ 0 & 0 & 1 & 2 & | & 3 \\ 0 & 0 & 2 & 1 & | & 3 \end{bmatrix}$$

$$R_2 \leftarrow -R_1 + R_2$$
$$R_3 \leftarrow -3R_1 + R_2$$

when we eliminate x_1 from all equations except the first. The problem now arises when we attempt to eliminate x_2 from all equations except the second. We find that the coefficient of x_2 in equation 2 is 0. When this has taken place in our previous examples we have merely scanned the elements of column 2 below the 2, 2 position until we found a non-zero element and then interchanged rows. There was always such a non-zero element unless the remaining equations were redundant and all elements in the succeeding rows were zeros. Such is not the case here and we are unable to eliminate x_2 from equation 1. In such a situation we skip x_2 and attempt to eliminate x_3 from all equations except *equation* 2. We can do this unless the element in the 2, 3 position is also 0. If it were 0, we would scan column 3 below the 2, 3 position for non-zero elements. If we found one, we would interchange rows and proceed as before. If not, we would repeat the above procedure for the remaining variables until a non-zero element was found. In this example the 2, 3 element is 1, so we use it to delete x_3 from all equations except the second, as follows:

$$\begin{bmatrix} 1 & 1 & 1 & 1 & | & 4 \\ 0 & 0 & 1 & 2 & | & 3 \\ 0 & 0 & 2 & 1 & | & 3 \end{bmatrix} \sim \begin{bmatrix} 1 & 1 & 0 & -1 & | & 1 \\ 0 & 0 & 1 & 2 & | & 3 \\ 0 & 0 & 0 & -3 & | & -3 \end{bmatrix}.$$

$$R_1 \leftarrow -R_2 + R_1$$
$$R_3 \leftarrow -2R_2 + R_3$$

We now delete x_4 from all equations except the third.

$$\begin{bmatrix} 1 & 1 & 0 & -1 & | & 1 \\ 0 & 0 & 1 & 2 & | & 3 \\ 0 & 0 & 0 & -3 & | & -3 \end{bmatrix} \sim \begin{bmatrix} 1 & 1 & 0 & 0 & | & 2 \\ 0 & 0 & 1 & 0 & | & 1 \\ 0 & 0 & 0 & 1 & | & 1 \end{bmatrix}.$$

$$R_3 \leftarrow (-1/3)R_3$$
$$R_2 \leftarrow -2R_3 + R_2$$
$$R_1 \leftarrow R_3 + R_1$$

Instead of assigning the last $n - m = 4 - 3 = 1$ variable(s) arbitrarily, we assign x_2 arbitrarily in this case to obtain

$$X = \begin{bmatrix} 2 - a \\ a \\ 1 \\ 1 \end{bmatrix}.$$

For emphasis, we again point out that we could express X as a sum

$$X = X_P + X_H = \begin{bmatrix} 2 \\ 0 \\ 1 \\ 1 \end{bmatrix} + a \begin{bmatrix} -1 \\ 1 \\ 0 \\ 0 \end{bmatrix},$$

where X_P is one particular solution to the original set of equations and X_H is the solution to the homogeneous set of equations with coefficient matrix A.

In Example 3.8.1 we had a variable x_3 for which there was no (non-redundant) equation 3. Thus we obviously could not use equation 3 to eliminate x_3 from all other equations as we did for x_1 and x_2. (We used equation 1 to eliminate x_1, equation 2 to eliminate x_2, etc.). Such a variable as x_3 we have called a free variable and we know that if there is any solution at all, this variable may be arbitrarily assigned.

In Example 3.8.2 we had a variable, namely x_2, which we were unable to eliminate from one of the previous equations, equation 1. In this case, x_2 would also be called a free variable and be freely assigned any value. If there is any solution at all, such a variable may receive an arbitrary assignment.

If we are dealing originally with m equations in n variables and it turns out that there are k redundant equations, as indicated in the final matrix by the number of rows consisting entirely of zeros, then the number of free variables is n − (m − k). Each of these free variables may be arbitrarily assigned values. We sometimes say that we have an $[n − (m − k)]$-dimensional infinity of solutions or that we have $n − (m − k)$ degrees of freedom.

For those readers who are familiar with vectors as arrows, and with the elementary ideas of 3-dimensional geometry, the following example may help to explain the workings of a free variable. It will not impede your progress to skip this example until after you have studied the early portions of Chapter 6.

Example 3.8.3

$$1x_1 + 0x_2 + 0x_3 = 2$$
$$0x_1 + 1x_2 + 0x_3 = 3.$$

Using Gauss-Jordan reduction, we obtain $\begin{bmatrix} 1 & 0 & 0 & | & 2 \\ 0 & 1 & 0 & | & 3 \end{bmatrix}$, from which we see that

$$\left\{ X \mid X = \begin{bmatrix} 2 \\ 3 \\ a \end{bmatrix} = \begin{bmatrix} 2 \\ 3 \\ 0 \end{bmatrix} + a \begin{bmatrix} 0 \\ 0 \\ 1 \end{bmatrix} \right\} = \{X_P + X_H\}$$

is the complete solution. Now, $x_1 = 2$ and $x_2 = 3$ each represent planes in 3-space as shown in Figure 3.8.1.

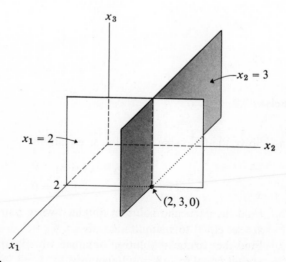

Figure 3.8.I

The dotted line of intersection is as shown. The entire line represents the solution set of the set of equations. When we split X into $\begin{bmatrix} 2 \\ 3 \\ 0 \end{bmatrix}$ and $a \begin{bmatrix} 0 \\ 0 \\ 1 \end{bmatrix}$ we are saying that any solution vector X may be written as a sum of two vectors X_P and X_H. Drawing $X_P = \begin{bmatrix} 2 \\ 3 \\ 0 \end{bmatrix}$ and $X_H = \begin{bmatrix} 0 \\ 0 \\ 2 \end{bmatrix}$, with $a = 2$, in Figure 3.8.2 we see that the solution vector $X = \begin{bmatrix} 2 \\ 3 \\ 2 \end{bmatrix}$ has been located.

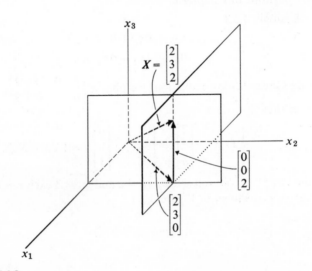

Figure 3.8.2

Exercises 3.8

1. a. Solve the following set of linear equations:

$$x_1 - x_2 + x_3 - x_4 = 0$$
$$x_3 + x_4 = 0.$$

   b. Find the particular solution obtained when both free variables are set equal to 1 simultaneously.

   c. Find the particular solution obtained when both free variables are set equal to -3 simultaneously.

   d. Let Y be the sum of the solutions in b. and c. Show that Y is a solution of the original problem.

2. a. Solve the equation $AX = B$ by Gauss-Jordan reduction:

$$A = \begin{bmatrix} 2 & 3 & 1 & 0 \\ 3 & 2 & 0 & 1 \end{bmatrix}, \quad B = \begin{bmatrix} 5 \\ 5 \end{bmatrix}.$$

   b. Find the particular solution that results when both free variables are set equal to 0.
   c. We have _____ non-redundant equations in _____ unknowns, and a _____-dimensional infinity of solutions.
   d. What matrix appears in columns 3 and 4 of the final augmented matrix?
   e. Decompose X into X_P and X_H. Verify that $AX_P = B$ and that $AX_H = 0$.

3. a. Solve the equation $AX = B$ by Gauss-Jordan reduction, where

$$A = \begin{bmatrix} 1 & 2 & -5 \\ 2 & 4 & -3 \end{bmatrix}, \quad B = \begin{bmatrix} 0 \\ 0 \end{bmatrix}.$$

   b. In this case we have _____ non-redundant equations in _____ unknowns, and a _____-dimensional infinity of solutions, as evidenced by the _____ free variable(s) in the solution.
   c. Find and verify the particular solution that results from setting the free variable equal to 2. Is any scalar multiple of this solution also a solution?

4. a. Solve the equation $AX = B$ where

$$A = \begin{bmatrix} 1 & 2 & -1 & 2 & 4 \\ 3 & -1 & 4 & 6 & -5 \\ 4 & 2 & -3 & -1 & -2 \end{bmatrix}, \quad B = \begin{bmatrix} 5 \\ 5 \\ -2 \end{bmatrix}.$$

   b. We have _____ non-redundant equations in _____ unknowns. There is a _____-dimensional infinity of solutions, as evidenced by the _____ free variables.
   c. Find and verify the particular solution that results when each of the free variables is set equal to 1.

5. a. Consider the equation $AX = B$ where

$$A = \begin{bmatrix} 1 & 1 & -2 & 1 & 3 \\ 2 & -1 & 2 & 2 & 6 \\ 3 & 2 & -4 & -3 & -9 \end{bmatrix}, \quad B = \begin{bmatrix} 2 \\ 4 \\ 6 \end{bmatrix}.$$

If there is 1 redundant equation then there should be a _____-dimensional infinity of solutions, while if none of the equations are redundant, there should be _____ free variables and a _____-dimensional infinity of solutions.

b. Solve the equation.

c. Decompose X into X_P and X_H, and verify that $AX_P = B$ and $AX_H = 0$.

3.9 Gauss-Jordan reduction. The general case—a synopsis

We have now covered all of the situations that may arise when A is not non-singular and there is at least one solution matrix X. To illustrate that not all sets of equations have solutions, consider the following example.

Example 3.9.1

$$x_1 + x_2 = 1$$

$$x_1 + x_2 = 2.$$

Clearly there are no matrices $X = \begin{bmatrix} x_1 \\ x_2 \end{bmatrix}$ the sum of whose elements is both 1 and 2. Thus there can be no solution.

How does this fact that the set of equations above has no solution become apparent in the solution algorithm? We answer the question by attempting to solve the system:

$$\begin{bmatrix} 1 & 1 & | & 1 \\ 1 & 1 & | & 2 \end{bmatrix} \sim \begin{bmatrix} 1 & 1 & | & 1 \\ 0 & 0 & | & 1 \end{bmatrix}.$$

$$R_2 \leftarrow -R_1 + R_2$$

The last row of the second matrix provides the clue, since it is a representation of the equation

$$0 \cdot x_1 + 0 \cdot x_2 = 1,$$

which obviously has no solution. At some point in the algorithm, *such a row will always be created in a problem which has no solution*. The algorithm should be terminated when this occurs. The geometrical situation is shown in Figure 3.9.1. The two equations represent non-intersecting parallel lines.

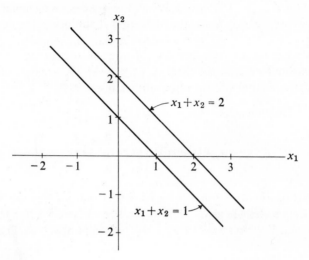

Figure 3.9.1

*How do we then proceed, in general, to find an X such that $AX = B$?
Using the ad hoc remedies of*

1. *Juggling the order of the rows (equations) as required, and*

2. *Skipping columns (variables that become free) as required,
we start with the augmented matrix $[A \mid B] = [A^{(1)} \mid B^{(1)}]$ and proceed
through a sequence of s equivalent augmented matrices until we reach the
matrix*

$$[A^{(s)} \mid B^{(s)}]$$

in which $A^{(s)}$ is of a very special form. To be specific, in the case where a
solution exists, suppose that we have m equations in n unknowns and
k of the original equations are redundant, with $k \leqslant m$. Then

1. The last $k \geqslant 0$ rows of $A^{(s)}$ consist entirely of zeros.

2. The first non-zero element in each of the first $m - k$ rows of
$A^{(s)}$ is a 1.

3. Each such "first 1" in a row is the only non-zero element in its
column.

4. These "first 1's" are in an echelon form; that is, if the first
1 in row 1 appears in column a_1, the first 1 in row 2 appears in column
a_2, and so forth, then

$$a_1 < a_2 < \cdots < a_{m-k}.$$

(the a_j here should not be confused with the matrix elements a_{ij})

Such a matrix is said to be in **row-reduced echelon form**. *The variables
$x_{a_1}, x_{a_2}, \ldots, x_{a_{m-k}}$ corresponding to the "first 1's" are then determined*

in terms of the constants of $B^{(s)}$ and the remaining variables (if any) which may be freely assigned arbitrary values. We emphasize that one does not usually know the number k at the beginning of the solution process.

Let us now consider several augmented matrices in row-reduced echelon form and use them to write down the general solutions to the corresponding systems of equations, if any exist.

Example 3.9.2

$$[A^{(s)} \mid B^{(s)}] = \begin{bmatrix} 1 & 0 & 2 & \big| & 3 \\ 0 & 1 & -1 & \big| & 4 \\ 0 & 0 & 0 & \big| & 0 \end{bmatrix}.$$

In this case, $m = 3$, $n = 3$, and $k = 1$ as indicated by the one row consisting entirely of zeros. Here x_3 is a free variable that may be arbitrarily assigned. Suppose we let $x_3 = a$. Then from row 2, we find that

$$x_2 = 4 + a,$$

and from row 1, then, we find that

$$x_1 = 3 - 2a,$$

so that

$$\left\{ X \mid X = \begin{bmatrix} 3 - 2a \\ 4 + a \\ a \end{bmatrix} = \begin{bmatrix} 3 \\ 4 \\ 0 \end{bmatrix} + a \begin{bmatrix} -2 \\ 1 \\ 1 \end{bmatrix} \right\} = \{X_P + X_H\}$$

is the general solution to the original matrix equation $AX = B$. (What is $A^{(s)}X_H$?) To check the above solution, we verify that

$$\begin{bmatrix} 1 & 0 & 2 \\ 0 & 1 & -1 \\ 0 & 0 & 0 \end{bmatrix} \begin{bmatrix} 3 - 2a \\ 4 + a \\ a \end{bmatrix} = \begin{bmatrix} 3 \\ 4 \\ 0 \end{bmatrix} = B^{(s)},$$

and recall that the matrix equation $A^{(s)}X = B^{(s)}$ is equivalent to the original matrix equation $AX = B$, whatever it was. (Can we tell what it was?) Geometrically, two of the three planes represented by the original three equations intersected in a straight line. The third plane contained this same straight line and was thus redundant. We thus have an $n - (m - k)$ or $3 - (3 - 1) = 1$ dimensional infinity of solutions (a straight line in 3-dimensional space as shown in Figure 3.9.2). Before continuing, the reader should insure that he understands what the situation would be, had the 3, 4 element of $[A^{(s)} \mid B^{(s)}]$ been 1 rather than 0.

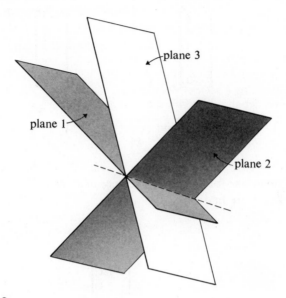

Figure 3.9.2

Example 3.9.3

$m = 3, n = 5.$

$$[A^{(s)} \mid B^{(s)}] = \begin{bmatrix} 1 & 0 & 0 & 2 & -5 & \big| & 2 \\ 0 & 1 & 0 & -1 & 2 & \big| & 4 \\ 0 & 0 & 1 & 4 & 3 & \big| & -3 \end{bmatrix}.$$

Here, $k = 0$, indicating that none of the original equations was redundant. The variables x_4 and x_5 may be freely assigned. Suppose that we let $x_4 = a$ and $x_5 = b$. Then, from the last row,

$$x_3 = -3 - 4a - 3b,$$

and proceeding upward through the matrix we obtain

$$x_2 = 4 + \quad a - 2b$$
$$x_1 = 2 - 2a + 5b,$$

so that our parametric solution vector (matrix) X in 5-space (the set of all column matrices with five elements) is

$$X = \begin{bmatrix} 2 - 2a + 5b \\ 4 + 1a - 2b \\ -3 - 4a - 3b \\ 0 + 1a + 0b \\ 0 + 0a + 1b \end{bmatrix}.$$

Again we note that X may be split into two parts, $X = X_P + X_H$, where

$$X_P = \begin{bmatrix} 2 \\ 4 \\ -3 \\ 0 \\ 0 \end{bmatrix} \quad \text{and} \quad X_H = a\begin{bmatrix} -2 \\ 1 \\ -4 \\ 1 \\ 0 \end{bmatrix} + b\begin{bmatrix} 5 \\ -2 \\ -3 \\ 0 \\ 1 \end{bmatrix}.$$

The reader should verify that

1. $A^{(s)}X_P = B^{(s)}$, and
2. $A^{(s)}X_H = 0$.

Here we have an $n - (m - k) = 5 - (3 - 0) = 2$-dimensional infinity of solutions, one for each specific choice of a and b. For instance, if we set $a = b = 1$, we find that

$$\begin{bmatrix} 5 \\ 3 \\ -10 \\ 1 \\ 1 \end{bmatrix}$$

is a solution.

Example 3.9.4

$m \doteq 4, n = 6$.

$$[A^{(s)} \mid B^{(s)}] = \begin{bmatrix} 1 & 2 & 0 & 0 & 1 & -2 & \vert & -1 \\ 0 & 0 & 1 & 0 & -1 & 3 & \vert & 2 \\ 0 & 0 & 0 & 1 & 2 & -4 & \vert & 0 \\ 0 & 0 & 0 & 0 & 0 & 0 & \vert & 0 \end{bmatrix}.$$

In this example $k = 1$. The 0 in the 2, 2 position indicates that column 2 was skipped and that x_2 is thus a free variable. The variables x_5 and x_6 are also free so we expect a 3-dimensional infinity of solutions, and find, letting $x_2 = a$, $x_5 = b$, $x_6 = c$, that

$$\left\{ X \mid X = \begin{bmatrix} -1 - 2a - 1b + 2c \\ 0 + 1a + 0b + 0c \\ 2 + 0a + 1b - 3c \\ 0 + 0a - 2b + 4c \\ 0 + 0a + 1b + 0c \\ 0 + 0a + 0b + 1c \end{bmatrix} = \begin{bmatrix} -1 \\ 0 \\ 2 \\ 0 \\ 0 \\ 0 \end{bmatrix} + a\begin{bmatrix} -2 \\ 1 \\ 0 \\ 0 \\ 0 \\ 0 \end{bmatrix} + b\begin{bmatrix} -1 \\ 0 \\ 1 \\ -2 \\ 1 \\ 0 \end{bmatrix} + c\begin{bmatrix} 2 \\ 0 \\ -3 \\ 4 \\ 0 \\ 1 \end{bmatrix} \right\}$$

is the general solution. It is left to the reader to consider the product of $A^{(s)}$ and the individual matrices shown in the above display of the general solution. By this time you should have some idea of what to expect.

Example 3.9.5

$m = 3, n = 4.$

$$\begin{bmatrix} 1 & 0 & 0 & 0 & | & 3 \\ 0 & 1 & 0 & 2 & | & 4 \\ 0 & 0 & 1 & 3 & | & -1 \\ 0 & 0 & 0 & 0 & | & 2 \end{bmatrix}$$

The last row indicates that no solution exists.

We note that in all those cases in which any solution exists, we found an $n - (m - k)$-dimensional infinity of solutions. That is, there were $n - (m - k)$ variables which could be freely assigned values. If the solution is to be unique, it must be true that $n - (m - k) = 0$ or that $n = m - k$. (What happens if $n < m - k$?)

At this point we now have a computational algorithm for solving any system of linear equations for which a solution exists (called a **consistent system**), and for discovering those systems which have no solution (**inconsistent** systems).

We pause now to allow the reader to gain some practical experience in actually solving systems of linear equations by using the Gauss-Jordan reduction process. The exercises have been chosen so that they exhibit all of the idiosyncrasies that may arise.

In the next chapter we shall introduce some new terminology pertaining to certain sets of matrices or vectors called *vector spaces*. We shall use it to formulate some of the standard results in the study of linear equations to which we have alluded from time to time in this chapter. If the reader works carefully through the following exercises, these results will appear natural and easy to understand.

Exercises 3.9

1. Use Gauss-Jordan reduction to solve the matrix equation $AX = B$. Before you start each problem, determine the minimum number of free variables that must be present if any solution exists.

   a. $A = \begin{bmatrix} 2 & 0 & 1 & 3 & -2 \\ -1 & 3 & 4 & 2 & -1 \\ 5 & -3 & -1 & 7 & -5 \end{bmatrix}, B = \begin{bmatrix} 0 \\ -2 \\ 0 \end{bmatrix}.$

   b. $A = \begin{bmatrix} 0 & 1 & 2 & 0 & 4 \\ -2 & 0 & 0 & 1 & 1 \end{bmatrix}, B = \begin{bmatrix} 6 \\ 1 \end{bmatrix}.$

   c. $A = \begin{bmatrix} 1 & 1 & 1 & 1 \\ -1 & -1 & -1 & 1 \\ -1 & -1 & 1 & 1 \\ -1 & 1 & 1 & 1 \end{bmatrix}, B = \begin{bmatrix} 8 \\ -4 \\ 0 \\ 6 \end{bmatrix}.$

d. $A = \begin{bmatrix} 1 & -1 & 2 & -2 \\ 3 & -3 & -4 & 5 \end{bmatrix}$, $B = \begin{bmatrix} 3 \\ 7 \end{bmatrix}$.

e. $A = \begin{bmatrix} 1 & 2 & 0 \\ -1 & 2 & 3 \\ 3 & 6 & 3 \\ 0 & 1 & 1 \end{bmatrix}$, $B = \begin{bmatrix} 3 \\ -2 \\ 6 \\ 0 \end{bmatrix}$.

f. $A = \begin{bmatrix} 1 & -1 & 1 \\ 0 & 1 & 1 \\ -2 & 3 & -1 \end{bmatrix}$, $B = \begin{bmatrix} -1 \\ -2 \\ 1 \end{bmatrix}$.

2. What occurs in the Gauss-Jordan reduction process which causes "juggling" the order of the rows as we proceed from some one of the equivalent augmented matrices to the next?

3. Let $A = \begin{bmatrix} 1 & 2 \\ 3 & 4 \end{bmatrix}$ and suppose that we form a new matrix C from A by letting $R_2 \leftarrow -3R_1 + R_2$, so that $C = \begin{bmatrix} 1 & 2 \\ 0 & -2 \end{bmatrix}$. We can perform this operation by using matrix multiplication appropriately. For example, if we let $E_1 = \begin{bmatrix} 1 & 0 \\ -3 & 1 \end{bmatrix}$ and compute $E_1 A = \begin{bmatrix} 1 & 0 \\ -3 & 1 \end{bmatrix} \begin{bmatrix} 1 & 2 \\ 3 & 4 \end{bmatrix} = \begin{bmatrix} 1 & 2 \\ 0 & -2 \end{bmatrix}$, we have C. How did we form E_1? Very simply, we performed upon the identity matrix I_2 the same operation we performed upon A to yield C. Matrices like E_1 are called **elementary** matrices. Now consider the matrix equation $AX = B$, where $A = \begin{bmatrix} 3 & 4 \\ 5 & 7 \end{bmatrix}$, $B = \begin{bmatrix} -2 \\ -4 \end{bmatrix}$.

   a. Use Gauss-Jordan reduction to solve the problem, and keep an account of the elementary matrices $E_1, E_2, \ldots, E_s$ that would perform steps $1, 2, \ldots, s$.
   b. Find the product $E_s E_{s-1} \ldots E_2 E_1$.
   c. Find the product $(E_s E_{s-1} \ldots E_2 E_1)A$.
   d. From the results of c. what is the matrix $E_s E_{s-1} \ldots E_2 E_1$ in relation to A?

4. Find A^{-1} by finding the product $E_s E_{s-1} \ldots E_2 E_1$, where the E_i are the elementary matrices that will reduce A to a row-reduced echelon matrix I if

   a. $A = \begin{bmatrix} 2 & 7 \\ 1 & 4 \end{bmatrix}$
   b. $A = \begin{bmatrix} -1 & 0 & 1 \\ 2 & 1 & 0 \\ 0 & 2 & 3 \end{bmatrix}$.

5. How do we determine the number of free variables that may be arbitrarily assigned? Which variables do we choose to freely assign values?

6. What do we mean when we say that a variable has been "skipped" as the Gauss-Jordan reduction algorithm proceeded? Give an example of an augmented matrix which has a variable that has been skipped.

7. Let $A_1 = \begin{bmatrix} 1 \\ 3 \end{bmatrix}$, $A_2 = \begin{bmatrix} 1 \\ 4 \end{bmatrix}$; $B = \begin{bmatrix} -1 \\ -5 \end{bmatrix}$. Find numbers x_1, x_2, if they exist, such that $x_1 A_1 + x_2 A_2 = B$. If such x's exist, then we say that B is a *linear combination* of A_1 and A_2.

8. Show that $\begin{bmatrix} -1 \\ 2 \\ 3 \end{bmatrix}$ is a linear combination of $\begin{bmatrix} 1 \\ 0 \\ 0 \end{bmatrix}$, $\begin{bmatrix} 0 \\ 1 \\ 0 \end{bmatrix}$, and $\begin{bmatrix} 0 \\ 0 \\ 1 \end{bmatrix}$. Is every column vector with three elements such a linear combination?

9. Let $A_1 = \begin{bmatrix} 1 \\ 0 \\ 1 \end{bmatrix}$, $A_2 = \begin{bmatrix} 1 \\ 1 \\ 0 \end{bmatrix}$, $A_3 = \begin{bmatrix} 0 \\ 1 \\ 1 \end{bmatrix}$. Decide whether $B = \begin{bmatrix} 0 \\ 0 \\ 2 \end{bmatrix}$ is a linear combination of the A_i.

New terms

[4] Vector spaces and systems of linear equations

4.1 Linear combinations and vector spaces

Many of the standard results about linear equations may be succinctly phrased in terminology developed from the study of so-called "vector spaces." In order to do this we now introduce the elementary ideas involved and then use them in Sections 4.5 and 4.6 in a discussion of our earlier questions about the existence and uniqueness of solutions of linear equations.

We have previously noted that any solution X of the matrix equation $AX = B$ may be decomposed into X_P and X_H in such a manner that $AX_P = B$ and $AX_H = 0$. You may have noticed that X_H is always of a particular form. In Example 3.9.3, where

$$X = \begin{bmatrix} 2 \\ 4 \\ -3 \\ 0 \\ 0 \end{bmatrix} + a \begin{bmatrix} -2 \\ 1 \\ -4 \\ 1 \\ 0 \end{bmatrix} + b \begin{bmatrix} 5 \\ -2 \\ -3 \\ 0 \\ 1 \end{bmatrix},$$

we have

$$X_P = \begin{bmatrix} 2 \\ 4 \\ -3 \\ 0 \\ 0 \end{bmatrix} \quad \text{and} \quad X_H = a \begin{bmatrix} -2 \\ 1 \\ -4 \\ 1 \\ 0 \end{bmatrix} + b \begin{bmatrix} 5 \\ -2 \\ -3 \\ 0 \\ 1 \end{bmatrix}.$$

In Example 3.9.4 in which

$$X = \begin{bmatrix} -1 \\ 0 \\ 2 \\ 0 \\ 0 \\ 0 \end{bmatrix} + a \begin{bmatrix} -2 \\ 1 \\ 0 \\ 0 \\ 0 \\ 0 \end{bmatrix} + b \begin{bmatrix} -1 \\ 0 \\ 1 \\ -2 \\ 1 \\ 0 \end{bmatrix} + c \begin{bmatrix} 2 \\ 0 \\ -3 \\ 4 \\ 0 \\ 1 \end{bmatrix},$$

we have

$$X_P = \begin{bmatrix} -1 \\ 0 \\ 2 \\ 0 \\ 0 \\ 0 \end{bmatrix} \quad \text{and} \quad X_H = a \begin{bmatrix} -2 \\ 1 \\ 0 \\ 0 \\ 0 \\ 0 \end{bmatrix} + b \begin{bmatrix} -1 \\ 0 \\ 1 \\ -2 \\ 1 \\ 0 \end{bmatrix} + c \begin{bmatrix} 2 \\ 0 \\ -3 \\ 4 \\ 0 \\ 1 \end{bmatrix}.$$

For a particular problem, we now consider the set of matrices $H = \{X_H\}$, where the constants a, b, c, etc. take on all real values. To begin with, we shall call any $n \times 1$ matrix a **vector of order n.** (Although we will not always say so explicitly, whenever we state a definition, theorem, or property that applies to a set of $n \times 1$ column matrices, we will suppose that an analogous statement holds for $1 \times n$ row matrices.) Any single matrix constructed above by particular choices of the scalars involved in X_H is called a linear combination of the defining matrices involved. To make our definition specific, we will say that if $A_1, A_2, \ldots, A_p$ are each $n \times 1$ column matrices and $x_1, x_2, \ldots, x_p$ are any scalars, then the column matrix

$$B = x_1 A_1 + x_2 A_2 + \cdots + x_p A_p$$

is a **linear combination** of the A_i.

For $a = b = 2$ in the first example,

$$X_H = \begin{bmatrix} 6 \\ -2 \\ -14 \\ 2 \\ 2 \end{bmatrix} = 2 \begin{bmatrix} -2 \\ 1 \\ -4 \\ 1 \\ 0 \end{bmatrix} + 2 \begin{bmatrix} 5 \\ -2 \\ -3 \\ 0 \\ 1 \end{bmatrix},$$

and we say that X_H is a linear combination of $[-2, 1, -4, 1, 0]^T$ and $[5, -2, -3, 0, 1]^T$. Similarly, in the second example, for $a = b = c = 1$, we see that

$$X_H = \begin{bmatrix} -1 \\ 1 \\ -2 \\ 2 \\ 1 \\ 1 \end{bmatrix} = 1 \begin{bmatrix} -2 \\ 1 \\ 0 \\ 0 \\ 0 \\ 0 \end{bmatrix} + 1 \begin{bmatrix} -1 \\ 0 \\ 1 \\ -2 \\ 1 \\ 0 \end{bmatrix} + 1 \begin{bmatrix} 2 \\ 0 \\ -3 \\ 4 \\ 0 \\ 1 \end{bmatrix}$$

is a linear combination of the vectors $[-2, 1, 0, 0, 0, 0]^T$, $[-1, 0, 1, -2, 1, 0]^T$, and $[2, 0, -3, 4, 0, 1]^T$.

The problem of finding scalars x_i which will express B as a linear combination of the A_i is just the general linear equation problem which we have examined in Chapter 3. On the other hand, if we are given a set of vectors A_i and a set of scalars x_i, then it is a simple matter to find B.

If S is a set of $n \times 1$ column matrices, then we shall call S a **vector space** provided that

1. S is closed under the operation of addition; that is, if Y_1 and Y_2 are in S, then $Y_1 + Y_2$ is in S.
2. S is closed under scalar multiplication; that is, if Y is in S and c is any scalar, then the vector cY is also in S.

Under this definition the set of all $n \times 1$ column matrices is a vector space.* There are many subsets of $\mathcal{M}_{n,1}$ which are also vector spaces. In a moment we shall show that if S is any subset of $\mathcal{M}_{n,1}$ which consists of all possible linear combinations of a finite set of vectors in $\mathcal{M}_{n,1}$ then S is a vector space.

To illustrate the method of proof numerically, consider the set

$$S = \left\{ Y \mid Y = x_1 A_1 + x_2 A_2, A_1 = \begin{bmatrix} 1 \\ 2 \\ 3 \end{bmatrix}, A_2 = \begin{bmatrix} -1 \\ 3 \\ -1 \end{bmatrix} \right\}.$$

That is, S is the set of all possible linear combinations of $[1, 2, 3]^T$ and $[-1, 3, -1]^T$. For $x_1 = 2$, $x_2 = 3$, we have

$$Y_1 = 2A_1 + 3A_2 = \begin{bmatrix} -1 \\ 13 \\ 3 \end{bmatrix} \text{ which is an element of } S;$$

and for $x_1 = -1$, $x_2 = -2$, we compute that

$$Y_2 = -A_1 - 2A_2 = \begin{bmatrix} 1 \\ -8 \\ -1 \end{bmatrix} \text{ is also in } S.$$

If S is to be closed under addition and scalar multiplication then it must be true, for example, that

$$Y_3 = Y_1 + Y_2 = \begin{bmatrix} 0 \\ 5 \\ 2 \end{bmatrix}$$

---

* For the definition of an abstract vector space, see Appendix C. Our vector space defined above is an important special case.

and

$$Y_4 = cY_1 = \begin{bmatrix} -1c \\ 13c \\ 3c \end{bmatrix}$$

are in S. Since

$$Y_3 = \begin{bmatrix} 0 \\ 5 \\ 2 \end{bmatrix} = 1 \begin{bmatrix} 1 \\ 2 \\ 3 \end{bmatrix} + 1 \begin{bmatrix} -1 \\ 3 \\ -1 \end{bmatrix} = 1A_1 + 1A_2,$$

we see that Y_3 is a linear combination of A_1 and A_2, and is thus an element of S. Similarly,

$$Y_4 = \begin{bmatrix} -c \\ 13c \\ 3c \end{bmatrix} = (2c) \begin{bmatrix} 1 \\ 2 \\ 3 \end{bmatrix} + (3c) \begin{bmatrix} -1 \\ 3 \\ -1 \end{bmatrix}$$

is also in S.

We now claim that if S consists of all possible linear combinations of a given finite set of p vectors, then S is a vector space. Since H, as defined above, is such a set, we will then know that H is a vector space. We present the proof for $p = 2$, and show that S is closed under addition and scalar multiplication.

Proof:

Let $S = \{Y \mid Y = x_1A_1 + x_2A_2\}$. For addition, suppose that $Y_1 = a_1A_1 + a_2A_2$ and $Y_2 = b_1A_1 + b_2A_2$ are in S. Then

$$\begin{aligned} Y_3 = Y_1 + Y_2 &= (a_1A_1 + a_2A_2) + (b_1A_1 + b_2A_2) \\ &= a_1A_1 + (a_2A_2 + b_1A_1) + b_2A_2 \quad &\text{(Why?)} \\ &= a_1A_1 + (b_1A_1 + a_2A_2) + b_2A_2 \quad &\text{(Why?)} \\ &= (a_1A_1 + b_1A_1) + (a_2A_2 + b_2A_2) \quad &\text{(Why?)} \\ &= (a_1 + b_1)A_1 + (a_2 + b_2)A_2 \quad &\text{(Why?)} \\ &= c_1A_1 + c_2A_2. \end{aligned}$$

Therefore Y_3 is a linear combination of the A_i and is in S, so that S is closed under addition.

For scalar multiplication, suppose that $Y_1 = a_1A_1 + a_2A_2$ as before, and let c be any scalar. Then

$$\begin{aligned} Y_4 = cY_1 = c(a_1A_1 + a_2A_2) &= c(a_1A_1) + c(a_2A_2) \quad &\text{(Why?)} \\ &= (ca_1)A_1 + (ca_2)A_2 = c_1A_1 + c_2A_2. \end{aligned}$$

Thus Y_4 is in S, implying that S is closed under scalar multiplication. □

To further illustrate the last property demonstrated in the proof, let

$$A_1 = \begin{bmatrix} 1 \\ 2 \\ 3 \end{bmatrix}, A_2 = \begin{bmatrix} -1 \\ 3 \\ -1 \end{bmatrix}$$

as previously, and let

$$Y = 2A_1 + 3A_2 = \begin{bmatrix} -1 \\ 13 \\ 3 \end{bmatrix}$$

be in S. For $c = 4$, for example, we want to show that

$$4Y = 4 \begin{bmatrix} -1 \\ 13 \\ 3 \end{bmatrix} = \begin{bmatrix} -4 \\ 52 \\ 12 \end{bmatrix}$$

is in S. Since

$$\begin{bmatrix} -4 \\ 52 \\ 12 \end{bmatrix} = 8 \begin{bmatrix} 1 \\ 2 \\ 3 \end{bmatrix} + 12 \begin{bmatrix} -1 \\ 3 \\ -1 \end{bmatrix} = 8A_1 + 12A_2,$$

it is also in S.

We should mention that not every set of vectors has the two closure properties, so that there do exist vector sets which are not vector spaces. First, the scalar multiplication property makes it evident that a vector space is an infinite set of vectors unless it contains the zero vector alone (see Exercise 7). However, there are many infinite vector sets which are not vector spaces. Consider the set of all positive multiples of $\begin{bmatrix} 1 \\ 0 \end{bmatrix}$. This set is closed under addition but not under scalar multiplication since, for example, $(-1)\begin{bmatrix} 1 \\ 0 \end{bmatrix} = \begin{bmatrix} -1 \\ 0 \end{bmatrix}$ is not in the set. As a do-it-yourself second illustration, let

$$T = \left\{ Y \mid Y = a \begin{bmatrix} 1 \\ 0 \end{bmatrix} \right\} \cup \left\{ Y \mid Y = b \begin{bmatrix} 0 \\ 1 \end{bmatrix} \right\},$$

where, as usual, a and b are arbitrary scalars. Is T closed under addition and scalar multiplication and thus a vector space (see Exercise 9)?

Any subset of S which is also a vector space will be called a **subspace** of S. Thus

$$S_1 = \left\{ Y \mid Y = x_1 \begin{bmatrix} 1 \\ 0 \\ 1 \end{bmatrix} + x_2 \begin{bmatrix} 0 \\ 1 \\ 2 \end{bmatrix} \right\}$$

is a subspace of

$$S = \left\{ Y \mid Y = x_1 \begin{bmatrix} 1 \\ 0 \\ 1 \end{bmatrix} + x_2 \begin{bmatrix} 0 \\ 1 \\ 2 \end{bmatrix} + x_3 \begin{bmatrix} 1 \\ 1 \\ 1 \end{bmatrix} \right\}.$$

Note in this example that the defining vectors of S_1 are a proper subset of the defining vectors of S. However, there are many subspaces of S other than those constructed strictly as the set of all linear combinations of a proper subset of the defining vectors of S. For example,

$$Y_1 = 2\begin{bmatrix} 1 \\ 0 \\ 1 \end{bmatrix} + 3\begin{bmatrix} 0 \\ 1 \\ 2 \end{bmatrix} + 0\begin{bmatrix} 1 \\ 1 \\ 1 \end{bmatrix} = \begin{bmatrix} 2 \\ 3 \\ 8 \end{bmatrix}$$

and

$$Y_2 = 1\begin{bmatrix} 1 \\ 0 \\ 1 \end{bmatrix} + 1\begin{bmatrix} 0 \\ 1 \\ 2 \end{bmatrix} + (-1)\begin{bmatrix} 1 \\ 1 \\ 1 \end{bmatrix} = \begin{bmatrix} 0 \\ 0 \\ 2 \end{bmatrix}$$

are in S, and $\{Y \mid Y = a_1 Y_1 + a_2 Y_2\}$ is another subspace of S.

In Chapter 6 we shall relate the elements of our vector spaces (which we call vectors) to the geometrical vectors with which you may already be familiar.

Exercises 4.1

1. Show that the following vectors are linear combinations of the vectors $E_1 = \begin{bmatrix} 1 \\ 0 \end{bmatrix}$ and $E_2 = \begin{bmatrix} 0 \\ 1 \end{bmatrix}$ by finding the appropriate scalars:

   a. $\begin{bmatrix} 2 \\ 0 \end{bmatrix}$ b. $\begin{bmatrix} 3 \\ 5 \end{bmatrix}$ c. $\begin{bmatrix} \pi \\ e \end{bmatrix}$ d. $\begin{bmatrix} 1/2 \\ 3/8 \end{bmatrix}$.

2. Use Gauss-Jordan reduction to show that the following vectors are linear combinations of the vectors $\begin{bmatrix} 1 \\ 2 \end{bmatrix}, \begin{bmatrix} -1 \\ 3 \end{bmatrix}$ by finding the appropriate scalars.

   a. $\begin{bmatrix} 0 \\ 5 \end{bmatrix}$ b. $\begin{bmatrix} 4 \\ 3 \end{bmatrix}$ c. $\begin{bmatrix} 2 \\ 0 \end{bmatrix}$ d. $\begin{bmatrix} -3 \\ -1 \end{bmatrix}$.

3. Solve simultaneously the four sets of equations $AX = B_1$, $AX = B_2$, $AX = B_3$, $AX = B_4$ represented by the augmented matrix $[A \mid B_1 B_2 B_3 B_4] = \begin{bmatrix} 1 & -1 & 0 & 4 & 2 & -3 \\ 2 & 3 & 5 & 3 & 0 & -1 \end{bmatrix}$. Relate your solution to Exercise 2.

4. By searching for the appropriate scalars, decide whether or not the following vectors are linear combinations of $\begin{bmatrix} 1 \\ 0 \\ 1 \end{bmatrix}$ and $\begin{bmatrix} 0 \\ 1 \\ 1 \end{bmatrix}$:

a. $\begin{bmatrix} 0 \\ 0 \\ 2 \end{bmatrix}$ 　　　 b. $\begin{bmatrix} -2 \\ 1 \\ -1 \end{bmatrix}$ 　　　 c. $\begin{bmatrix} 2 \\ 3 \\ 4 \end{bmatrix}$.

5. Consider the set $S = \left\{ Y \mid Y = x_1 \begin{bmatrix} 0 \\ 1 \\ 1 \end{bmatrix} + x_2 \begin{bmatrix} 1 \\ 0 \\ 0 \end{bmatrix} \right\}$.

   a. Is S a vector space?
   b. Find two different vectors A and B in S.
   c. Find the scalars which prove that $A + B$ is in S.
   d. Find a proper subset T of S which is a subspace of S.

6. Consider the set

$$S = \left\{ Y \mid Y = x_1 \begin{bmatrix} 1 \\ 0 \\ 1 \\ 0 \end{bmatrix} + x_2 \begin{bmatrix} 0 \\ -1 \\ 0 \\ 0 \end{bmatrix} + x_3 \begin{bmatrix} 1 \\ 1 \\ 1 \\ 1 \end{bmatrix} \right\}.$$

   a. Is S a vector space?
   b. Find a vector Y_1 in S other than the three listed.
   c. Find scalars which verify that $3Y_1$ is in S.
   d. Find scalars which verify that 0 is in S.

7. Is $\{0\}$ a vector space? Why?

8. Consider the set S from Exercise 5. Let

$$T = \left\{ Y \mid Y = y_1 \begin{bmatrix} 0 \\ 2 \\ 2 \end{bmatrix} + y_2 \begin{bmatrix} 2 \\ 0 \\ 0 \end{bmatrix} \right\}.$$

   Show that $S = T$ by showing that $T \subseteq S$ and $S \subseteq T$.

9. Consider the set $T = \left\{ Y \mid Y = a \begin{bmatrix} 1 \\ 0 \end{bmatrix} \right\} \cup \left\{ Y \mid Y = b \begin{bmatrix} 0 \\ 1 \end{bmatrix} \right\}$ in the text.
   Show that this set is not closed under addition, but that it is closed under scalar multiplication.

10. Show that 0 is in every vector space.

11. Prove that the non-empty intersection of two vector spaces is a vector space.

12. Verify that $T = \left\{ Y \mid Y = a \begin{bmatrix} 1 \\ 0 \\ 1 \end{bmatrix} + b \begin{bmatrix} 0 \\ 1 \\ 1 \end{bmatrix} \right\}$ is a subspace of

$$S = \left\{ Y \mid Y = a \begin{bmatrix} 1 \\ -1 \\ 0 \end{bmatrix} + b \begin{bmatrix} 2 \\ 1 \\ 3 \end{bmatrix} + c \begin{bmatrix} 3 \\ 0 \\ 0 \end{bmatrix} \right\}.$$

New terms

4.2 Spanning sets and linear dependence

We shall say that a finite set of vectors $T \subseteq S$ **spans** a vector space S provided that any vector in S may be written as a linear combination of the vectors in T.

Example 4.2.1

Let

$$S = \left\{ Y \mid Y = a_1 \begin{bmatrix} 1 \\ 0 \\ 0 \end{bmatrix} + a_2 \begin{bmatrix} 0 \\ 1 \\ 0 \end{bmatrix} \right\}.$$

Then

$$T_1 = \left\{ \begin{bmatrix} 1 \\ 0 \\ 0 \end{bmatrix}, \begin{bmatrix} 0 \\ 1 \\ 0 \end{bmatrix} \right\}$$

spans S as does

$$T_2 = \left\{ \begin{bmatrix} 2 \\ 0 \\ 0 \end{bmatrix}, \begin{bmatrix} 0 \\ 2 \\ 0 \end{bmatrix} \right\}.$$

However,

$$T_3 = \left\{ \begin{bmatrix} 2 \\ 0 \\ 0 \end{bmatrix}, \begin{bmatrix} 0 \\ 0 \\ 2 \end{bmatrix} \right\}$$

does not span S since, for example,

$$\begin{bmatrix} 1 \\ 1 \\ 0 \end{bmatrix}$$

is in S and is not in the set of all linear combinations of vectors in T_3.

With the definition of a spanning set in mind one might wonder what the knowledge of such a subset T of S tells us about S. One could attempt, for example, to define a measure of the size of S as the number of vectors in T. For this integer to serve as a definition of a unique size for S, however, it is apparent that each spanning set for S would have to contain the same number of vectors.

Example 4.2.1 (continued)

$$T_4 = \left\{ \begin{bmatrix} 1 \\ 0 \\ 0 \end{bmatrix} \begin{bmatrix} 0 \\ 1 \\ 0 \end{bmatrix}, \begin{bmatrix} 0 \\ 2 \\ 0 \end{bmatrix} \right\}$$

is a spanning set for S which contains 3 vectors as opposed to the 2 vectors in each of T_1 and T_2.

From this example we are forced to conclude that there may be different spanning sets for a given vector space and that the spanning sets may contain different numbers of vectors. Such a measure of size for S would not be unique, so another approach to the idea of size is required. We shall examine this question later.

The next example portrays what must be done to show that a given set of vectors spans a vector space when the latter has been constructed as a set of linear combinations.

Example 4.2.2

Let $S = \{Y \mid Y = x_1 A_1 + x_2 A_2 + x_3 A_3\}$, and consider the three sets

$$T_1 = \{A_1, A_2, A_3\}, \quad T_2 = \{2A_1, 2A_2, 2A_3\},$$

and

$$T_3 = \{A_1, A_2, A_3, A_1 + A_2, A_1 + A_3, A_2 + A_3\}.$$

T_1 spans S by definition. We may show that T_2 spans S by showing that we may write any Y in S as a linear combination of the vectors in T_2, namely, $2A_1$, $2A_2$, $2A_3$. Since $Y = x_1 A_1 + x_2 A_2 + x_3 A_3 = (\frac{1}{2}x_1)(2A_1) + (\frac{1}{2}x_2)(2A_2) + (\frac{1}{2}x_3)(2A_3)$ is such a linear combination, T_2 does span S. Can you now show that T_3 spans S?

Realizing that the number of vectors in different spanning sets may differ, we pursue the following question: *Does there exist a spanning set for S which contains a minimum number of vectors*? The answer to this question is "Yes." Such sets are of pre-eminent importance as we shall see later. To find out how we can determine which spanning sets contain "surplus" vectors which could be discarded to obtain such a minimal spanning set, we consider the concept of linear dependence.

In general, we shall say that the set $\{A_1, A_2, \ldots, A_p\}$ of $n \times 1$

column vectors is a **linearly dependent set of vectors** provided that there exist scalars $c_1, c_2, \ldots, c_p$ *not all* 0, such that

$$c_1 A_1 + c_2 A_2 + \cdots + c_p A_p = 0.$$

You may already be familiar with this idea in its simplest form,* that of a set of 2 vectors in the plane which happen to lie in the same line, as shown in Figure 4.2.1.

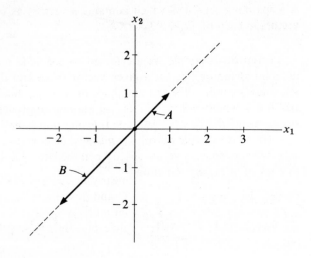

Figure 4.2.1

In the figure, B is merely a scalar multiple of A; and it happens here that $B = -2A$. To put this in a form which is more useful when more than 2 vectors are being considered, we note that

$$2A + 1B = 0.$$

We have found constants $c_1 = 2$ and $c_2 = 1$, not both zero, such that

$$c_1 A + c_2 B = 0.$$

We have satisfied our general definition in this case. In reality, we have found a fancy way of saying that B is a non-zero multiple of A.

Example 4.2.3

Let A, B, C be the vectors shown in Figure 4.2.2. In this case $C = 2A + B$, so that

$$2A + B + (-1)C = 0.$$

_____
* See the first part of Chapter 6 if you are not familiar with plane vectors.

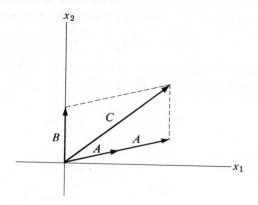

Figure 4.2.2

Although none of the 3 vectors is a scalar multiple of any other one, there do exist scalars $c_1 = 2$, $c_2 = 1$, $c_3 = -1$, such that

$$c_1 A + c_2 B + c_3 C = 0.$$

Thus $\{A, B, C\}$ is a linearly dependent set.

If a set of vectors is not linearly dependent, then it is said to be **linearly independent**. If we let C and D denote the vectors in Figure 4.2.3, we see that neither is a scalar multiple of the other and it should be intuitively clear that the only values of c_1 and c_2 such that

$$c_1 C + c_2 D = 0$$

are $c_1 = c_2 = 0$. Thus $\{C, D\}$ is a linearly independent set. Rather than saying the latter, we may sometimes say that C and D are linearly independent vectors.

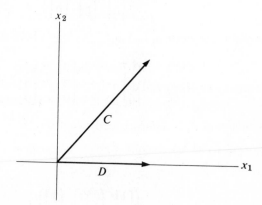

Figure 4.2.3

We now reconsider the general definition of linear dependence. Suppose that we have a set of vectors and a set of scalars such that

$$c_1 A_1 + c_2 A_2 + \cdots + c_p A_p = 0,$$

and that $c_1 \neq 0$. Then $c_1^{-1} = 1/c_1$ exists, and multiplying both sides of the equation by $1/c_1$, we have

$$A_1 + \frac{c_2}{c_1} A_2 + \cdots + \frac{c_p}{c_1} A_p = 0,$$

or

$$A_1 = -\frac{c_2}{c_1} A_2 - \cdots - \frac{c_p}{c_1} A_p.$$

We have just shown that if $c_1 \neq 0$ then A_1 is a linear combination of the remaining $p - 1$ vectors $A_2, \ldots, A_p$—an immediate generalization of the idea of being a scalar multiple of one vector. Since, in general, at least one of the $c_i \neq 0$, we know that in a linearly dependent set we could solve for at least one of the A_i in a similar fashion, and that *at least one of the p vectors is a linear combination of the remaining ones.* Thus the concept of a linearly dependent set of vectors is intimately associated with the idea of scalar multiple and linear combination.

In order to build our confidence in our knowledge of these fundamental definitions, let us consider some further examples.

Example 4.2.4

Consider

$$T_4 = \left\{ \begin{bmatrix} 1 \\ 0 \\ 0 \end{bmatrix}, \begin{bmatrix} 0 \\ 1 \\ 0 \end{bmatrix}, \begin{bmatrix} 0 \\ 2 \\ 0 \end{bmatrix} \right\}$$

of Example 4.2.1. Since

$$0 \begin{bmatrix} 1 \\ 0 \\ 0 \end{bmatrix} + 2 \begin{bmatrix} 0 \\ 1 \\ 0 \end{bmatrix} + (-1) \begin{bmatrix} 0 \\ 2 \\ 0 \end{bmatrix} = \begin{bmatrix} 0 \\ 0 \\ 0 \end{bmatrix},$$

we conclude that T_4 is a linearly dependent set.

Example 4.2.5

Let

$$T = \left\{ \begin{bmatrix} 1 \\ 0 \\ 1 \end{bmatrix}, \begin{bmatrix} 0 \\ 1 \\ -1 \end{bmatrix}, \begin{bmatrix} 1 \\ 1 \\ 0 \end{bmatrix} \right\}.$$

Are there constants c_1, c_2, c_3, not all zero, such that

$$c_1 \begin{bmatrix} 1 \\ 0 \\ 1 \end{bmatrix} + c_2 \begin{bmatrix} 0 \\ 1 \\ -1 \end{bmatrix} + c_3 \begin{bmatrix} 1 \\ 1 \\ 0 \end{bmatrix} = \begin{bmatrix} 0 \\ 0 \\ 0 \end{bmatrix} ?$$

We recognize this as a homogeneous linear equation problem with the c_i as unknowns. Solving, we find that

$$1 \begin{bmatrix} 1 \\ 0 \\ 1 \end{bmatrix} + 1 \begin{bmatrix} 0 \\ 1 \\ -1 \end{bmatrix} + (-1) \begin{bmatrix} 1 \\ 1 \\ 0 \end{bmatrix} = \begin{bmatrix} 0 \\ 0 \\ 0 \end{bmatrix},$$

so that T is another linearly dependent set.

Example 4.2.6

Consider

$$T_2 = \left\{ \begin{bmatrix} 2 \\ 0 \\ 0 \end{bmatrix}, \begin{bmatrix} 0 \\ 2 \\ 0 \end{bmatrix} \right\}$$

of Example 4.2.1. We wish to find scalars c_1, c_2, not both zero, such that

$$c_1 \begin{bmatrix} 2 \\ 0 \\ 0 \end{bmatrix} + c_2 \begin{bmatrix} 0 \\ 2 \\ 0 \end{bmatrix} = \begin{bmatrix} 0 \\ 0 \\ 0 \end{bmatrix}.$$

By observation, however, we see that both c_1 and c_2 *must* be 0 in order to solve this equation. Thus, T_2 is a linearly independent set. It is apparent that neither of the vectors is a linear combination (multiple) of the other one.

We conclude this section by pointing out that *if we have a set of non-zero vectors* $\{A_1, A_2, \ldots, A_p\}$, *and some one of them is a linear combination of the others, then the entire set is linearly dependent.* Suppose, for example, that

$$A_3 = c_1 A_1 + c_2 A_2 + c_4 A_4 + \cdots + c_p A_p.$$

Then we know that

$$c_1 A_1 + c_2 A_2 + (-1)A_3 + c_4 A_4 + \cdots + c_p A_p = 0.$$

Since $(-1) \neq 0$, the set is linearly dependent.

Example 4.2.7

Consider

$$A_1 = \begin{bmatrix} 1 \\ 2 \\ 3 \end{bmatrix}, A_2 = \begin{bmatrix} -1 \\ 3 \\ 4 \end{bmatrix}, A_3 = 2A_1 - A_2 = \begin{bmatrix} 3 \\ 1 \\ 2 \end{bmatrix}.$$

Since $2A_1 + (-1)A_2 + (-1)A_3 = 0$, we have that $\{A_1, A_2, A_3\}$ is linearly dependent.

Exercises 4.2

1. What do we mean when we say that a set T spans a vector space S?

2. Let $S = \left\{ Y \mid Y = a\begin{bmatrix} 1 \\ 0 \\ 2 \end{bmatrix} + b\begin{bmatrix} 0 \\ 1 \\ -1 \end{bmatrix} \right\}$. Find a spanning set T for S.

3. The set $T = \{A_1, A_2, A_3\}$ is said to be a linearly dependent set provided that there exist scalars c_i, _____, such that _____. On the other hand, T is said to be a linearly independent set if _____.

4. If $c_1 A_1 + c_2 A_2 = 0$ holds only in case $c_1 = c_2 = 0$, we say that $\{A_1, A_2\}$ is _____.

5. Use the definition of linear dependence to decide whether or not the following sets are linearly dependent. If dependent, find scalars required by the definition.

   a. $T = \left\{ \begin{bmatrix} 1 \\ 2 \end{bmatrix}, \begin{bmatrix} -1 \\ 3 \end{bmatrix} \right\}$ b. $T = \left\{ \begin{bmatrix} 1 \\ 0 \\ 1 \end{bmatrix}, \begin{bmatrix} 2 \\ -4 \\ -4 \end{bmatrix}, \begin{bmatrix} 0 \\ 2 \\ 3 \end{bmatrix} \right\}$

   c. $T = \left\{ \begin{bmatrix} 1 \\ 2 \end{bmatrix}, \begin{bmatrix} -1 \\ 3 \end{bmatrix}, \begin{bmatrix} 1 \\ 0 \end{bmatrix} \right\}$ d. $T = \left\{ \begin{bmatrix} 1 \\ 2 \end{bmatrix}, \begin{bmatrix} 1 \\ 0 \end{bmatrix} \right\}$.

6. Is $B = [3, -2, 1]^T$ in the space spanned by $[2, 0, 2]^T$, $[-1, 1, 1]^T$, and $[3, 0, 1]^T$?

7. Use the definition of linear dependence to decide which of the following sets of vectors are linearly dependent. For those which are, express one of the vectors as a linear combination of the others.

   a. $T_1 = \left\{ \begin{bmatrix} 1 \\ 1 \\ 1 \\ 1 \end{bmatrix}, \begin{bmatrix} 1 \\ 0 \\ 1 \\ 0 \end{bmatrix}, \begin{bmatrix} 1 \\ 0 \\ 3 \\ 1 \end{bmatrix}, \begin{bmatrix} -1 \\ -1 \\ 1 \\ 0 \end{bmatrix} \right\}$

   b. $T_2 = \left\{ \begin{bmatrix} 1 \\ 1 \\ 1 \\ 1 \end{bmatrix}, \begin{bmatrix} -1 \\ 2 \\ 1 \\ 2 \end{bmatrix}, \begin{bmatrix} 0 \\ 0 \\ 0 \\ 1 \end{bmatrix} \right\}$

c. $T_3 = \left\{ \begin{bmatrix} 1 \\ 0 \end{bmatrix}, \begin{bmatrix} 0 \\ 3 \end{bmatrix} \right\}$ d. $T_4 = \left\{ \begin{bmatrix} 1 \\ 0 \\ 0 \end{bmatrix}, \begin{bmatrix} 0 \\ 0 \\ 3 \end{bmatrix}, \begin{bmatrix} 0 \\ 2 \\ 0 \end{bmatrix} \right\}$

e. $T_5 = \left\{ \begin{bmatrix} 1 \\ 0 \\ 0 \end{bmatrix}, \begin{bmatrix} 0 \\ 0 \\ 3 \end{bmatrix}, \begin{bmatrix} 0 \\ 2 \\ 0 \end{bmatrix}, \begin{bmatrix} 2 \\ -4 \\ 6 \end{bmatrix} \right\}.$

8. Which of the sets in Exercise 7 could have at least one vector deleted and still span the same space?

9. Show that

$$T_1 = \left\{ \begin{bmatrix} 1 \\ 0 \\ 2 \end{bmatrix}, \begin{bmatrix} 0 \\ 2 \\ 1 \end{bmatrix} \right\} \quad \text{and} \quad T_2 = \left\{ \begin{bmatrix} 2 \\ -2 \\ 3 \end{bmatrix}, \begin{bmatrix} 3 \\ -4 \\ 4 \end{bmatrix} \right\}$$

span the same subspace of 3×1 column vectors.

10. Let $\{A_1, A_2, A_3\}$ be a linearly independent set. Show that if A_4 is not a linear combination of A_1, A_2, A_3, then $\{A_1, A_2, A_3, A_4\}$ is linearly independent also.

11. Let $\{A_1, A_2, A_3\}$ be a linearly dependent set. Show that at least one of the A_i is a linear combination of the others.

12. Show that if 0 is an element of any finite set of vectors, T, then the set T is linearly dependent.

13. Let A and B be finite sets of vectors such that $A \subseteq B$. Show that a sufficient condition that B be linearly dependent is that A be linearly dependent. Is this condition also necessary?

14. Refer to sets A and B in Exercise 13. Show that a necessary condition that B be linearly independent is that A be linearly independent. Is this condition also sufficient?

15. If $\{A_1, A_2, A_3\}$ is a linearly independent set, show that $\{A_1, A_1 + A_2, A_1 + A_2 + A_3\}$ is also a linearly independent set.

16. Is the following statement true? If the set T spans the vector space S, then T is linearly independent?

New terms

spans, 112   linearly independent set of vectors, 115
linearly dependent set of vectors, 114

4.3   Basis and dimension

If $T \subseteq S$ is a linearly independent spanning set for the vector space S, we say that T is a **basis** for S.

Example 4.3.1

Since

$$T_1 = \left\{ \begin{bmatrix} 1 \\ 0 \\ 0 \end{bmatrix}, \begin{bmatrix} 0 \\ 1 \\ 0 \end{bmatrix} \right\}$$

is a linearly independent spanning set for

$$S = \left\{ Y \mid Y = a_1 \begin{bmatrix} 1 \\ 0 \\ 0 \end{bmatrix} + a_2 \begin{bmatrix} 0 \\ 1 \\ 0 \end{bmatrix} \right\},$$

T_1 is a basis for S. Similarly,

$$T_2 = \left\{ \begin{bmatrix} 2 \\ 0 \\ 0 \end{bmatrix}, \begin{bmatrix} 0 \\ 2 \\ 0 \end{bmatrix} \right\}$$

is also a basis for S. However, neither

$$T_3 = \left\{ \begin{bmatrix} 2 \\ 0 \\ 0 \end{bmatrix}, \begin{bmatrix} 0 \\ 0 \\ 2 \end{bmatrix} \right\} \quad \text{nor} \quad T_4 = \left\{ \begin{bmatrix} 1 \\ 0 \\ 0 \end{bmatrix}, \begin{bmatrix} 0 \\ 1 \\ 0 \end{bmatrix}, \begin{bmatrix} 0 \\ 2 \\ 0 \end{bmatrix} \right\}$$

is a basis for S (Why?).

Example 4.3.2

If

$$S = \left\{ Y \mid Y = a_1 \begin{bmatrix} 1 \\ 0 \end{bmatrix} + a_2 \begin{bmatrix} 0 \\ 1 \end{bmatrix} \right\},$$

then

$$T_1 = \left\{ \begin{bmatrix} 1 \\ 0 \end{bmatrix}, \begin{bmatrix} 0 \\ 1 \end{bmatrix} \right\}$$

is a basis for S, while

$$\left\{ \begin{bmatrix} 1 \\ 0 \end{bmatrix}, \begin{bmatrix} 0 \\ 1 \end{bmatrix}, \begin{bmatrix} 0 \\ 0 \end{bmatrix} \right\}$$

is not (Why?).

We conclude from Example 4.3.2 that the zero vector cannot be an element of any basis (or, indeed, of any linearly independent set).

Suppose that we have a vector space S and a basis $B \subseteq S$. We wish to show that it is the number of vectors in B which should serve as the measure of the size of S. In order that this be a meaningful definition, it must be true that each basis for S has the same number of vectors. We shall show that this is the case in two steps.

LEMMA 4.3.1

If $\{A_1, A_2, \ldots, A_n\}$ is a linearly dependent set of non-zero vectors, then there is some one of the vectors which is a linear combination of those preceding it in the list.

Proof:

The set $\{A_1\}$ is linearly independent, since $A_1 \neq 0$. If $\{A_1, A_2\}$ is a linearly dependent set, in which case A_2 is a linear combination (scalar multiple) of A_1, the proof is complete. If not, then $\{A_1, A_2\}$ is an independent set and we then consider $\{A_1, A_2, A_3\}$. If this set is linearly dependent, then there exist constants c_1, c_2, c_3, not all zero, such that

$$c_1 A_1 + c_2 A_2 + c_3 A_3 = 0.$$

Now $c_3 \neq 0$, because that would imply that $\{A_1, A_2\}$ was linearly dependent (How?). Thus, c_3^{-1} exists, and we can solve for A_3 as a linear combination of A_1, A_2. If $\{A_1, A_2, A_3\}$ is linearly independent, we consider $\{A_1, A_2, A_3, A_4\}$ and so forth. In general, we reason as follows. Consider the set $T_k = \{A_1, A_2, \ldots, A_k\}$. If T_k is linearly independent, then we consider the set $\{A_1, A_2, \ldots, A_k, A_{k+1}\}$. If T_k is the first such set that is linearly dependent, then there are scalars c_i, not all zero, such that

$$c_1 A_1 + c_2 A_2 + \cdots + c_k A_k = 0.$$

Further, $c_k \neq 0$, since this would imply that $\{A_1, A_2, \ldots, A_{k-1}\}$ was linearly dependent, contrary to our assumption that we are considering the first dependent set. Since $c_k \neq 0$, then $c_k^{-1} = 1/c_k$ exists, and

$$A_k = -\frac{c_1}{c_k} A_1 - \frac{c_2}{c_k} A_2 - \cdots - \frac{c_{k-1}}{c_k} A_{k-1},$$

and we thus have expressed A_k as a linear combination of the A's preceding it. Since there were only n vectors to start with and the original set was dependent, in no more than n steps we must find a vector which is a linear combination of those preceding it. This completes the proof of the lemma. □

Example 4.3.3

Let

$$\left\{ A_1 = \begin{bmatrix} 1 \\ 0 \\ 0 \end{bmatrix}, A_2 = \begin{bmatrix} 1 \\ 2 \\ 1 \end{bmatrix}, A_3 = \begin{bmatrix} 0 \\ 2 \\ 1 \end{bmatrix}, A_4 = \begin{bmatrix} -1 \\ 2 \\ 3 \end{bmatrix} \right\}$$

be a spanning set for a vector space S. $\{A_1\}$ is a linearly independent set. $\{A_1, A_2\}$ is also independent since A_2 is not a scalar multiple of A_1. Consider $\{A_1, A_2, A_3\}$. Since $(-1)A_1 + 1A_2 + (-1)A_3 = 0$, as we see by solving the system of equations

$$\begin{bmatrix} 1 & 1 & 0 \\ 0 & 2 & 2 \\ 0 & 1 & 1 \end{bmatrix} \begin{bmatrix} c_1 \\ c_2 \\ c_3 \end{bmatrix} = \begin{bmatrix} 0 \\ 0 \\ 0 \end{bmatrix},$$

we conclude that $A_3 = -A_1 + A_2$ is a linear combination of the preceding vectors A_1, A_2. We note that A_4 is not a linear combination of A_1, A_2, A_3, so the conjecture that the last vector must be a linear combination of the preceding is false.

We next show in Theorem 4.3.1 that the number of vectors in a spanning set for S cannot be less than the number of vectors in any given linearly independent subset of S. We shall use this fact in the proof of Theorem 4.3.2, the main result of this section.

THEOREM 4.3.1

Let S be the vector space spanned by $\{A_1, A_2, \ldots, A_n\}$ and let $\{B_1, B_2, \ldots, B_m\}$ be a linearly independent subset of S. Then $m \leqslant n$.

Proof:

Consider the set $T_1 = \{B_1, A_1, A_2, \ldots, A_n\}$. This set is linearly dependent since B_1 is a linear combination of the A_i (the A_i span S). Thus, by Lemma 4.3.1, some vector X of the set T_1 is a linear combination of those preceding it. Since X cannot be B_1, suppose it is A_k. We discard A_k from the set to form

$$\{B_1, A_1, \ldots, A_{k-1}, A_{k+1}, \ldots, A_n\}.$$

This new set also spans S (Why?). Thus, in particular, the vector B_2 is a linear combination of its elements and

$$T_2 = \{B_2, B_1, A_1, \ldots, A_{k-1}, A_{k+1}, \ldots, A_n\}$$

is a linearly dependent set. Again, some vector of the set is a linear combination of the preceding. This vector can not be one of the B_j since the B_j are independent. Thus it must be one of the A_i. We call this vector A_r and discard it from T_2. The resulting set also spans S. Continuing in this fashion, we delete one of the A_i vectors and add one of the B_j vectors, each time creating a new spanning set for S consisting of n vectors. We want to show that $n \geqslant m$. We suppose to the contrary that $n < m$ and see that this leads us to conclude that the set of B_j vectors is dependent, contradicting our assumption that the B_j are independent. If $n < m$ we will eventually run out of A_i to delete before we have all m of the B_j in the set. We might, for example, have

$$T_k = \{B_k, B_{k-1}, \ldots, B_1\}$$

with $k < m$, so that, in particular, B_m is not in T_k. Since T_k is a spanning set for S, B_m would have to be a linear combination of the vectors in T_k. Thus the set of all the B_j would be linearly dependent, in contradiction to our original assumption. Thus $m \leqslant n$, as we wished to show.   ☐

THEOREM 4.3.2

Every basis for S contains the same number of vectors.

Proof:

Suppose that we have two bases for S—both linearly independent spanning sets for S. Call them B_1 and B_2 and let n_1 and n_2 denote the number of vectors in B_1, B_2 respectively. We wish to show that $n_1 = n_2$. Since B_1 spans S and B_2 is linearly independent, $n_1 \geqslant n_2$ by Theorem 4.3.1. However, B_2 spans S and B_1 is also linearly independent, so that $n_2 \geqslant n_1$. Thus $n_1 = n_2$ and the proof is complete.   ☐

Given a spanning set $T = \{A_1, A_2, \ldots, A_n\}$ for a vector space S, we can create a basis for S by starting with A_1. If $A_1 \neq 0$, we consider $\{A_1, A_2\}$. If this set is independent, we consider $\{A_1, A_2, A_3\}$ and so forth, until we find a vector which is a linear combination of the preceding ones. We discard this vector and continue until we check all of the vectors in T, and discard those which are linear combinations of the preceding.

We have shown in Theorem 4.3.2 that the number of vectors in a basis for S is unique. This non-negative integer, which represents both the maximum number of linearly independent vectors in S and the minimum number of vectors required to span S, is called the **dimension** of S. If we happen to know the dimension of S, then the process of finding a basis for S must terminate when we have found the correct number of linearly independent vectors. We thus need not continue and check every element of the spanning set being examined.

Example 4.3.4

Suppose that

$$S = \left\{ Y \,\middle|\, Y = a_1 \begin{bmatrix} 1 \\ 0 \\ 0 \\ 0 \end{bmatrix} + a_2 \begin{bmatrix} 1 \\ 2 \\ 1 \\ 0 \end{bmatrix} + a_3 \begin{bmatrix} 0 \\ 2 \\ 1 \\ 0 \end{bmatrix} + a_4 \begin{bmatrix} 0 \\ 0 \\ 1 \\ 1 \end{bmatrix} + a_5 \begin{bmatrix} 1 \\ 4 \\ 3 \\ 1 \end{bmatrix} \right\}.$$

S has dimension 3, and we wish to pick an independent subset of the defining vectors as a basis. Now $\{A_1, A_2\}$ is clearly independent; but $A_3 = A_2 - A_1$, so that $\{A_1, A_2, A_3\}$ is dependent. However, we can observe that A_4 is not a linear combination of A_1 and A_2. Thus $\{A_1, A_2, A_4\}$ is independent and will serve as a basis for S. Suppose we had started with A_2. What would the basis have been?

When we speak of " 2-space " we shall mean

$$\left\{ Y \mid Y = a\begin{bmatrix} 1 \\ 0 \end{bmatrix} + b\begin{bmatrix} 0 \\ 1 \end{bmatrix} \right\};$$

that is, the set of all 2×1 column matrices with real elements. This space has dimension 2. The obvious extensions to 3-space and to n-space will also be exploited. However, when we speak of "a 2-space," we merely mean some subset of a vector space which is a vector space of dimension 2. The vectors themselves may have 5 components, for example. Thus, we will say that

$$\left\{ Y \mid Y = a\begin{bmatrix} 1 \\ 0 \\ 0 \end{bmatrix} + b\begin{bmatrix} 0 \\ 1 \\ 0 \end{bmatrix} \right\}$$

is a subspace of 3-space of dimension 2, or simply a 2-space.

Exercises 4.3

1. We say that the set $T \subseteq S$ is a basis for the vector space S provided that T is _____ and that T _____.

2. If the dimension of a vector space S is 4, then any basis for S contains __4__.

3. Decide which of the following statements are true:
    a. A subset of a basis consists of linearly independent vectors.
    b. A basis for a vector space is unique.
    c. If T is a basis for S, then no proper subset of T spans S.

4. Suppose that we know that a given vector space S is spanned by a set T which contains 6 vectors. What, if anything, can be said about the dimension of S?

5. Which of the following sets are not a basis for the vector space

$$S = \left\{ Y \mid Y = x_1\begin{bmatrix} 1 \\ 0 \\ 0 \end{bmatrix} + x_2\begin{bmatrix} 0 \\ 1 \\ 0 \end{bmatrix} + x_3\begin{bmatrix} 0 \\ 0 \\ 1 \end{bmatrix} \right\} ?$$

a. $T_1 = \left\{ \begin{bmatrix} 1 \\ 0 \\ 0 \end{bmatrix}, \begin{bmatrix} 0 \\ 1 \\ 1 \end{bmatrix}, \begin{bmatrix} 1 \\ -1 \\ -1 \end{bmatrix} \right\}$

b. $T_2 = \left\{ \begin{bmatrix} 0 \\ 0 \\ 1 \end{bmatrix}, \begin{bmatrix} 1 \\ 0 \\ 1 \end{bmatrix}, \begin{bmatrix} 2 \\ 3 \\ 4 \end{bmatrix}, \begin{bmatrix} -1 \\ 0 \\ 0 \end{bmatrix} \right\}$.

6. If

$$H = \left\{ X_H \mid X_H = a \begin{bmatrix} 1 \\ 0 \\ 1 \\ 0 \end{bmatrix} + b \begin{bmatrix} 0 \\ 1 \\ 1 \\ 0 \end{bmatrix} + c \begin{bmatrix} 0 \\ 0 \\ 3 \\ 1 \end{bmatrix} \right\}$$

what is the dimension of H?

7. Let a basis for 2-space consist of $\{A_1, A_2\} = \left\{ \begin{bmatrix} 2 \\ 1 \end{bmatrix}, \begin{bmatrix} 1 \\ 2 \end{bmatrix} \right\}$. Which, if any, of these vectors could be replaced by $\begin{bmatrix} 6 \\ 3 \end{bmatrix}$ to form a new basis?

8. Suppose that A_1, A_2, A_3, A_4 are 4 vectors in 3-space such that $\{A_1, A_2, A_3\}$ is a basis for the space spanned by all 4 A_i. If $A_4 = A_1 + A_2$, which of the 3 vectors, if any, could be replaced by A_4 to obtain a new basis?

9. Suppose that $Y = A_1 + 2A_2 + 3A_3$ is a representation of Y in terms of the basis vectors in Exercise 8. Find the new representation of Y if A_2 is replaced by A_4 to form a new basis $\{A_1, A_4, A_3\}$.

10. Let $\{B_1, B_2, \ldots, B_m\}$ be a basis for m-space, and suppose that $A = y_1 B_1 + y_2 B_2 + \cdots + y_m B_m$ with $y_1 \neq 0$. Prove that $\{A, B_2, \ldots, B_m\}$ is also a basis for m-space.

11. Let S be the space spanned by

$$T = \left\{ \begin{bmatrix} 1 \\ 0 \\ 1 \\ 1 \end{bmatrix}, \begin{bmatrix} -1 \\ -3 \\ 1 \\ 0 \end{bmatrix}, \begin{bmatrix} 2 \\ 3 \\ 0 \\ 1 \end{bmatrix}, \begin{bmatrix} 2 \\ 0 \\ 2 \\ 2 \end{bmatrix} \right\}.$$

Find the dimension of S and a subset of T which could serve as a basis for S.

New terms

4.4   The coordinates of a vector

A basis for a vector space S provides another advantage over a spanning set which happens to be linearly dependent. *A basis may be used to define a coordinate system for S which provides a unique set of coordinates for each vector in S.* A merely linearly dependent spanning set will not suffice.   Let $S = \left\{ Y \mid Y = a_1 \begin{bmatrix} 1 \\ 0 \\ 0 \end{bmatrix} + a_2 \begin{bmatrix} 0 \\ 1 \\ 0 \end{bmatrix} + a_3 \begin{bmatrix} 0 \\ 2 \\ 0 \end{bmatrix} \right\}$.   Some 3×1 column matrices are elements of S and some are not (Can you name one which is not?). For $a_1 = a_2 = a_3 = 1$, we see that

$$Y_1 = \begin{bmatrix} 1 \\ 3 \\ 0 \end{bmatrix} = 1 \begin{bmatrix} 1 \\ 0 \\ 0 \end{bmatrix} + 1 \begin{bmatrix} 0 \\ 1 \\ 0 \end{bmatrix} + 1 \begin{bmatrix} 0 \\ 2 \\ 0 \end{bmatrix}$$

is in S. With respect to this particular spanning set, we could say that Y_1 is represented by the coordinate set $\{1, 1, 1\}$ since, knowing the A_i and this triple of constants, we could re-create Y_1. However, it is also the case that

$$Y_1 = \begin{bmatrix} 1 \\ 3 \\ 0 \end{bmatrix} = 1 \begin{bmatrix} 1 \\ 0 \\ 0 \end{bmatrix} + 3 \begin{bmatrix} 0 \\ 1 \\ 0 \end{bmatrix} + 0 \begin{bmatrix} 0 \\ 2 \\ 0 \end{bmatrix},$$

so that $\{1, 3, 0\}$ would also be a candidate for a coordinate set for Y_1. Here we have an example of non-uniqueness that is undesirable. We prefer to use a set of vectors with the property that such a **coordinate set for a given vector** is unique (much as you prefer to be known by *one* name). A basis for S provides such a set. We show that this is true for a 3-dimensional vector space.

THEOREM 4.4.1

If $\{A_1, A_2, A_3\}$ is a basis for 3-space and $Y = a_1 A_1 + a_2 A_2 + a_3 A_3 = b_1 A_1 + b_2 A_2 + b_3 A_3$ then $a_1 = b_1$, $a_2 = b_2$, $a_3 = b_3$.

Proof:

We demonstrate that the contrapositive is true; that is, we shall show that if $a_i \neq b_i$ for some i, then $\{A_1, A_2, A_3\}$ is not a basis for S. We see that, from the hypothesis of the theorem,

$$(a_1 - b_1)A_1 + (a_2 - b_2)A_2 + (a_3 - b_3)A_3 = 0.$$

Since $a_i \neq b_i$ for some i, we have a set of scalars $c_i = a_i - b_i$, not all zero, such that $c_1 A_1 + c_2 A_2 + c_3 A_3 = 0$, and the A_i cannot be linearly independent. Thus $\{A_1, A_2, A_3\}$ is not a basis for S. Recalling that establishing the contrapositive is equivalent to establishing the original theorem, we are finished.   □

This uniqueness of coordinate sets, or "names" of vectors, which is provided by a basis for a vector space is one which we will exploit often.

Example 4.4.1

Let $S = \left\{ Y \mid Y = a \begin{bmatrix} 1 \\ 0 \end{bmatrix} + b \begin{bmatrix} 0 \\ 1 \end{bmatrix} \right\}$. In this basis it is a simple matter to find coordinates. Let $Y_1 = \begin{bmatrix} 3 \\ 2 \end{bmatrix} = 3 \begin{bmatrix} 1 \\ 0 \end{bmatrix} + 2 \begin{bmatrix} 0 \\ 1 \end{bmatrix}$. Thus $\{3, 2\}$ is the coordinate set denoting $\begin{bmatrix} 3 \\ 2 \end{bmatrix}$.

Example 4.4.2

Let

$$S = \left\{ Y \mid Y = a \begin{bmatrix} 1 \\ 0 \\ 1 \end{bmatrix} + b \begin{bmatrix} 0 \\ 1 \\ 0 \end{bmatrix} + c \begin{bmatrix} -1 \\ 2 \\ 3 \end{bmatrix} \right\}.$$

If we know that $Y_1 = \begin{bmatrix} 0 \\ 3 \\ 4 \end{bmatrix}$ is in S, we may wish to find its coordinates with respect to this basis. Thus we wish to solve the set of equations

$$x_1 \begin{bmatrix} 1 \\ 0 \\ 1 \end{bmatrix} + x_2 \begin{bmatrix} 0 \\ 1 \\ 0 \end{bmatrix} + x_3 \begin{bmatrix} -1 \\ 2 \\ 3 \end{bmatrix} = \begin{bmatrix} 0 \\ 3 \\ 4 \end{bmatrix}.$$

By Gauss-Jordan reduction we find that $x_1 = x_2 = x_3 = 1$. The coordinate set is thus $\{1, 1, 1\}$.

Because of the notational advantages which it provides, we now consider the concept of a coordinate matrix of a given vector X with respect to a fixed basis. Let $\{U_1, U_2, \ldots, U_m\}$ be a fixed basis for $\mathscr{M}_{m,1}$. If X is in $\mathscr{M}_{m,1}$ such that

$$X = u_1 U_1 + u_2 U_2 + \cdots + u_m U_m,$$

then the column matrix

$$X_U = \begin{bmatrix} u_1 \\ u_2 \\ \vdots \\ u_m \end{bmatrix}$$

is called the **coordinate matrix** of X with respect to the U basis. We can then represent X as the matrix product

$$[U_1, U_2, \ldots, U_m] \begin{bmatrix} u_1 \\ u_2 \\ \vdots \\ u_m \end{bmatrix} = UX_U = X,$$

where the square matrix $U = [U_1, U_2, \ldots, U_m]$ is the **basis matrix** whose columns are the basis vectors U_i, and X_U is the column matrix of coordinates of X with respect to the U basis.

Example 4.4.3

In $\mathcal{M}_{2,1}$, let $\{U_1, U_2\} = \left\{ \begin{bmatrix} 1 \\ 2 \end{bmatrix}, \begin{bmatrix} 1 \\ 3 \end{bmatrix} \right\}$ be a basis, so that $U = [U_1, U_2] = \begin{bmatrix} 1 & 1 \\ 2 & 3 \end{bmatrix}$ is the corresponding basis matrix. Since $X = \begin{bmatrix} 2 \\ 7 \end{bmatrix}$ is in $\mathcal{M}_{2,1}$, there are scalars u_1, u_2 such that $\begin{bmatrix} 2 \\ 7 \end{bmatrix} = u_1 \begin{bmatrix} 1 \\ 2 \end{bmatrix} + u_2 \begin{bmatrix} 1 \\ 3 \end{bmatrix} = \begin{bmatrix} 1 & 1 \\ 2 & 3 \end{bmatrix} \begin{bmatrix} u_1 \\ u_2 \end{bmatrix}$, or such that $X = UX_U$. Noting that this is nothing more than a linear equation problem to solve, and that $U^{-1} = \begin{bmatrix} 3 & -1 \\ -2 & 1 \end{bmatrix}$, we can find

$$X_U = U^{-1}X = \begin{bmatrix} 3 & -1 \\ -2 & 1 \end{bmatrix} \begin{bmatrix} 2 \\ 7 \end{bmatrix} = \begin{bmatrix} -1 \\ 3 \end{bmatrix}.$$

We verify that X_U is valid by computing

$$X = -1 \begin{bmatrix} 1 \\ 2 \end{bmatrix} + 3 \begin{bmatrix} 1 \\ 3 \end{bmatrix} = \begin{bmatrix} 2 \\ 7 \end{bmatrix}.$$

Let us now consider a very special case in

Example 4.4.4

Let $\{U_1, U_2\} = \left\{ \begin{bmatrix} 1 \\ 0 \end{bmatrix}, \begin{bmatrix} 0 \\ 1 \end{bmatrix} \right\}$, so that $U = \begin{bmatrix} 1 & 0 \\ 0 & 1 \end{bmatrix}$. If $X = \begin{bmatrix} 2 \\ 7 \end{bmatrix}$, then, since

$$X = 2U_1 + 7U_2 = \begin{bmatrix} 1 & 0 \\ 0 & 1 \end{bmatrix} \begin{bmatrix} 2 \\ 7 \end{bmatrix},$$

we see that $X = UX_U = I_2 X_U$, so that $X = X_U$.

This last example demonstrates that if we have the special case in which our basis matrix is the identity matrix, then the vector X and its coordinate matrix X_U are indistinguishable. In a particular application, the context of the discussion must make it clear whether a matrix is being used to represent a vector or the coordinates of a vector.

The previous discussion in this section should make it very clear that it is important to know when a given set of vectors is a basis. Certain sets of vectors can be quickly identified as linearly independent sets and thus as a basis for the vector space which they span. Consider $\left\{ \begin{bmatrix} 2 \\ 0 \end{bmatrix}, \begin{bmatrix} 0 \\ 1 \end{bmatrix} \right\}$. Because of the 0 in the second vector, it is clear that the second vector could not be a non-zero multiple of the first, and thus that the two vectors are linearly independent.

Now let us look at a set containing three vectors

$$\left\{ \begin{bmatrix} 1 \\ 0 \\ 0 \end{bmatrix}, \begin{bmatrix} 0 \\ 2 \\ 0 \end{bmatrix}, \begin{bmatrix} 0 \\ 0 \\ 4 \end{bmatrix} \right\}.$$

The placement of the zeros again makes it clear that these three vectors are also linearly independent. Of course, we could always use the definition and look for scalars c_1, c_2, c_3 such that

$$c_1 \begin{bmatrix} 1 \\ 0 \\ 0 \end{bmatrix} + c_2 \begin{bmatrix} 0 \\ 2 \\ 0 \end{bmatrix} + c_3 \begin{bmatrix} 0 \\ 0 \\ 4 \end{bmatrix} = \begin{bmatrix} 0 \\ 0 \\ 0 \end{bmatrix}.$$

Since this requires that $c_1 = 0$, $2c_2 = 0$, and $4c_3 = 0$—that is, each $c_i = 0$—the set of vectors is linearly independent. In general, then, we note that if we have a set of p vectors $\{A_1, A_2, \ldots, A_p\}$ with the property that each A_i has at least $p - 1$ zeros and each A_i has a non-zero element in a row in which all of the other vectors have a 0, then the set must be linearly independent. We recall that the set H of Example 3.9.3 was constructed as the set of all linear combinations of the vectors in the

$$\left\{ \begin{bmatrix} -2 \\ 1 \\ -4 \\ 1 \\ 0 \end{bmatrix}, \begin{bmatrix} 5 \\ -2 \\ -3 \\ 0 \\ 1 \end{bmatrix} \right\},$$

which has this property, as does the corresponding set of vectors

$$\left\{ \begin{bmatrix} -2 \\ 1 \\ 0 \\ 0 \\ 0 \\ 0 \end{bmatrix}, \begin{bmatrix} -1 \\ 0 \\ 1 \\ -2 \\ 1 \\ 0 \end{bmatrix}, \begin{bmatrix} 2 \\ 0 \\ -3 \\ 4 \\ 0 \\ 1 \end{bmatrix} \right\}$$

of Example 3.9.4. A reconsideration of the manner in which X_H was constructed should convince you that this will always be the case. *Thus,*

*our H vector spaces are constructed as sets of linear combinations of
linearly independent vectors to start with.* These defining vectors form a
basis for H in each case, and the dimension of H is readily obtainable.

Exercises 4.4

1. Let $\left\{ \begin{bmatrix} 1 \\ 0 \end{bmatrix}, \begin{bmatrix} 0 \\ 1 \end{bmatrix} \right\}$ be a basis for 2-space. Find the coordinates of
$\begin{bmatrix} 1 \\ -1 \end{bmatrix}$ and $\begin{bmatrix} 3 \\ 4 \end{bmatrix}$ with respect to this basis.

2. Determine by observation which of the following sets are linearly
independent.

   a. $\left\{ \begin{bmatrix} 1 \\ 0 \\ 0 \end{bmatrix}, \begin{bmatrix} 0 \\ 0 \\ 3 \end{bmatrix}, \begin{bmatrix} 0 \\ 2 \\ 0 \end{bmatrix} \right\}$
       b. $\left\{ \begin{bmatrix} 2 \\ 0 \\ 0 \\ 3 \end{bmatrix}, \begin{bmatrix} 0 \\ 2 \\ 0 \\ 1 \end{bmatrix}, \begin{bmatrix} 0 \\ 0 \\ 5 \\ 4 \end{bmatrix} \right\}$

   c. $\left\{ \begin{bmatrix} 1 \\ 0 \\ 1 \end{bmatrix}, \begin{bmatrix} 2 \\ 4 \\ 0 \end{bmatrix}, \begin{bmatrix} -2 \\ 0 \\ -2 \end{bmatrix} \right\}$
       d. $\left\{ \begin{bmatrix} 3 \\ 4 \\ 1 \\ 0 \\ 0 \end{bmatrix}, \begin{bmatrix} 2 \\ 3 \\ 0 \\ 1 \\ 0 \end{bmatrix}, \begin{bmatrix} -1 \\ 2 \\ 0 \\ 0 \\ 1 \end{bmatrix} \right\}$

3. Let $\left\{ \begin{bmatrix} 1 \\ 2 \end{bmatrix}, \begin{bmatrix} 2 \\ 1 \end{bmatrix} \right\}$ be a basis for 2-space. Find the coordinates of
$\begin{bmatrix} 1 \\ 2 \end{bmatrix}, \begin{bmatrix} 3 \\ 3 \end{bmatrix}$, and $\begin{bmatrix} -3 \\ 0 \end{bmatrix}$ with respect to this basis.

4. Let $\left\{ \begin{bmatrix} 1 \\ 0 \\ 0 \end{bmatrix}, \begin{bmatrix} 0 \\ 1 \\ 0 \end{bmatrix}, \begin{bmatrix} 0 \\ 0 \\ 1 \end{bmatrix} \right\}$ and $\left\{ \begin{bmatrix} 1 \\ 0 \\ 0 \end{bmatrix}, \begin{bmatrix} 1 \\ 1 \\ 0 \end{bmatrix}, \begin{bmatrix} 1 \\ 1 \\ 1 \end{bmatrix} \right\}$ be bases for 3-space.

   Find the coordinates of $\begin{bmatrix} 3 \\ 2 \\ 1 \end{bmatrix}$ and $\begin{bmatrix} 2 \\ 2 \\ 1 \end{bmatrix}$ with respect to each basis.

5. The results of this problem will be of special interest for those who
plan to study Chapter 7.

   Let $A = \begin{bmatrix} 2 & 3 & 1 & 0 \\ 3 & 2 & 0 & 1 \end{bmatrix} = [A_1, A_2, A_3, A_4]$ and let S be the
space spanned by the columns A_i of A.

   a. Which possible pairs $\{A_i, A_j\}$ could serve as a basis for S?

   b. If $\{A_3, A_4\}$ is chosen, find the coordinate sets which represent
each of the A_i with respect to this basis.

    c. If $\{A_3, A_1\}$ is chosen, find the coordinate sets.

    d. If $\{A_2, A_1\}$ is chosen, find the coordinate sets.

    e. Express $\begin{bmatrix} 6 \\ 6 \end{bmatrix}$ as a linear combination of the basis vectors in d.

6. Let $A = \begin{bmatrix} 2 & 1 & 1 & 0 \\ 1 & 1 & 0 & 1 \end{bmatrix} = [A_1, A_2, A_3, A_4]$, and let S be the space spanned by the columns A_i of A. Find the coordinates of each of the A_i if the following bases are chosen for S.

    a. $\{A_3, A_4\}$ b. $\{A_1, A_4\}$ c. $\{A_1, A_2\}$.

7. Fill in the blanks.

    a. In $\mathcal{M}_{2,1}$, let $U_1 = \begin{bmatrix} 1 \\ 4 \end{bmatrix}$ and $U_2 = \begin{bmatrix} 4 \\ 2 \end{bmatrix}$ so that $U = \begin{bmatrix} & \end{bmatrix}$.

    b. If $X = \begin{bmatrix} -2 \\ 6 \end{bmatrix}$ is in $\mathcal{M}_{2,1}$, then $X = UX_U$ where $X_U = \begin{bmatrix} & \end{bmatrix}$.

    c. If $X = \begin{bmatrix} 1 \\ 0 \end{bmatrix}$ is in $\mathcal{M}_{2,1}$, then $X_U = \begin{bmatrix} & \end{bmatrix}$.

    d. If $X = \begin{bmatrix} & \end{bmatrix}$ is in $\mathcal{M}_{2,1}$ then $X_U = \begin{bmatrix} 1 \\ 1 \end{bmatrix}$.

New terms

coordinate set for a vector, 126   basis matrix, 128
coordinate matrix, 128

4.5 Vector spaces and homogeneous linear equations

We have seen that the problem of finding X such that $AX = 0$ is equivalent to finding x_i such that

$$x_1 A_1 + x_2 A_2 + \cdots + x_n A_n = 0, \quad \text{where the } A_i \text{ are the columns of } A.$$

We are asking for the set of all linear combinations of the A_i which yield 0, if any. We recall from Section 4.1 that the solution set H is a vector space. We shall call upon your knowledge of the Gauss-Jordan reduction process and the method of constructing H to formulate some general results about the dimension of H. First we note that H is a subspace of **n-space**, or $\mathcal{M}_{n,1}$.

We suppose, as before, that we are dealing with a situation in which we have m equations in n unknowns with $k < m$ of the equations redundant and $m - k \leqslant n$. By Gauss-Jordan reduction we obtain a row-reduced echelon form as shown below in which the asterisks represent real numbers which may or may not be 0.

$$m-k\begin{array}{c} \\ \\ \\ \\ \\ \end{array}\quad k\begin{array}{c} \\ \\ \\ \end{array}\begin{bmatrix} * & * & \cdots & * & 0 \\ * & * & \cdots & * & 0 \\ \cdot & \cdot & \cdots & \cdot & \cdot \\ * & * & \cdots & * & 0 \\ \hline 0 & 0 & \cdots & 0 & 0 \\ \cdot & \cdot & \cdots & \cdot & \cdot \\ 0 & 0 & \cdots & 0 & 0 \end{bmatrix}$$

There are two possibilities. Either $m - k = n$ or $m - k < n$. If $m - k = n$, then the matrix of asterisks is an $n \times n$ identity matrix implying that we have a unique solution 0. We say that $\{0\}$ is a vector space of dimension 0. On the other hand, if $m - k < n$, then there will be $d = n - (m - k)$ free variables. By assigning these as in Chapter 3, we obtain a solution set of the form

$$H = \{X_H \mid X_H = a_1 B_1 + a_2 B_2 + \cdots + a_d B_d\},$$

in such a way that the set $\{B_1, B_2, \ldots, B_d\}$ is linearly independent. Thus H is of dimension $d = n - (m - k)$. A typical example of such a row-reduced echelon matrix is

$$\begin{bmatrix} 1 & 0 & -2 & 0 & -4 & -7 & 0 \\ 0 & 1 & -3 & 0 & -5 & -8 & 0 \\ 0 & 0 & 0 & 1 & -6 & -9 & 0 \\ 0 & 0 & 0 & 0 & 0 & 0 & 0 \end{bmatrix}.$$

In this particular case we know that we may freely assign values for x_6, x_5, and x_3. Thus, if we let $x_3 = a$, $x_5 = b$, and $x_6 = c$, we find that

$$H = \left\{ X_H \mid X_H = \begin{bmatrix} 2a + 4b + 7c \\ 3a + 5b + 8c \\ 1a + 0b + 0c \\ 0a + 6b + 9c \\ 0a + 1b + 0c \\ 0a + 0b + 1c \end{bmatrix} \right\}$$

is the general solution. We know that in this particular case H is a vector space because we can rewrite it as

$$H = \left\{ X_H \mid X_H = a\begin{bmatrix} 2 \\ 3 \\ 1 \\ 0 \\ 0 \\ 0 \end{bmatrix} + b\begin{bmatrix} 4 \\ 5 \\ 0 \\ 6 \\ 1 \\ 0 \end{bmatrix} + c\begin{bmatrix} 7 \\ 8 \\ 0 \\ 9 \\ 0 \\ 1 \end{bmatrix} \right\}.$$

Since each X_H is a linear combination of 3 linearly independent vectors from 6-space, we know that the solution space is a subspace of 6-space of dimension 3.

Now let us consider the original questions that we asked in Chapter 3 concerning linear equations as they apply in general to $AX = 0$.

1. Does a solution exist? Yes, although it may only be the trivial one.

2. If so, is the solution unique? The solution will be unique only in case $n = m - k$, in which case there will remain no free variables. In this case the dimension of the solution space is 0.

3. If there is at least one solution, and it is not unique, then how many solutions are there? If there is one non-trivial solution, then there are certainly an infinite number, since every scalar multiple of the one solution is also a solution. Thus, the dimension of the solution space is at least 1.

4. What is the complete set of solutions? The vector space of dimension d as constructed above constitutes the complete solution set. The vectors constructed serve as one possible basis for this space.

One of the words which you will see if you continue your study of matrices is the term "rank". We shall define the **rank of a matrix** A to be the number $(m - k)$ of non-redundant rows of A when A is thought of as the coefficient matrix of a set of homogeneous linear equations. We use the symbol $r(A)$ to stand for the rank of A. Thus $r(A)$ can be calculated as the number of non-zero rows remaining after A is transformed to row-reduced echelon form.

For convenience, we now list some of the standard results from the study of homogeneous linear equations. The reader should have no trouble reconciling our phraseology here with that of our previous statements.

THEOREM 4.5.1

Consider the set $AX = 0$ of m linear equations in n unknowns in which k of the equations are redundant. Then

1. There is at least one X, namely 0, such that $AX = 0$.

2. The complete set of solutions is a subspace of n-space of dimension

$$d = n - (m - k) = n - r(A).$$

3. A necessary and sufficient condition that $X = 0$ be the unique solution is that $d = 0$; that is, $n = (m - k) = r(A)$.

4. If $n > m - k = r(A)$, then there are exactly $n - r(A)$ linearly independent solutions.

Exercises 4.5

1. Suppose that A is an $m \times n$ matrix with $m \leqslant n$. Decide whether the following statements are true or false.
   a. A system $AX = 0$ has a non-trivial solution if $m < n$.
   b. A system $AX = 0$ has a non-trivial solution only if $m < n$.
   c. If A is non-singular, then 0 is the only solution of $AX = 0$.
   d. The solution set of $AX = 0$ forms a vector space.
   e. The dimension of $\{X \mid AX = 0\}$ is greater than or equal to $n - m$.
   f. 0 is in the set of vectors spanned by the columns of A.
   g. The set of $n - r(A)$ solution vectors created as a result of Gauss-Jordan reduction of $[A \mid 0]$ may be linearly dependent.
   h. A necessary condition that 0 be a solution of $AX = 0$ is that $m < n$.
   i. A homogeneous linear equation $AX = 0$ is always consistent.
   j. $r(A) \leqslant m$.
   k. $r(A) \leqslant n$.

2. Verify, from the definition of vector space, that $\{X \mid AX = 0\}$ is a vector space.

3. Consider the set of equations $AX = 0$ with A an $m \times n$ matrix and $k < m$ redundant equations. Find the dimension of the solution space if
   a. $n = 5, m = 3, k = 1$.
   b. $n = m = 5, k = 0$.
   c. $n = 6, m = 4, k = 1$.
   d. $n = 10, m = 5 = r(A)$.
   e. $n = 4, m = 4, r(A) = 3$.

4. Use our results from the theory of homogeneous linear equations to show that the set $\left\{ \begin{bmatrix} 1 \\ 2 \end{bmatrix}, \begin{bmatrix} 2 \\ 1 \end{bmatrix}, \begin{bmatrix} 4 \\ 3 \end{bmatrix} \right\}$ is a linearly dependent set. (*Hint:* Find the dimension of the solution space of $AC = 0$, where $A = \begin{bmatrix} 1 & 2 & 4 \\ 2 & 1 & 3 \end{bmatrix}$ and C is the matrix of the coefficients in the definition of linear dependence.)

New terms

n-space, 131　　　　　　　　　　　rank of a matrix, 133

4.6   Vector spaces and non-homogeneous linear equations

We now use our results for $AX = 0$ to study the case where $AX = B$ and $B \neq 0$. Suppose first that we have a particular solution X_P such that $AX_P = B$ and some other vector X_H such that $AX_H = 0$. Consider the vector $Y = X_P + X_H$. Is Y also a solution of $AX = B$? Since

$$AY = A(X_P + X_H) = AX_P + AX_H = B + 0 = B,$$

we see that Y is such a solution. Therefore, if we know any particular solution to $AX = B$ and any homogeneous solution X_H, we can find another particular solution easily. Is every solution to $AX = B$ of the form $X_P + X_H$? If any solution X_P exists then certainly it is of this form since 0 is a solution to $AX = 0$ and $X_P = X_P + 0$. If Y is any other solution such that $AY = B$, then Y can be expressed as

$$Y = X_P + (Y - X_P),$$

and

$$A(Y - X_P) = AY - AX_P = B - B = 0,$$

so that $Y - X_P$ is a solution of $AX = 0$. Thus Y is of the form $X_P + X_H$, with $X_H = Y - X_P$. We have therefore proved that

1. If $Y = X_P + X_H$, then Y is a solution of $AX = B$.
2. If Y is a solution of $AX = B$, then Y is of the form $Y = X_P + X_H$.

We may rephrase the preceding results as

THEOREM 4.6.1

A necessary and sufficient condition that Y be a solution of $AX = B$ is that $Y = X_P + X_H$ where $AX_P = B$ and $AX_H = 0$.

Reconsideration of the Gauss-Jordan process shows that it is a method which provides solutions to $AX = B$ and $AX = 0$ simultaneously. For, since the matrix A is the same in both cases, and $AX = 0$ has only a constant column of zeros, we have, in reality, been solving a related homogeneous set of equations each time we solved a non-homogeneous set. At the same time, we have been solving for one particular solution of $AX = B$, namely X_P. Any vector in the complete set of solutions for $AX = B$ can then be formed as a sum of X_P and some vector in the vector space of solutions $\{X_H\} = H$.

With these ideas in mind, we see that if there is at least one solution to $AX = B$, then there will be a unique solution only in case $\{X_H\}$ is $\{0\}$. Otherwise, there will be an infinite number of solutions. It will be instructional for you to consider whether or not the complete set of solutions to $AX = B$, $B \neq 0$ is a vector space itself.

The following theorem relates the existence of particular solutions to the concept of rank.

THEOREM 4.6.2

There will exist a solution of $AX = B$ if and only if the rank of the augmented matrix $[A \mid B]$ is equal to the rank of A.

Proof:

When we attempt to solve $AX = B$ by Gauss-Jordan reduction we will reach an equivalent augmented matrix of the form

$$
\begin{array}{c}
 \\
m - k \\
 \\
 \\
k \\
 \\
\end{array}
\begin{array}{c}
n \\
\left[
\begin{array}{cccc|c}
* & * & \cdots & * & * \\
\cdot & \cdot & \cdots & \cdot & \cdot \\
* & * & \cdots & * & * \\
\hline
0 & 0 & \cdots & 0 & a_1 \\
\cdot & \cdot & \cdots & \cdot & \cdot \\
0 & 0 & \cdots & 0 & a_k
\end{array}
\right]
\end{array}
$$

where the asterisks and a_i indicate any real number. If there is a solution then $a_1 = a_2 = \cdots = a_k = 0$, and $r(A) = ([A \mid B])$. On the other hand, if $r(A) = r([A \mid B])$, then the a_i are 0, and there will be a solution. □

Exercises 4.6

1. Show that if $X = X_P + X_H$ then X is a solution of $AX = B$.

2. Show that if $AX = B$ then X is of the form $X_P + X_H$.

3. Determine whether or not a particular solution exists in the following cases with augmented matrices $[A \mid B]$ as shown. If one exists, find the complete solution in the form $\{X_P + X_H\}$. Verify your solution by substitution in the original equations.

a. $\begin{bmatrix} 1 & 2 & | & 1 \\ 0 & 0 & | & 1 \end{bmatrix}$ b. $\begin{bmatrix} 1 & 2 & | & 0 \\ 0 & 0 & | & 1 \end{bmatrix}$

c. $\begin{bmatrix} 1 & 3 & | & 1 \\ 2 & 1 & | & 1 \end{bmatrix}$ d. $\begin{bmatrix} 1 & 3 & | & 1 \\ 3 & 9 & | & 1 \end{bmatrix}$

e. $\begin{bmatrix} 0 & 0 & | & 0 \\ 1 & 2 & | & 1 \end{bmatrix}$ f. $\begin{bmatrix} 1 & 0 & 1 & | & 1 \\ 0 & 1 & 0 & | & 2 \\ 0 & 0 & 0 & | & 3 \end{bmatrix}$

g. $\begin{bmatrix} 1 & 1 & 2 & | & 0 \\ 0 & 1 & 0 & | & -1 \\ 1 & 0 & 2 & | & 1 \end{bmatrix}$ h. $\begin{bmatrix} 1 & 1 & 1 & | & 1 \\ 0 & 1 & 0 & | & 1 \\ 1 & 0 & 0 & | & 1 \end{bmatrix}$

$\begin{bmatrix} 5 \end{bmatrix}$ Determinants

5.1 Definition and evaluation of determinants

In this chapter we wish to describe an important function—a function which associates with each *square* matrix A a real number, called the **determinant** of A. The value of the determinant function at a square matrix A is commonly denoted as det A or as $|A|$. In case the elements of A are given explicitly as

$$A = \begin{bmatrix} a_{11} & \cdots & a_{1n} \\ a_{21} & \cdots & a_{2n} \\ \cdot & \cdots & \cdot \\ a_{n1} & \cdots & a_{nn} \end{bmatrix},$$

we may write

$$\det \begin{bmatrix} a_{11} & \cdots & a_{1n} \\ a_{21} & \cdots & a_{2n} \\ \cdot & \cdots & \cdot \\ a_{n1} & \cdots & a_{nn} \end{bmatrix} \quad \text{or} \quad \begin{vmatrix} a_{11} & \cdots & a_{1n} \\ a_{21} & \cdots & a_{2n} \\ \cdot & \cdots & \cdot \\ a_{n1} & \cdots & a_{nn} \end{vmatrix}$$

for the value of the determinant function at A. Our choice of the following defining properties is motivated by the Gauss-Jordan reduction operations of Chapter 3. By themselves, they provide a straightforward method for computation. That there exists a unique determinant function with these properties is proven in the textbook of D. Finkbeiner (see Suggested Reading).

The four defining properties of the determinant function are:

Property 1. If any two rows of a square matrix are interchanged, then the determinant of the resulting matrix is the negative of the determinant of the original matrix.

Example 5.1.1

$$\begin{vmatrix} 1 & 2 & 3 \\ 4 & 5 & 6 \\ 7 & 8 & 9 \end{vmatrix} = - \begin{vmatrix} 4 & 5 & 6 \\ 1 & 2 & 3 \\ 7 & 8 & 9 \end{vmatrix}.$$

Property 2. If any row of a square matrix is multiplied by a non-zero scalar (real number) k, then the determinant of the resulting matrix is k times the determinant of the original matrix.

Example 5.1.2

$$\begin{vmatrix} 1 & 2 & 3 \\ 4k & 5k & 6k \\ 7 & 8 & 9 \end{vmatrix} = (k) \begin{vmatrix} 1 & 2 & 3 \\ 4 & 5 & 6 \\ 7 & 8 & 9 \end{vmatrix}.$$

Property 3. If a scalar multiple of one row of a square matrix is added to another row, then the determinant of the resulting matrix is the *same* as the determinant of the original matrix.

Example 5.1.3

$$\begin{vmatrix} 1 & 2 & 3 \\ 4 & 5 & 6 \\ 7 & 8 & 9 \end{vmatrix} = \begin{vmatrix} 1 & 2 & 3 \\ 6 & 9 & 12 \\ 7 & 8 & 9 \end{vmatrix},$$

where in the first matrix we added twice the first row to the second row to obtain the second matrix.

Property 4. The determinant of an upper triangular matrix (all the elements below the main diagonal are zero) is the *product* of the diagonal elements.

Example 5.1.4

$$\begin{vmatrix} 2 & 5 \\ 0 & 3 \end{vmatrix} = 6; \qquad \begin{vmatrix} 0 & 0 & 0 \\ 0 & 0 & 0 \\ 0 & 0 & 0 \end{vmatrix} = 0;$$

$$\begin{vmatrix} 1 & 0 & 0 \\ 0 & 1 & 0 \\ 0 & 0 & 1 \end{vmatrix} = 1; \qquad \begin{vmatrix} 1 & 17 & 39 \\ 0 & -1 & 68 \\ 0 & 0 & -2 \end{vmatrix} = 2.$$

In the special case of a 1×1 matrix, its determinant is simply the single element of the matrix.

Example 5.1.5

Let us now, by way of illustration, find the value of the determinant function at the matrix

$$\begin{bmatrix} 1 & -1 & 2 \\ -2 & 4 & -3 \\ 3 & -3 & 9 \end{bmatrix}.$$

Applying Property 3, we add 2 times the first row to the second, and subtract 3 times the first row from the third, so that

$$\begin{vmatrix} 1 & -1 & 2 \\ -2 & 4 & -3 \\ 3 & -3 & 9 \end{vmatrix} = \begin{vmatrix} 1 & -1 & 2 \\ 0 & 2 & 1 \\ 0 & 0 & 3 \end{vmatrix}.$$

Now from Property 4, we find that since the last result is triangular, the determinant has the value 6.

Example 5.1.6

As another example, let us find the determinant of

$$\begin{bmatrix} 1 & 2 & 3 \\ 4 & 5 & 6 \\ 7 & 8 & 9 \end{bmatrix}.$$

Using Property 3 twice we see that

$$\begin{vmatrix} 1 & 2 & 3 \\ 4 & 5 & 6 \\ 7 & 8 & 9 \end{vmatrix} = \begin{vmatrix} 1 & 2 & 3 \\ 0 & -3 & -6 \\ 0 & -6 & -12 \end{vmatrix}.$$

Now using Property 2, we see that

$$\begin{vmatrix} 1 & 2 & 3 \\ 0 & -3 & -6 \\ 0 & -6 & -12 \end{vmatrix} = (-3) \begin{vmatrix} 1 & 2 & 3 \\ 0 & 1 & 2 \\ 0 & -6 & -12 \end{vmatrix};$$

and now re-applying Property 3, we find that

$$(-3) \begin{vmatrix} 1 & 2 & 3 \\ 0 & 1 & 2 \\ 0 & -6 & -12 \end{vmatrix} = (-3) \begin{vmatrix} 1 & 2 & 3 \\ 0 & 1 & 2 \\ 0 & 0 & 0 \end{vmatrix} = (-3)(1 \cdot 1 \cdot 0) = 0.$$

The reader should observe that in the foregoing examples it is only necessary to *triangularize* rather than reduce to echelon form; that is, we need not zero out a column above a pivotal element, but only below it.

We digress briefly to assure the reader that the determinant function described in Properties 1–4 above is the very same determinant often studied in high-school mathematics. There, the determinant of a 2×2 matrix $\begin{bmatrix} a & b \\ c & d \end{bmatrix}$ is usually defined as $\begin{vmatrix} a & b \\ c & d \end{vmatrix} = ad - bc$, while the determinant of a 3×3 matrix

$$\begin{bmatrix} a & b & c \\ d & e & f \\ g & h & i \end{bmatrix}$$

is given as $(aei - afh - bdi + bfg + cdh - ceg)$. Let us examine the 2×2 matrix $\begin{bmatrix} a & b \\ c & d \end{bmatrix}$. If $a \neq 0$, then by virtue of Property 2, $\begin{vmatrix} a & b \\ c & d \end{vmatrix} =$ $a \begin{vmatrix} 1 & b/a \\ c & d \end{vmatrix}$; and by Property 3, $a \begin{vmatrix} 1 & b/a \\ c & d \end{vmatrix} = a \begin{vmatrix} 1 & b/a \\ 0 & d - cb/a \end{vmatrix}$. This, by Property 4, is equal to $a(d - cb/a) = ad - bc$, the familiar 2×2 determinant recalled above. If $a = 0$, then $\begin{vmatrix} a & b \\ c & d \end{vmatrix} = \begin{vmatrix} 0 & b \\ c & d \end{vmatrix} = -\begin{vmatrix} c & d \\ 0 & b \end{vmatrix}$. But the last result is upper triangular, so that

$$\begin{vmatrix} a & b \\ c & d \end{vmatrix} = -\begin{vmatrix} c & d \\ 0 & b \end{vmatrix} = -cb = ad - bc, \qquad \text{since } a = 0.$$

We leave it to the reader to verify from our definition that the 3×3 matrix

$$\begin{bmatrix} a & b & c \\ d & e & f \\ g & h & i \end{bmatrix}$$

does indeed have the determinant value shown above. If the reader is familiar with 3×3 determinants, he has probably learned certain patterns for obtaining their value. We regret to say that no such nice patterns exist for large matrices; or rather, patterns exist, but are so elaborately complicated that they are unsuited for practical calculations. An efficient way to find the determinant of a large matrix is to triangularize it using the analogues of the Gauss-Jordan reduction rules, although there are other methods which have theoretical and practical significance. We shall discuss some of these in the next section of this chapter.

Exercises 5.1

In Exercises 1–10, find the determinant of the given matrix.

1. $\begin{bmatrix} 1 & 2 \\ 3 & 4 \end{bmatrix}$
2. $\begin{bmatrix} -3 & 2 \\ 1 & 2 \end{bmatrix}$

3. $\begin{bmatrix} 1 & -1 & 0 \\ 2 & 1 & 3 \\ 1 & 0 & 1 \end{bmatrix}$

4. $\begin{bmatrix} 0 & 2 & 1 \\ -1 & 1 & -2 \\ 2 & 2 & 3 \end{bmatrix}$

5. $\begin{bmatrix} 2 & -4 & 2 & 0 \\ -1 & 0 & 1 & 2 \\ 1 & 0 & 1 & 3 \\ 3 & 2 & 1 & 0 \end{bmatrix}$

6. $\begin{bmatrix} 1 & 0 & 4 & -1 \\ -4 & 0 & 2 & 0 \\ 3 & 2 & 2 & 1 \\ 2 & 5 & 3 & 2 \end{bmatrix}$

7. $\begin{bmatrix} 1 & 0 & 1 & 1 & 0 \\ 0 & 1 & 0 & 0 & 1 \\ 1 & 0 & 1 & 1 & 0 \\ 0 & 1 & 0 & 1 & 0 \\ 0 & 0 & 1 & 0 & 1 \end{bmatrix}$

8. $\begin{bmatrix} 1 & 0 & 1 & 1 & 1 \\ -1 & 2 & -1 & 3 & 1 \\ 2 & 1 & 2 & 1 & 1 \\ 1 & -1 & 0 & 2 & 1 \\ 3 & 1 & 2 & 0 & 1 \end{bmatrix}$

9. $\begin{bmatrix} 0 & 0 & 2 \\ 0 & 3 & 0 \\ 4 & 0 & 0 \end{bmatrix}$

10. $\begin{bmatrix} 0 & 0 & 0 & 2 \\ 0 & 0 & 3 & 0 \\ 0 & 4 & 0 & 0 \\ 5 & 0 & 0 & 0 \end{bmatrix}$

11. Verify that $\begin{vmatrix} a & b & c \\ d & e & f \\ g & h & i \end{vmatrix} = aei - afh - bdi + bfg + cdh - ceg.$

12. In Chapter 2 we defined the result of multiplying a matrix A by a scalar s to be the matrix whose elements are the elements of A each multiplied by s. With $s = 3$ and $A = \begin{bmatrix} 1 & 2 \\ 3 & 4 \end{bmatrix}$ what is $|sA|$ and how is it related to $|A|$? What is the result if A is a 3×3 matrix?

We now wish to point out three related facts which are useful in evaluating determinants.

FACT I

If in the Gauss-Jordan reduction of a determinant, a zero appears on the diagonal and all elements below it in that column are zero, then the determinant is zero.

That this is true may be seen from the following considerations. Suppose that we have reduced the determinant through k steps, so that in the first k diagonal positions there is a 1, and in the $(k + 1)$th diagonal position, and everywhere below it in the $(k + 1)$th column, there is a zero.

$$
k\text{-}\left(\begin{array}{ccccccccc}
\overbrace{}^{k} \\
1 & X & X & \cdots & X & X & \cdots & X \\
0 & 1 & X & \cdots & X & X & \cdots & X \\
0 & 0 & 1 & \cdots & X & X & \cdots & X \\
\cdot & \cdot & \cdot & \cdots & \cdot & \cdot & \cdots & \cdot \\
0 & 0 & 0 & \cdots & 1 & X & \cdots & X \\
0 & 0 & 0 & \cdots & 0 & 0 & \cdots & X \\
\cdot & \cdot & \cdot & \cdots & \cdot & \cdot & \cdots & \cdot \\
0 & 0 & 0 & \cdots & 0 & 0 & \cdots & X
\end{array}\right)
$$

In the Gauss-Jordan process, as applied to systems of linear equations, we have learned that in this situation we merely skip over the $(k + 1)$th column and proceed to reduce the $(k + 2)$th column using the element in the $(k + 1, k + 2)$ position. But now observe that if we do that, then, when we have completed the reduction process and the determinant is reduced to triangular form, there will still be a zero in the $(k + 1, k + 1)$ position. No matter what the following reduction process has wrought, the triangular final matrix will have a 0 on the main diagonal and its determinant will have the value 0. Thus, in practice, we would have stopped our work at the $(k + 1)$th step, since the determinant must be zero.

Example 5.1.7

Find the determinant of

$$
\begin{bmatrix}
1 & -1 & 1 & -1 & 1 \\
1 & 0 & 2 & 1 & 0 \\
-1 & 1 & -1 & 0 & 1 \\
2 & -2 & 2 & -1 & 3 \\
2 & -1 & 3 & 1 & 3
\end{bmatrix}.
$$

The result of zeroing out the first column below the 1, 1 position is

$$
\begin{vmatrix}
1 & -1 & 1 & -1 & 1 \\
0 & 1 & 1 & 2 & -1 \\
0 & 0 & 0 & -1 & 2 \\
0 & 0 & 0 & 1 & 1 \\
0 & 1 & 1 & 3 & 1
\end{vmatrix}.
$$

Now using the 2, 2 position to zero out below it, we obtain

$$\begin{vmatrix} 1 & -1 & 1 & -1 & 1 \\ 0 & 1 & 1 & 2 & -1 \\ 0 & 0 & 0 & -1 & 2 \\ 0 & 0 & 0 & 1 & 1 \\ 0 & 0 & 0 & 1 & 2 \end{vmatrix}.$$

Now observe that the 3, 3 element *and all elements of the column below it are zeros.* Hence, by our preceding argument, the determinant must be zero. This is verified by continuing the reduction using the 3, 4 element to obtain

$$\begin{vmatrix} 1 & -1 & 1 & -1 & 1 \\ 0 & 1 & 1 & 2 & -1 \\ 0 & 0 & 0 & -1 & 2 \\ 0 & 0 & 0 & 0 & 3 \\ 0 & 0 & 0 & 0 & 4 \end{vmatrix},$$

which is in triangular form. The presence of the 0 in the 3, 3 position now assures us that the determinant (being the product of the diagonal elements) is zero.

FACT 2

If a row of a matrix consists entirely of zeros, then the determinant of that matrix is 0.

This also is easily seen to be true. For, if any row of the matrix A is zero and we multiply that row by a non-zero scalar k, the result is still the matrix A. But by Property 2, the determinant is k times the determinant of A. Thus $k\,|A| = |A|$ for any $k \neq 0$. It must then be true that $|A| = 0$.

Example 5.1.8

$$A = \begin{bmatrix} 1 & -1 & 1 & 2 \\ 0 & 0 & 0 & 0 \\ 2 & -1 & 1 & -3 \\ 1 & -1 & 3 & 7 \end{bmatrix} = \begin{bmatrix} 1 & -1 & 1 & 2 \\ k \cdot 0 & k \cdot 0 & k \cdot 0 & k \cdot 0 \\ 2 & -1 & 1 & -3 \\ 1 & -1 & 3 & 7 \end{bmatrix}.$$

Thus

$$\begin{vmatrix} 1 & -1 & 1 & 2 \\ 0 & 0 & 0 & 0 \\ 2 & -1 & 1 & -3 \\ 1 & -1 & 3 & 7 \end{vmatrix} = \begin{vmatrix} 1 & -1 & 1 & 2 \\ k \cdot 0 & k \cdot 0 & k \cdot 0 & k \cdot 0 \\ 2 & -1 & 1 & -3 \\ 1 & -1 & 3 & 7 \end{vmatrix}$$

$$= k \begin{vmatrix} 1 & -1 & 1 & 2 \\ 0 & 0 & 0 & 0 \\ 2 & -1 & 1 & -3 \\ 1 & -1 & 3 & 7 \end{vmatrix}.$$

The validity of our second fact may also be demonstrated in another way. Using the above example, and interchanging the zero row with the last row, we obtain

$$\begin{vmatrix} 1 & -1 & 1 & 2 \\ 0 & 0 & 0 & 0 \\ 2 & -1 & 1 & -3 \\ 1 & -1 & 3 & 7 \end{vmatrix} = - \begin{vmatrix} 1 & -1 & 1 & 2 \\ 1 & -1 & 3 & 7 \\ 2 & -1 & 1 & -3 \\ 0 & 0 & 0 & 0 \end{vmatrix}.$$

We now reduce the last result to triangular form, obtaining

$$- \begin{vmatrix} 1 & -1 & 1 & 2 \\ 0 & 0 & 2 & 5 \\ 0 & 1 & -1 & -7 \\ 0 & 0 & 0 & 0 \end{vmatrix} = \begin{vmatrix} 1 & -1 & 1 & 2 \\ 0 & 1 & -1 & -7 \\ 0 & 0 & 2 & 5 \\ 0 & 0 & 0 & 0 \end{vmatrix}.$$

But the presence of the zero in the 4, 4 position assures us that the determinant is zero.

FACT 3

If two rows of a matrix are proportional, the determinant of the matrix is zero.

This is now very easy to see, for if some row is k times another row we subtract k times the one row from the other and produce a matrix with one row zero. By Fact 2, the determinant is 0.

These facts will be useful in evaluating the determinants in the following exercises.

Exercises 5.1 (continued)

In Exercises 13–20 use the facts just developed to show that each determinant is zero.

13. $\begin{vmatrix} 1 & 2 & 1 \\ 1 & 2 & 4 \\ 2 & 4 & 4 \end{vmatrix}$

14. $\begin{vmatrix} 1 & 2 & 3 \\ 2 & 4 & 6 \\ 1 & 5 & 8 \end{vmatrix}$

15. $\begin{vmatrix} 1 & -1 & 2 & 1 & 3 \\ 1 & 0 & 4 & 2 & 2 \\ 1 & 0 & 4 & 3 & 3 \\ 2 & 0 & 8 & 4 & 7 \\ 3 & 0 & 12 & 8 & 10 \end{vmatrix}$

16. $\begin{vmatrix} 1 & 2 & 3 & 3 & 4 \\ -1 & -1 & -1 & 0 & -1 \\ 2 & 6 & 10 & 12 & 14 \\ 1 & 3 & 6 & 6 & 9 \\ 3 & 5 & 8 & 9 & 13 \end{vmatrix}$

17.
$$\begin{vmatrix} 1 & 2 & 1 & 3 \\ 2 & 5 & 1 & 8 \\ 3 & 7 & 2 & 11 \\ 3 & 5 & 1 & 1 \end{vmatrix}$$

18.
$$\begin{vmatrix} 1 & -1 & 0 & 1 \\ 2 & 1 & -3 & 4 \\ 0 & 3 & -3 & 2 \\ 1 & 5 & 4 & 7 \end{vmatrix}$$

19.
$$\begin{vmatrix} 2 & 4 & 6 & 8 \\ 1 & 2 & 3 & 4 \\ 5 & 1 & 3 & 7 \\ 6 & 1 & 5 & 4 \end{vmatrix}$$

20.
$$\begin{vmatrix} a & b & c \\ a^2 - ab & ab - b^2 & ac - bc \\ a^2 - b^2 & a^2 + b^2 & a^3 + b^3 \end{vmatrix}$$

Suggested reading

C. Curtis, *Linear Algebra*, Allyn & Bacon, Boston (1968).
D. Finkbeiner, *Introduction to Matrices and Linear Transformations*, 2nd Ed., W. H. Freeman and Company, San Franciso (1966).

New terms

determinant, 137

5.2   Some further properties of determinants

For the sake of completeness, and for some theoretical advantages, we here present some results of a more traditional approach to determinants.

To begin with, let us consider an $n \times n$ matrix $A = [a_{ij}]$, and a particular element in that matrix, say a_{ks}. We define the **cofactor** A_{ks} of a_{ks} to be

$$A_{ks} = (-1)^{k+s} D_{ks},$$

where D_{ks} denotes the determinant of the $(n-1) \times (n-1)$ submatrix of A found by deleting the kth row and the sth column from A.

Example 5.2.1

In the matrix

$$A = \begin{bmatrix} 1 & 2 & 3 \\ 4 & 5 & 6 \\ 7 & 8 & 9 \end{bmatrix}$$

the cofactor of the element 6, which is in the 2, 3 position is

$$A_{23} = (-1)^{2+3} \begin{vmatrix} 1 & 2 \\ 7 & 8 \end{vmatrix} = 6.$$

Here, $D_{23} = \begin{vmatrix} 1 & 2 \\ 7 & 8 \end{vmatrix}$ is seen to be the determinant of the submatrix obtained from A by deleting the row and column of A in which 6 lies.

The cofactor of 5 in the above example is (since 5 is in the 2, 2 position)

$$A_{22} = (-1)^{2+2} \begin{vmatrix} 1 & 3 \\ 7 & 9 \end{vmatrix} = -12.$$

The cofactors of the other elements of A are:

$$A_{11} = -3, \ A_{12} = 6, \ A_{13} = -3, \ A_{21} = 6, \ A_{31} = -3, \ A_{32} = 6,$$
$$A_{33} = -3,$$

which you should now verify.

Exercises 5.2

Find the cofactors of each element of

1. $\begin{bmatrix} 3 & 1 & 5 \\ 2 & 0 & 3 \\ 1 & 1 & 2 \end{bmatrix}.$
　　　　2. $\begin{bmatrix} 3 & 0 & 1 \\ 2 & 1 & 1 \\ 1 & 2 & 3 \end{bmatrix}.$

Find the cofactors of the elements of the second row of

3. $\begin{bmatrix} 1 & 1 & 2 & 3 \\ -1 & 1 & 2 & 1 \\ 0 & 1 & 1 & 2 \\ 3 & 0 & -1 & 1 \end{bmatrix}.$
　　4. $\begin{bmatrix} 0 & 2 & 4 & 4 \\ 2 & 0 & 1 & 3 \\ 0 & 1 & 1 & 2 \\ 3 & 1 & 0 & 3 \end{bmatrix}.$

Find the cofactors of the elements of the second column of

5. $\begin{bmatrix} 2 & 1 & 0 & 3 \\ 1 & -1 & 1 & 2 \\ 1 & 1 & 2 & 1 \\ 2 & 2 & 3 & 4 \end{bmatrix}.$
　　6. $\begin{bmatrix} 3 & -1 & 1 & 1 \\ 3 & 1 & -4 & 1 \\ 2 & 2 & 6 & 4 \\ 1 & 2 & 7 & 1 \end{bmatrix}.$

7. Let

$$\begin{bmatrix} 1 & 2 & 3 \\ -1 & 0 & 4 \\ 2 & 1 & 2 \end{bmatrix} = A.$$

Find the cofactors of the elements of the first row of A.

8.   Find the cofactors of the elements of the first column of A^T with A as in Exercise 7. Compare your results with those of Exercise 7.

Our first result is the following:

THEOREM 5.2.1

The determinant of a matrix $A = [a_{ij}]$ is the sum of the products of the elements of any row multiplied by the corresponding cofactors of those elements. That is, for any row, say the ith,

$$|A| = a_{i1}A_{i1} + a_{i2}A_{i2} + \cdots + a_{in}A_{in}.$$

Example 5.2.2

Consider the matrix

$$A = \begin{bmatrix} 1 & 2 & 3 \\ 4 & 5 & 6 \\ 7 & 8 & 9 \end{bmatrix},$$

the cofactors of which we computed above. Let us calculate the determinant of A (which we already know is zero from Example 5.16) by applying the above result to the first row of A.

$$|A| = a_{11}A_{11} + a_{12}A_{12} + a_{13}A_{13} = 1(-3) + 2(6) + 3(-3) = 0.$$

Let us now calculate the determinant of A using the other rows, just to verify that it makes no difference which row we use to expand the determinant of A. Using the second row, for instance, we have

$$|A| = a_{21}A_{21} + a_{22}A_{22} + a_{23}A_{23} = 4(6) + 5(-12) + 6(6) = 0;$$

and if we use the third row, we have

$$|A| = a_{31}A_{31} + a_{32}A_{32} + a_{33}A_{33} = 7(-3) + 8(6) + 9(-3) = 0.$$

Example 5.2.3

Consider the matrix of Example 5.1.5,

$$A = \begin{bmatrix} 1 & -1 & 2 \\ -2 & 4 & -3 \\ 3 & -3 & 9 \end{bmatrix}.$$

In that example we had already seen that $|A| = 6$. Let us now expand the determinant of A using the first row. We find that $A_{11} = 27$, $A_{12} = 9$, and $A_{13} = -6$. Then

$$|A| = (1)A_{11} + (-1)A_{12} + (2)A_{13} = 27 - 9 + 2(-6) = 6.$$

The reader should now continue this example by expanding $|A|$ by its second row and by its third row.

The next result, which is a companion theorem to the first, is interesting in itself, and, with the first, will be used in the next section to establish a connection between the determinant and the inverse of a square matrix.

THEOREM 5.2.2

The sum of the products of the elements of any row of a square matrix A and the cofactors of the corresponding elements of a different row of A is zero. In symbols, for $i \neq k$,

$$a_{i1}A_{k1} + a_{i2}A_{k2} + \cdots + a_{in}A_{kn} = 0.$$

Example 5.2.4

Consider the matrix of the previous example. If we form the sum of the products of the elements of the second row ($i = 2$) with the cofactors of the elements of the first row ($k = 1$), we obtain

$$(-2)(27) + 4(9) - 3(-6) = -54 + 36 + 18 = 0.$$

Similarly, the third row elements along with the first row cofactors yield

$$3(27) - 3(9) + 9(-6) = 81 - 27 - 54 = 0.$$

Exercises 5.2 (continued)

In Exercises 9–12, find the determinant by applying Theorem 5.2.1. to the *first row*. Verify that the same value is obtained by applying Theorem 5.2.1 to the *third* row.

9. $\begin{vmatrix} 1 & -1 & 2 \\ 3 & 2 & -4 \\ 6 & -1 & 1 \end{vmatrix}$

10. $\begin{vmatrix} 1 & 4 & 7 \\ 2 & 5 & 8 \\ 3 & 6 & 9 \end{vmatrix}$

11. $\begin{vmatrix} 1 & -1 & 2 & 3 \\ 2 & 1 & 4 & -1 \\ 1 & 1 & 2 & -2 \\ -3 & 4 & 1 & 2 \end{vmatrix}$

12. $\begin{vmatrix} 1 & 0 & 5 & 0 \\ 0 & 3 & 0 & 7 \\ 2 & 0 & 6 & 0 \\ 0 & 4 & 0 & 8 \end{vmatrix}$

13. Apply Theorem 5.2.2 to the first ($i = 1$) and third ($k = 3$) rows of each of the determinants in Exercises 9–12 above to obtain the value zero.

14. Find the determinants of the transposes of the matrices in Exercises 9 and 11 above and compare them with the determinants of the original matrices.

15.   Prove Theorem 5.2.1 for arbitrary 2 × 2 matrices.

16.   Prove Theorem 5.2.2 for arbitrary 2 × 2 matrices.

Before passing to our next two theorems, we ask the reader to consider the following: we evaluate the determinant of the 5 × 5 matrix below by the Gauss-Jordan triangularization process, listing the results of the reduction of the successive columns.

$$
\begin{vmatrix}
1 & 1 & -1 & 1 & 1 \\
2 & 3 & 0 & 1 & 3 \\
-1 & 1 & 6 & 0 & -1 \\
3 & 5 & 3 & 8 & 3 \\
1 & 0 & -3 & 7 & 3
\end{vmatrix}
=
\begin{vmatrix}
1 & 1 & -1 & 1 & 1 \\
0 & 1 & 2 & -1 & 1 \\
0 & 2 & 5 & 1 & 0 \\
0 & 2 & 6 & 5 & 0 \\
0 & -1 & -2 & 6 & 2
\end{vmatrix}
$$

$$
=
\begin{vmatrix}
1 & 1 & -1 & 1 & 1 \\
0 & 1 & 2 & -1 & 1 \\
0 & 0 & 1 & 3 & -2 \\
0 & 0 & 2 & 7 & -2 \\
0 & 0 & 0 & 5 & 3
\end{vmatrix}
$$

$$
=
\begin{vmatrix}
1 & 1 & -1 & 1 & 1 \\
0 & 1 & 2 & -1 & 1 \\
0 & 0 & 1 & 3 & -2 \\
0 & 0 & 0 & 1 & 2 \\
0 & 0 & 0 & 5 & 3
\end{vmatrix}
$$

$$
=
\begin{vmatrix}
1 & 1 & -1 & 1 & 1 \\
0 & 1 & 2 & -1 & 1 \\
0 & 0 & 1 & 3 & -2 \\
0 & 0 & 0 & 1 & 2 \\
0 & 0 & 0 & 0 & -7
\end{vmatrix}
$$

$$= -7.$$

In the above display, the first equality shows the reduction of the first column, the second equality shows the reduction of the second column, etc., so that the determinant is available as the product of the diagonal elements of the final triangular matrix.

Now, contrast this method of evaluating the above determinant with the method of cofactors. Using the latter method, we find that if we use the elements of the first row, for example, we obtain

$$
\begin{vmatrix}
1 & 1 & -1 & 1 & 1 \\
2 & 3 & 0 & 1 & 3 \\
-1 & 1 & 6 & 0 & -1 \\
3 & 5 & 3 & 8 & 3 \\
1 & 0 & -3 & 7 & 3
\end{vmatrix}
= 1(-1)^{1+1}
\begin{vmatrix}
3 & 0 & 1 & 3 \\
1 & 6 & 0 & -1 \\
5 & 3 & 8 & 3 \\
0 & -3 & 7 & 3
\end{vmatrix}
+
$$

$$+ 1(-1)^{1+2} \begin{vmatrix} 2 & 0 & 1 & 3 \\ -1 & 6 & 0 & -1 \\ 3 & 3 & 8 & 3 \\ 1 & -3 & 7 & 3 \end{vmatrix}$$

$$- 1(-1)^{1+3} \begin{vmatrix} 2 & 3 & 1 & 3 \\ -1 & 1 & 0 & -1 \\ 3 & 5 & 8 & 3 \\ 1 & 0 & 7 & 3 \end{vmatrix}$$

$$+ 1(-1)^{1+4} \begin{vmatrix} 2 & 3 & 0 & 3 \\ -1 & 1 & 6 & -1 \\ 3 & 5 & 3 & 3 \\ 1 & 0 & -3 & 3 \end{vmatrix}$$

$$+ 1(-1)^{1+5} \begin{vmatrix} 2 & 3 & 0 & 1 \\ -1 & 1 & 6 & 0 \\ 3 & 5 & 3 & 8 \\ 1 & 0 & -3 & 7 \end{vmatrix}.$$

In order to evaluate the original determinant we now have to evaluate each of the *five* 4 × 4 determinants. Each one, expanded by some row, is given in terms of *four* 3 × 3 determinants, each one of which is given in terms of *three* 2 × 2 determinants. Thus, to evaluate the original determinant by this method, we will need to calculate $5 \cdot 4 \cdot 3 = 60$ different 2 × 2 determinants. We recommend that the reader *not* complete the calculations!

Our next theorem is an interesting algebraic result.

THEOREM 5.2.3

If A and B are each $n \times n$ matrices, then $|AB| = |A| \, |B|$. That is, the determinant of the product of two square matrices is the product of their determinants.

Example 5.2.5

Let $A = \begin{bmatrix} 1 & 2 \\ 3 & 4 \end{bmatrix}$, $B = \begin{bmatrix} 2 & -1 \\ 3 & 2 \end{bmatrix}$. Then $|A| = -2$, $|B| = 7$, so that

$|A| \, |B| = -14$. And $|AB| = \begin{vmatrix} 8 & 3 \\ 18 & 5 \end{vmatrix} = 40 - 54 = -14$.

Example 5.2.6

$$A = \begin{bmatrix} 1 & 2 & 3 \\ 1 & -1 & 2 \\ 2 & 1 & -3 \end{bmatrix}, \qquad B = \begin{bmatrix} 1 & 2 & 1 \\ 1 & 0 & -1 \\ 0 & -1 & 2 \end{bmatrix}.$$

Then

$$|A| = \begin{vmatrix} 1 & 2 & 3 \\ 0 & -3 & -1 \\ 0 & -3 & -9 \end{vmatrix} = \begin{vmatrix} 1 & 2 & 3 \\ 0 & -3 & -1 \\ 0 & 0 & -8 \end{vmatrix} = 24,$$

and

$$|B| = \begin{vmatrix} 1 & 2 & 1 \\ 0 & -2 & -2 \\ 0 & -1 & 2 \end{vmatrix} = -\begin{vmatrix} 1 & 2 & 1 \\ 0 & -1 & 2 \\ 0 & -2 & -2 \end{vmatrix} = -\begin{vmatrix} 1 & 2 & 1 \\ 0 & -1 & 2 \\ 0 & 0 & -6 \end{vmatrix} = -6,$$

so that $|A|\,|B| = -144$. In addition

$$|AB| = \begin{vmatrix} 3 & -1 & 5 \\ 0 & 0 & 6 \\ 3 & 7 & -5 \end{vmatrix} = -\begin{vmatrix} 3 & -1 & 5 \\ 3 & 7 & -5 \\ 0 & 0 & 6 \end{vmatrix}$$

$$= -\begin{vmatrix} 3 & -1 & 5 \\ 0 & 8 & -10 \\ 0 & 0 & 6 \end{vmatrix} = -144.$$

Unfortunately, no such nice result as Theorem 5.2.3 holds for addition or subtraction of matrices as the following example shows: let

$$A = \begin{bmatrix} 1 & 0 & 0 \\ 0 & 0 & 0 \\ 0 & 0 & 1 \end{bmatrix}, \qquad B = \begin{bmatrix} 0 & 0 & 0 \\ 0 & 1 & 0 \\ 0 & 0 & 0 \end{bmatrix}.$$

Then $|A| = 0$, $|B| = 0$, but $|A + B| = 1$, while $|A - B| = -1$.

COROLLARY 5.2.1

For any $n \times n$ matrices A and B,

$$|AB| = |BA|.$$

Proof:

$|AB| = |A|\,|B| = |B|\,|A| = |BA|$. The first and third equalities are true by Theorem 5.2.3. The second equality is also true, since $|A|$ and $|B|$ are scalars and hence commute. □

Our final theorem of this section is one which has both practical and theoretical significance.

THEOREM 5.2.4

The determinant of a matrix A is equal to the determinant of the transpose A^T of A.

Example 5.2.7

Let $A = \begin{bmatrix} 1 & 2 \\ 3 & 4 \end{bmatrix}$, so that $A^T = \begin{bmatrix} 1 & 3 \\ 2 & 4 \end{bmatrix}$. Then $|A| = 4 - 6 = -2$ and $|A^T| = 4 - 6 = -2$.

Example 5.2.8

With A as in Example 5.1.5,

$$A^T = \begin{bmatrix} 1 & -2 & 3 \\ -1 & 4 & -3 \\ 2 & -3 & 9 \end{bmatrix},$$

so that

$$|A^T| = \begin{vmatrix} 1 & -2 & 3 \\ 0 & 2 & 0 \\ 0 & 1 & 3 \end{vmatrix} = 2 \begin{vmatrix} 1 & -2 & 3 \\ 0 & 1 & 0 \\ 0 & 1 & 3 \end{vmatrix}$$

$$= 2 \begin{vmatrix} 1 & -2 & 3 \\ 0 & 1 & 0 \\ 0 & 0 & 3 \end{vmatrix} = 6 = |A|.$$

The practical significance of this theorem to us at this stage is the following:

Properties 1–3 of determinants as listed in Section 5.1 are now valid if the word *row* is replaced by the word *column*; and property 4 is valid if *upper triangular* is replaced by *lower triangular*.

Thus we may use column interchanges, divide or multiply a column by a non-zero scalar, and subtract a multiple of one column from another in reducing to triangular form. Moreover, Theorems 5.2.1 and 5.2.2 have valid column analogues, so that we may expand the determinant by the elements and cofactors of a column instead of by a row.

Exercises 5.2 (continued)

In Exercises 17–22, verify Theorem 5.2.3 by separately calculating $|A|$, $|B|$ and $|AB|$.

17. $A = \begin{bmatrix} 1 & 2 \\ 3 & 4 \end{bmatrix}, B = \begin{bmatrix} 5 & 6 \\ 7 & 8 \end{bmatrix}$ 18. $A = \begin{bmatrix} 1 & 2 \\ 1 & 3 \end{bmatrix}, B = \begin{bmatrix} -1 & 4 \\ -3 & 2 \end{bmatrix}$

19. $A = \begin{bmatrix} 1 & 0 & -1 \\ 2 & 1 & 3 \\ 1 & 4 & 1 \end{bmatrix}, B = \begin{bmatrix} 0 & 2 & -1 \\ 0 & 1 & 0 \\ 1 & 4 & 2 \end{bmatrix}$

20. $A = \begin{bmatrix} 4 & -1 & 2 \\ -1 & 0 & 2 \\ 2 & 1 & 1 \end{bmatrix}, B = \begin{bmatrix} 1 & 1 & 1 \\ 0 & 2 & 2 \\ 0 & 0 & 3 \end{bmatrix}$

21. $A = \begin{bmatrix} 1 & 1 & 2 & 1 \\ 1 & 0 & 1 & 1 \\ -1 & 1 & 3 & 0 \\ 2 & 4 & 1 & 1 \end{bmatrix}, B = \begin{bmatrix} 4 & 1 & -1 & 1 \\ 2 & 2 & 2 & 1 \\ 3 & 3 & 1 & 0 \\ 1 & 4 & 3 & 1 \end{bmatrix}$

22. $A = \begin{bmatrix} 1 & 0 & 1 & 1 \\ 0 & 1 & 1 & 0 \\ 2 & -1 & 1 & 2 \\ 2 & 2 & -1 & 1 \end{bmatrix}, B = \begin{bmatrix} 1 & 2 & 3 & 4 \\ -1 & 1 & -3 & 1 \\ 0 & 1 & 0 & 0 \\ 2 & 1 & 1 & 2 \end{bmatrix}$

In Exercises 23–28, verify Theorem 5.2.4 by finding $|A|$ and $|A^T|$ separately.

23. $A = \begin{bmatrix} 2 & 1 \\ 2 & 3 \end{bmatrix}$

24. $A = \begin{bmatrix} 1 & 4 \\ -1 & 2 \end{bmatrix}$

25. $A = \begin{bmatrix} 1 & 1 & 2 \\ -1 & 2 & 3 \\ 1 & 1 & 2 \end{bmatrix}$

26. $A = \begin{bmatrix} 1 & 2 & 3 \\ 2 & 4 & 5 \\ 3 & 5 & 1 \end{bmatrix}$

27. $A = \begin{bmatrix} 1 & 1 & 4 & -1 \\ 2 & 1 & 5 & 3 \\ 1 & 1 & 2 & 1 \\ 1 & 0 & 1 & 2 \end{bmatrix}$

28. $A = \begin{bmatrix} 1 & 2 & 3 & 4 \\ -1 & 1 & 2 & 1 \\ 0 & 1 & 1 & 0 \\ 1 & 0 & 0 & 1 \end{bmatrix}$

29. Prove Theorems 5.2.3 and 5.2.4 for arbitrary 2×2 matrices.

New terms

cofactor, 145

5.3   Some applications of determinants

We can now apply our foregoing theorems to find a "formula" for calculating the inverse of a square matrix, if it exists. Let us consider by way of example a 3×3 matrix

$$A = \begin{bmatrix} a_{11} & a_{12} & a_{13} \\ a_{21} & a_{22} & a_{23} \\ a_{31} & a_{32} & a_{33} \end{bmatrix};$$

and let us construct a new 3×3 matrix B in the following way. To construct the first row of B, we write

$$B = \begin{bmatrix} A_{11} & A_{21} & A_{31} \\ \underline{\hspace{1cm}} & \underline{\hspace{1cm}} & \underline{\hspace{1cm}} \\ \underline{\hspace{1cm}} & \underline{\hspace{1cm}} & \underline{\hspace{1cm}} \end{bmatrix};$$

that is, the first *row* of B consists of the cofactors of the elements of the first *column* of A. Similarly, the second *row* of B consists of the cofactors of the second *column* of A, and the third row of B consists of the cofactors of the third column of A, so that we have

$$B = \begin{bmatrix} A_{11} & A_{21} & A_{31} \\ A_{12} & A_{22} & A_{32} \\ A_{13} & A_{23} & A_{33} \end{bmatrix}.$$

Let us now form the matrix product AB and apply Theorems 5.2.1 and 5.2.2 to obtain

$$\begin{bmatrix} a_{11} & a_{12} & a_{13} \\ a_{21} & a_{22} & a_{23} \\ a_{31} & a_{32} & a_{33} \end{bmatrix} \begin{bmatrix} A_{11} & A_{21} & A_{31} \\ A_{12} & A_{22} & A_{32} \\ A_{13} & A_{23} & A_{33} \end{bmatrix} = \begin{bmatrix} \det A & 0 & 0 \\ 0 & \det A & 0 \\ 0 & 0 & \det A \end{bmatrix}.$$

That this is actually the result may be seen from considering that the element in the 1, 1 position in the product matrix is

$$a_{11}A_{11} + a_{12}A_{12} + a_{13}A_{13},$$

which is, by Theorem 5.2.1, equal to det A. The element in the 1, 2 position of the product is $a_{11}A_{21} + a_{12}A_{22} + a_{13}A_{23}$, which is, by Theorem 5.2.2, equal to zero. The elements of the second and third rows of the product matrix are obtained in a similar manner. Thus

$$AB = \begin{bmatrix} \det A & 0 & 0 \\ 0 & \det A & 0 \\ 0 & 0 & \det A \end{bmatrix} = (\det A) \begin{bmatrix} 1 & 0 & 0 \\ 0 & 1 & 0 \\ 0 & 0 & 1 \end{bmatrix}$$

$$= (\det A)I_3.$$

Moreover, from the column analogues of Theorems 5.2.1 and 5.2.2, we see that

$$BA = \begin{bmatrix} \det A & 0 & 0 \\ 0 & \det A & 0 \\ 0 & 0 & \det A \end{bmatrix} = (\det A) \begin{bmatrix} 1 & 0 & 0 \\ 0 & 1 & 0 \\ 0 & 0 & 1 \end{bmatrix}$$

$$= (\det A)I_3.$$

Thus, if det $A \neq 0$, the preceding equations may be rewritten as

$$A\left(\frac{1}{\det A} B\right) = I_3 = \left(\frac{1}{\det A} B\right)A.$$

Thus we have the important result that

$$A^{-1} = \frac{1}{\det A} B.$$

Example 5.3.1

Let us calculate the inverse of the matrix $A = \begin{bmatrix} 1 & -1 & 2 \\ 2 & -1 & 3 \\ 1 & 1 & 2 \end{bmatrix}$.

Here the determinant of A is found to be 2. The cofactors of the elements are:

$$
\begin{array}{lll}
A_{11} = -5 & A_{12} = -1 & A_{13} = 3 \\
A_{21} = 4 & A_{22} = 0 & A_{23} = -2 \\
A_{31} = -1 & A_{32} = 1 & A_{33} = 1.
\end{array}
$$

Thus our matrix B is

$$\begin{bmatrix} -5 & 4 & -1 \\ -1 & 0 & 1 \\ 3 & -2 & 1 \end{bmatrix},$$

and

$$
A^{-1} = \frac{1}{\det A} B = 1/2 \begin{bmatrix} -5 & 4 & -1 \\ -1 & 0 & 1 \\ 3 & -2 & 1 \end{bmatrix}
$$

$$
= \begin{bmatrix} -5/2 & 2 & -1/2 \\ -1/2 & 0 & 1/2 \\ 3/2 & -1 & 1/2 \end{bmatrix}.
$$

The reader may now verify by multiplication that this is, indeed, the inverse of A.

The matrix B in the foregoing discussion is often called the **adjoint** of the matrix A, and is denoted by adj A. Our result, exhibited for 3×3 matrices, is, of course, valid for any order square matrix A, and may be briefly stated as:

THEOREM 5.3.1

$A(\text{adj } A) = (\text{adj } A)A = (\det A)I_n$. (We remind the reader that adj A is a square matrix, while det A is a scalar.)

Thus we have seen that if $\det A \neq 0$ then A has an inverse—namely, $A^{-1} = (1/\det A)(\text{adj } A)$. The converse of this statement is true also; that is, if A has an inverse, then $\det A \neq 0$. For if A has an inverse, then using Theorem 5.2.3, we have $|A|\,|A^{-1}| = |AA^{-1}| = |I_n| = 1$, so that $|A| \neq 0$. As a side result, we also see that $\det |A^{-1}| = 1/\det A$. Thus we have the following fundamental relationship between inverses and determinants:

THEOREM 5.3.2

A square matrix A has an inverse if and only if its determinant is non-zero.

While the preceding theorem is useful, we hasten to point out that the method of calculating the inverse of a matrix, as illustrated in Example 5.3.1, is extremely time-consuming for large matrices, and is essentially useless as a method of calculation. Just consider that finding the inverse of a 10×10 matrix by that method would require computing the determinants of one 10×10 matrix and one hundred 9×9 matrices. Recall from Section 3.6 that the Gauss-Jordan reduction method only requires reduction of $[A \,|\, I_n]$ to $[I \,|\, A^{-1}]$. The computation is scarcely double that needed for finding $|A|$.

Exercises 5.3

In Exercises 1–4, verify Theorem 5.3.1 by calculating the products $A(\operatorname{adj} A)$ and $(\operatorname{adj} A)A$.

1. $\begin{bmatrix} 1 & 3 \\ 1 & 2 \end{bmatrix}$
2. $\begin{bmatrix} 3 & 1 \\ 6 & 2 \end{bmatrix}$

3. $\begin{bmatrix} 4 & 1 & 2 \\ 1 & 1 & -3 \\ 5 & 2 & -1 \end{bmatrix}$
4. $\begin{bmatrix} 1 & 2 & 1 \\ 1 & 1 & 0 \\ 0 & 2 & 3 \end{bmatrix}$

In Exercises 5–10, use the method of this section and the method of Section 3.6 to calculate the inverses of the given matrix.

5. $\begin{bmatrix} 1 & 2 \\ 3 & 4 \end{bmatrix}$
6. $\begin{bmatrix} -1 & 1 \\ 4 & 6 \end{bmatrix}$

7. $\begin{bmatrix} 1 & 2 & 1 \\ 1 & 3 & 1 \\ 2 & 1 & 4 \end{bmatrix}$
8. $\begin{bmatrix} 0 & 1 & 2 \\ 0 & 0 & 2 \\ 2 & 1 & 3 \end{bmatrix}$

9. $\begin{bmatrix} 4 & 2 & 0 & 1 \\ 1 & 1 & 1 & 1 \\ 3 & 1 & 0 & 1 \\ -1 & 2 & 3 & 2 \end{bmatrix}$
10. $\begin{bmatrix} 1 & 1 & 2 & 3 \\ 1 & 2 & 3 & 0 \\ 0 & 0 & 1 & 2 \\ 0 & 0 & 2 & 5 \end{bmatrix}$

We now consider **Cramer's Rule**, which is a method for solving certain special types of systems of equations.

Consider the system of three equations in three unknowns

$$a_{11}x_1 + a_{12}x_2 + a_{13}x_3 = b_1$$
$$a_{21}x_1 + a_{22}x_2 + a_{23}x_3 = b_2$$
$$a_{31}x_1 + a_{32}x_2 + a_{33}x_3 = b_3.$$

Cramer's Rule states that if the determinant of the coefficient matrix is not zero—that is, if $|A| \neq 0$, then the (unique) solution of this system is given in terms of determinants by

$$x_1 = \frac{\begin{vmatrix} b_1 & a_{12} & a_{13} \\ b_2 & a_{22} & a_{23} \\ b_3 & a_{32} & a_{33} \end{vmatrix}}{|A|}, \quad x_2 = \frac{\begin{vmatrix} a_{11} & b_1 & a_{13} \\ a_{21} & b_2 & a_{23} \\ a_{31} & b_3 & a_{33} \end{vmatrix}}{|A|}, \quad x_3 = \frac{\begin{vmatrix} a_{11} & a_{12} & b_1 \\ a_{21} & a_{22} & b_2 \\ a_{31} & a_{32} & b_3 \end{vmatrix}}{|A|}.$$

In general, *for a system of n equations in n unknowns in which the coefficient matrix A has a non-zero determinant, the kth unknown is the quotient of two determinants. The denominator determinant is the determinant of A, and the numerator is the determinant of the matrix formed by replacing the kth column of A by B.*

The reader may have used Cramer's Rule to solve two equations in two unknowns, or to solve three equations in three unknowns. If not, there are several exercises at the end of this section on which he may try his hand. We illustrate Cramer's Rule with a system of four equations in four unknowns.

Example 5.3.2

Solve (by Cramer's Rule) the system

$$x_1 - x_2 + x_3 - x_4 = 6$$
$$2x_1 + x_2 \qquad + x_4 = -1$$
$$x_1 + 2x_2 + x_3 - 2x_4 = 5$$
$$3x_1 - x_2 - 2x_3 + x_4 = -2.$$

In matrix form, this system may be written as $AX = B$, where

$$A = \begin{bmatrix} 1 & -1 & 1 & -1 \\ 2 & 1 & 0 & 1 \\ 1 & 2 & 1 & -2 \\ 3 & -1 & -2 & 1 \end{bmatrix}, \quad X = \begin{bmatrix} x_1 \\ x_2 \\ x_3 \\ x_4 \end{bmatrix}, \quad B = \begin{bmatrix} 6 \\ -1 \\ 5 \\ -2 \end{bmatrix}.$$

The reader should now verify, by hook or by crook, that

$$|A| = \begin{vmatrix} 1 & -1 & 1 & -1 \\ 2 & 1 & 0 & 1 \\ 1 & 2 & 1 & -2 \\ 3 & -1 & -2 & 1 \end{vmatrix} = -32.$$

By Cramer's Rule, then,

$$x_1 = \frac{\begin{vmatrix} 6 & -1 & 1 & -1 \\ -1 & 1 & 0 & 1 \\ 5 & 2 & 1 & -2 \\ -2 & -1 & -2 & 1 \end{vmatrix}}{-32}, \qquad x_2 = \frac{\begin{vmatrix} 1 & 6 & 1 & -1 \\ 2 & -1 & 0 & 1 \\ 1 & 5 & 1 & -2 \\ 3 & -2 & -2 & 1 \end{vmatrix}}{-32},$$

$$x_3 = \frac{\begin{vmatrix} 1 & -1 & 6 & -1 \\ 2 & 1 & -1 & 1 \\ 1 & 2 & 5 & -2 \\ 3 & -1 & -2 & 1 \end{vmatrix}}{-32}, \quad \text{and} \quad x_4 = \frac{\begin{vmatrix} 1 & -1 & 1 & 6 \\ 2 & 1 & 0 & -1 \\ 1 & 2 & 1 & 5 \\ 3 & -1 & -2 & -2 \end{vmatrix}}{-32}.$$

The reader should verify that $x_1 = 1$, $x_2 = -1$, $x_3 = 2$, and $x_4 = -2$; moreover, he should now substitute these values in the original system to verify that this is, indeed, a solution.

We note the obvious drawbacks to Cramer's Rule as a computational method.

1. It is only applicable directly to systems of equations with a square coefficient matrix.

2. It fails as a method if the coefficient matrix has a zero determinant.

3. For n equations in n unknowns, it requires the calculation of $n + 1$ determinants each of order n. For large matrices, a great deal more work is required than for Gauss-Jordan reduction.

Despite these serious objections, Cramer's Rule is a well-known method of solving small systems of equations, or of computing the values for one or two of the variables in larger systems. Moreover, it provides a sometimes convenient tool when an explicit representation of the solution is required.

Exercises 5.3 (continued)

Solve the following systems by Cramer's Rule.

11. $x_1 + 2x_2 = 3$
$2x_1 - x_2 = 4$

12. $2x_1 + x_2 = 1$
$x_1 - 3x_2 = 2$

13. $x_1 + 2x_2 + 3x_3 = 5$
$2x_1 + 3x_2 - x_3 = -3$
$3x_1 + 7x_2 + x_3 = -2$

14. $x_1 + x_2 + x_3 = 2$
$x_1 - x_2 - x_3 = -6$
$x_1 + 2x_2 + 3x_3 = 9$

15. (for the masochist) Solve the following system of equations by Cramer's Rule, evaluating all determinants by the cofactor method.

$$x_1 - x_2 - x_3 - x_4 - x_5 - x_6 = 2$$
$$2x_1 + x_2 + x_3 + x_4 + x_5 + x_6 = 1$$
$$x_1 - x_2 + x_3 - x_4 + x_5 - x_6 = 0$$
$$x_1 + 2x_2 + x_3 - x_4 - x_5 - x_6 = 3$$
$$2x_1 - x_2 - x_3 + x_4 - x_5 + x_6 = 1$$
$$x_1 + x_2 + x_3 + x_4 + x_5 - x_6 = 0$$

New terms

5.4   The rank of a matrix

In the previous chapter the notion of *rank* was discussed and some connections between rank and linear independence were explored. Here we use the same definition for rank but connect this notion with the primary subject of this chapter—determinants—with several interesting and informative results.

Recall that we considered A to be the matrix of a homogeneous system of m equations in n unknowns, and let k denote the number of rows of zeros in the final augmented matrix reduced by the Gauss-Jordan process. The presence of these last k rows of zeros signalled to us that there were k redundant equations in the original system; or, to put it another way, that there were $m - k$ non-redundant equations in the original system. We then defined the rank of A to be the number $m - k$ of non-zero rows in the final augmented matrix. Thus, it is apparent that we may determine the rank of A by first performing the Gauss-Jordan process and then simply counting the number of non-zero rows.

Example 5.4.1

The matrix

$$A = \begin{bmatrix} 1 & 1 & 1 & 3 \\ 2 & -1 & 2 & 3 \\ 4 & 1 & 4 & 9 \end{bmatrix} \quad \text{may be reduced to} \quad \begin{bmatrix} 1 & 0 & 1 & 2 \\ 0 & 1 & 0 & 1 \\ 0 & 0 & 0 & 0 \end{bmatrix}.$$

Thus, in the matrix equation $AX = 0$, there are $k = 1$ redundant equations. Hence the rank of A is 2.

Example 5.4.2

Let A be the matrix

$$A = \begin{bmatrix} 1 & 1 & 1 & 1 \\ 1 & 1 & 2 & 3 \\ 3 & 3 & 5 & 4 \end{bmatrix} \quad \text{which may be reduced to} \quad \begin{bmatrix} 1 & 1 & 1 & 1 \\ 0 & 0 & 1 & 2 \\ 0 & 0 & 2 & 1 \end{bmatrix},$$

and then successively to

$$\begin{bmatrix} 1 & 1 & 0 & -1 \\ 0 & 0 & 1 & 2 \\ 0 & 0 & 0 & -3 \end{bmatrix}, \quad \text{and finally to} \quad \begin{bmatrix} 1 & 1 & 0 & 0 \\ 0 & 0 & 1 & 0 \\ 0 & 0 & 0 & 1 \end{bmatrix},$$

which is in the row-echelon form. We thus see that $k = 0$ and that the rank of A is $m - k = 3$.

Exercises 5.4

By inspection determine the rank of each of the following matrices.

1. $\begin{bmatrix} 1 \\ 0 \end{bmatrix}$

2. $\begin{bmatrix} 1 & 1 \end{bmatrix}$

3. $\begin{bmatrix} 1 & 1 & 0 & 0 \\ 0 & 0 & 1 & 0 \\ 0 & 0 & 0 & 1 \\ 0 & 0 & 0 & 0 \end{bmatrix}$

4. $\begin{bmatrix} 1 & 0 & 0 & 0 & 0 \\ 0 & 0 & 0 & 0 & 0 \\ 0 & 1 & 0 & 0 & 0 \\ 0 & 0 & 0 & 0 & 0 \end{bmatrix}$

Find the rank of each of the following matrices.

5. $\begin{bmatrix} 1 & 2 & 0 & 1 \\ 3 & 1 & 5 & 2 \end{bmatrix}$

6. $\begin{bmatrix} 0 & 1 & 4 & 1 \\ 1 & 2 & 3 & 4 \end{bmatrix}$

7. $\begin{bmatrix} 1 & -1 & 2 & 4 \\ 0 & 2 & 4 & 6 \\ -1 & 3 & -4 & -4 \end{bmatrix}$

8. $\begin{bmatrix} 1 & -2 & -1 \\ 2 & 3 & 5 \\ -1 & 5 & 4 \end{bmatrix}$

9. $\begin{bmatrix} 1 & 2 & -3 & 4 \\ -2 & -3 & 0 & 4 \\ -1 & -1 & -3 & 8 \\ 1 & 3 & -9 & 16 \end{bmatrix}$

10. $\begin{bmatrix} 1 & 2 & -3 & 4 & 1 \\ -2 & -3 & 0 & 4 & 4 \\ -1 & -1 & -3 & 8 & 5 \\ 1 & 3 & -9 & 16 & 7 \end{bmatrix}$

We now proceed to justify the presence of our discussion of *rank* in this chapter on determinants. Let us first note that in order to determine the rank of a matrix, we do not have to completely reduce it to echelon form. That is, it is not necessary in a particular column to reduce the elements *above* the diagonal (or pivotal) element in the reduction process, since this in no way affects the number of zero rows.

Example 5.4.3

$$A = \begin{bmatrix} 1 & 3 & 2 & 3 \\ 0 & 0 & 1 & 4 \\ 0 & 0 & 0 & 7 \end{bmatrix}$$

clearly has rank 3 even though it may be further reduced to the echelon form

$$\begin{bmatrix} 1 & 3 & 0 & 0 \\ 0 & 0 & 1 & 0 \\ 0 & 0 & 0 & 1 \end{bmatrix}.$$

So let us now consider the 3×4 matrix A in the partially reduced form

$$A = \begin{bmatrix} 1 & 2 & 1 & 2 \\ 0 & 1 & 2 & 3 \\ 0 & 0 & 0 & 0 \end{bmatrix};$$

A has rank 2 and we note that any 3×3 submatrix, found by selecting some three of the columns of A must necessarily have determinant zero, since any such 3×3 submatrix will have its last row zero. Thus the submatrix

$$\begin{bmatrix} 1 & 1 & 2 \\ 0 & 2 & 3 \\ 0 & 0 & 0 \end{bmatrix}$$

formed from the first, third and fourth columns of A has determinant 0. And in general, for the partially reduced $m \times n$ matrix

$$r \begin{cases} \\ \\ \\ \\ \end{cases} k \text{ rows of zeros} \begin{cases} \\ \\ \\ \end{cases} \begin{bmatrix} 1 & a_{12} & a_{13} & \cdots & a_{1r} & \cdots & a_{1n} \\ 0 & 1 & a_{23} & \cdots & a_{2r} & \cdots & a_{2n} \\ \cdot & \cdot & \cdot & \cdots & \cdot & \cdots & \cdot \\ 0 & 0 & 0 & \cdots & 1 & \cdots & a_{rn} \\ 0 & 0 & 0 & \cdots & 0 & \cdots & 0 \\ \cdot & \cdot & \cdot & \cdots & \cdot & \cdots & \cdot \\ 0 & 0 & 0 & \cdots & 0 & \cdots & 0 \end{bmatrix},$$

with rank $r = m - k$, it is certainly true that any square submatrix of order $r + 1$ or larger has a zero determinant, since any such submatrix must contain at least one of the last k rows of zeros.

On the other hand, we see that in the matrix

$$A = \begin{bmatrix} 1 & 2 & 1 & 2 \\ 0 & 1 & 2 & 3 \\ 0 & 0 & 0 & 0 \end{bmatrix},$$

which has rank 2, it is possible to find *at least one* 2 × 2 submatrix which has non-zero determinant; for example, the matrix $\begin{bmatrix} 1 & 2 \\ 0 & 1 \end{bmatrix}$ lying in the first two rows and first two columns of A has non-zero determinant. Similarly, in the 4 × 5 matrix B of rank 3,

$$B = \begin{bmatrix} 1 & 2 & 1 & 2 & 3 \\ 0 & 1 & 2 & -1 & 2 \\ 0 & 0 & 0 & 1 & 4 \\ 0 & 0 & 0 & 0 & 0 \end{bmatrix},$$

each 4 × 4 submatrix has zero determinant, while we can find at least one 3 × 3 submatrix with non-zero determinant. Here such a matrix is found by choosing the submatrix lying in the first three rows and the first, second, and fourth columns, namely,

$$\begin{bmatrix} 1 & 2 & 2 \\ 0 & 1 & -1 \\ 0 & 0 & 1 \end{bmatrix}.$$

That is, we choose the columns which contain the "first 1's" in each row, and thus construct, since there are exactly $m - k$ such columns, a triangular submatrix of order $m - k$ which has non-zero determinant; indeed, its diagonal elements are all 1's.

Thus we see that the rank of a *reduced matrix A* can be realized as the order (size) of the highest order submatrix of A with non-zero determinant.

So much for reduced matrices. But what about non-reduced ones? For them the answer is the same, as stated in the following:

THEOREM 5.4.1

The rank of a matrix is the order of the highest order square submatrix with non-zero determinant.

The truth of this theorem may be made plausible by the following remarks. In the Gauss-Jordan reduction process used to reduce A to echelon form, three types of operations are allowed:

1. *Row interchange.* This type of operation does not alter the zero-ness or non-zero-ness of the determinant of any submatrix containing the interchanged rows, since it merely changes the algebraic sign of any such determinant.

2. *Multiplying a row by a non-zero scalar c.* Such an operation does not alter the zero-ness or non-zero-ness of the determinant of any submatrix containing the row multiplied, since the operation merely multiplies such a determinant by the scalar c.

3. *Adding a multiple of one row to another row.* This operation does not alter the values of subdeterminants containing the rows involved.

While the foregoing is not a proof of Theorem 5.4.1, a proof can be constructed from this type of consideration. In the classical presentation of matrix algebra, Theorem 5.4.1 is often taken as the definition of rank, with our definition following as a theorem.

Exercises 5.4 (continued)

Find the rank of each of the following matrices by finding an appropriate order submatrix with non-zero determinant.

11.
$$\begin{bmatrix} 1 & -1 & 2 \\ 2 & 1 & -1 \\ 3 & 0 & 1 \end{bmatrix}$$

12.
$$\begin{bmatrix} 1 & 2 & 3 \\ -1 & 1 & 0 \\ 2 & -1 & 2 \end{bmatrix}$$

13.
$$\begin{bmatrix} 2 & 2 & 3 \\ 0 & -1 & 2 \\ 2 & 2 & 3 \\ 2 & 0 & 6 \end{bmatrix}$$

14.
$$\begin{bmatrix} 1 & 2 & 1 \\ 0 & 1 & -1 \\ 2 & 4 & 2 \\ 1 & 4 & -1 \end{bmatrix}$$

We conclude this section with a few elementary observations concerning rank: first, a given submatrix of A^T is the transpose of a corresponding submatrix of A. By our previous results, their determinants are equal. Thus the rank of A^T is the same as the rank of A. That is, if r is the rank of A, then each subdeterminant of A of order $r + 1$ and larger is 0. Hence the same is true for A^T. In addition, there is at least one subdeterminant of order r in A which is not 0 and the obvious one corresponding to it in A^T is non-zero also. Thus we have

THEOREM 5.4.2

The rank of a matrix A is the same as the rank of its transpose A^T.

Second, since rank is defined as the number of non-redundant rows, we know that if A is an $m \times n$ matrix, then the rank of $A \leqslant m$. But by Theorem 5.4.2, we must also have the rank of $A \leqslant n$. Hence we have

THEOREM 5.4.3

If A is an $m \times n$ matrix, then

$$\text{rank of } A \leqslant \min\{m, n\}.$$

Third, two extremes occur for the rank of a matrix. If the matrix A has all its entries zero, then we say that the rank of A is *zero*. If A is $m \times n$, and the rank of A is equal to the minimum of m and n, then we say that A has **full rank**; that is, it has the maximum rank possible for its dimensions.

Example 5.4.4

The matrices

$$[0], \quad [0 \ \ 0 \ \ 0], \quad \begin{bmatrix} 0 & 0 & 0 & 0 & 0 \\ 0 & 0 & 0 & 0 & 0 \end{bmatrix}, \quad \text{and} \quad \begin{bmatrix} 0 & 0 & 0 \\ 0 & 0 & 0 \\ 0 & 0 & 0 \end{bmatrix}$$

all have rank 0. The matrices

$$[7]; \quad \begin{bmatrix} -4 & 0 \\ 2 & 0 \end{bmatrix}, \quad \begin{bmatrix} 2 \\ 1 \end{bmatrix}, \quad [1 \ \ 2 \ \ 3 \ \ 4 \ \ 5], \quad \text{and} \quad \begin{bmatrix} 1 & 2 & 3 \\ 0 & 0 & 0 \\ 2 & 4 & 6 \end{bmatrix}$$

all have rank 1. The matrices

$$[1], \quad \begin{bmatrix} 2 & 3 \\ 4 & 5 \end{bmatrix}, \quad \text{and} \quad \begin{bmatrix} 2 & 3 & 0 & 0 & 0 \\ 4 & 5 & 0 & 0 & 0 \end{bmatrix}$$

are all of *full rank*.

Finally, suppose that A is an $n \times n$ square matrix of rank n. Then the determinant of A is non-zero so that by Theorem 5.3.2, A has an inverse. Thus we have the following connection between rank and inverses:

THEOREM 5.4.4

The $n \times n$ matrix A has an inverse if and only if the rank of A is n.

Exercises 5.4 (continued)

In Exercises 15–20, row reduce separately the matrix and its transpose to find their ranks. Which matrices have full rank?

15. $\begin{bmatrix} 2 & 1 \\ 4 & 2 \\ 1 & 1 \end{bmatrix}$

16. $\begin{bmatrix} 2 & 2 & 1 \\ 3 & 3 & 2 \end{bmatrix}$

17. $\begin{bmatrix} 1 & -1 & 2 & 1 \\ 1 & 0 & 5 & 0 \\ 0 & -3 & 2 & 5 \end{bmatrix}$

18. $\begin{bmatrix} 1 & -2 & 1 \\ -2 & 6 & 2 \\ -1 & 7 & 9 \end{bmatrix}$

19. $\begin{bmatrix} 1 & 2 & 1 & -1 \\ 2 & 5 & 2 & -1 \\ 3 & 7 & 3 & -2 \\ 1 & 3 & 2 & 0 \end{bmatrix}$ 20. $\begin{bmatrix} -1 & 2 & 1 & 3 & 4 \\ 1 & 1 & 2 & 1 & 3 \\ 2 & 1 & -1 & 1 & 2 \end{bmatrix}$

21. Let $A = \begin{bmatrix} 1 & -1 & 1 & 0 \\ 2 & -1 & 0 & 1 \end{bmatrix}$. Show that AA^T has an inverse, and find $(AA^T)^{-1}$. Prove that $A^T A$ has no inverse.

22. a. In each of the indicated matrix products, find the rank of each factor and the rank of the product matrix.

$$\begin{bmatrix} 0 & 1 \\ 0 & 0 \end{bmatrix}\begin{bmatrix} 0 & 0 \\ 0 & 1 \end{bmatrix}; \quad \begin{bmatrix} 0 & 1 \\ 0 & 0 \end{bmatrix}\begin{bmatrix} 1 & 0 \\ 0 & 1 \end{bmatrix}; \quad \begin{bmatrix} 1 & 0 & 0 \\ 0 & 0 & 1 \\ 1 & 0 & 1 \end{bmatrix}\begin{bmatrix} 0 & 1 & 0 \\ 1 & 0 & 0 \\ 1 & 1 & 0 \end{bmatrix}.$$

What conclusions can you draw about the rank of AB relative to the ranks of A and of B?

b. In each of the products in a. above, calculate the product in reverse order and its rank. Can you draw a conclusion about the rank of BA relative to the rank of AB?

c. Find some examples among 2×2 matrices which *disprove* each of the following non-theorems:

    i. rank of $(A + B) =$ rank of $A +$ rank of B.
    ii. rank of $(A - B) =$ rank of $A -$ rank of B.

New terms

full rank, 164

[6] Linear transformations and applications in geometry

6.1 Arrows and vectors

In Chapter 4, we defined a vector of order n to be an ordered n-tuple of real numbers—that is, a $1 \times n$ row matrix or an $n \times 1$ column matrix. The set of all $1 \times n$ row matrices forms a vector space under the usual addition and scalar multiplication of matrices described in Chapter 2; similarly, the set of all $n \times 1$ column vectors forms a vector space. We now describe a geometrical interpretation of vectors which we will find convenient to use throughout the remainder of this chapter.

In the three-dimensional space in which we live, it is common to adopt some sort of **rectangular coordinate system** to describe points in space. This is done by selecting an origin (a point denoted in the figures by O) from which all distances are measured, coordinate directions in which distances are measured, and a convenient unit of measure. Thus the top of the telephone pole across the street may be described (with one's self as origin) as 45 feet north, 20 feet east, and 25 feet up. We call the coordinate system in this example rectangular because the coordinate directions are at right angles to each other. One conventional coordinate system for 3-space is shown in Figure 6.1.1 with origin O, and directions x, y, and z. A point P in this space may be described in this system as being a units in the x-direction, b units in the y-direction, and c units in the z-direction (see Figure 6.1.2). In this

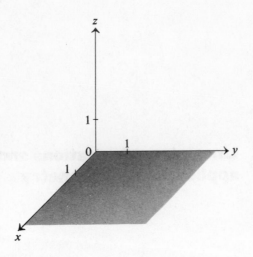

Figure 6.1.1

way we associate the point P in space with the triple of numbers (a, b, c). Thus the triple (a, b, c) serves as a name for the point P relative to the given coordinate system. Were we to change the coordinate system, the point P would correspond to another triple, and the triple (a, b, c) would correspond to a different point.

Now, with a fixed coordinate system, we interpret the vector $[a, b, c]$ as the **arrow** (directed line segment) whose tail is at the origin and whose head is at the point associated with the triple (a, b, c) (Figure 6.1.3).

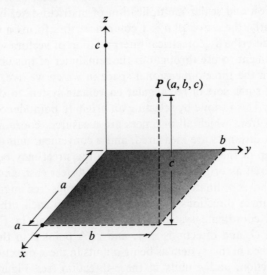

Figure 6.1.2

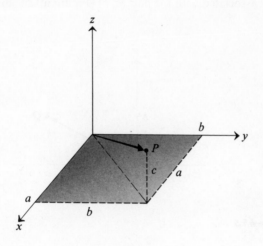

Figure 6.1.3

In the same way we interpret the column vector

$$\begin{bmatrix} a \\ b \\ c \end{bmatrix}$$

as the arrow from the origin to the point P, associated with (a, b, c).

For our geometric interpretation of 1×2 row matrices, we take a fixed coordinate system in the plane and in terms of that system we make correspond to every point an ordered pair (a, b) (Figure 6.1.4). We

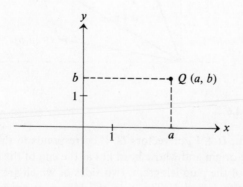

Figure 6.1.4

then interpret the row vector $[a, b]$ as the arrow from the origin to the point associated with the pair (a, b) (Figure 6.1.5). In a similar manner

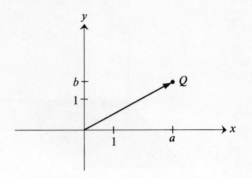

Figure 6.1.5

the column vector $\begin{bmatrix} a \\ b \end{bmatrix}$ is associated with the same arrow in the plane as is $[a, b]$.

We have already established in Chapter 2 an algebra for 1×2 matrices. That is, we defined the sum $[a, b] + [c, d]$ to be $[a + c, b + d]$ and the scalar product $\alpha[a, b]$ to be $[\alpha a, \alpha b]$. In terms of arrows in the plane, or in 3-space, addition may be realized as follows (Figure 6.1.6).

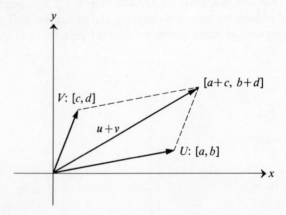

Figure 6.1.6

The sum, $U + V$, of vectors U, V corresponds to the arrow whose tail is at the origin and whose head lies at the end of the diagonal (from the origin) of the parallelogram, two sides of which are the arrows corresponding to U and V. This rule of addition of arrows is often referred to as the **Parallelogram Law**. One may verify that this addition is associative and commutative, and that the degenerate arrow 0 (the arrow from the origin to the origin—corresponding to the vector $[0, 0]$) acts as additive identity, and that, as shown in Figure 6.1.7,

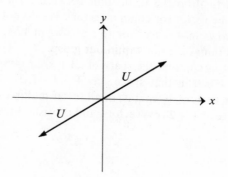

Figure 6.1.7

the additive inverse $(-U)$ of the arrow U is an arrow of the same length as U but in the opposite direction. Further, a scalar multiple aV of an arrow V is an arrow whose length is $|a|$ times the length of V and is in the same direction as V if $a > 0$ and in the opposite direction if $a < 0$ (Figure 6.1.8).

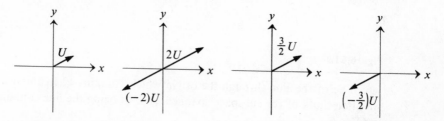

Figure 6.1.8

This scalar multiplication of arrows may be easily shown to satisfy the same properties (Section 2.7) as does our scalar multiplication of matrices. Thus the set of arrows from the origin is a vector space under these operations. Since the space of arrows is essentially the same as that of 1×2 vectors (matrices) we will henceforth drop the distinction and refer to the arrows as vectors also. Whether we interpret an arrow as a 1×2 row vector or as a 2×1 column vector depends entirely upon the context of a given discussion and we shall have occasion to use both interpretations.

All that we have said about arrows in the plane may be repeated for arrows in 3-space. With each such arrow we associate a 1×3 row vector or a 3×1 column vector. The Parallelogram Law is the rule by which we add arrows in 3-space. Scalar multiplication is defined as before. As a result, the arrows in 3-space also form a vector space and we will henceforth drop the distinction between an arrow in 3-space and a 1×3 row vector (or column vector). We do not extend this discussion to "arrows in 4-space" or to "arrows in 17-space" because pictures of such things are not within our grasp.

Let us consider the space of all 1×2 row vectors and a particular vector $V \neq 0$ in that space, say $V = [-1, 2]$. The set S of all linear combinations of V (that is, of all scalar multiples of V) is a subspace of the space of 1×2 row vectors, and consists (Figure 6.1.9) of all vectors

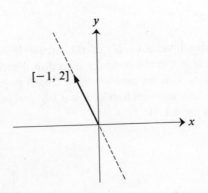

Figure 6.1.9

which lie in the line through the origin which contains V. In this way we often think of the subspace spanned by V as being the line containing V.

If U and V are 1×2 row vectors, then either they are linearly independent, or one of them is a scalar multiple of the other. In the latter case, the space spanned by them may be thought of as the line through the origin which contains them (Figure 6.1.10). In the former case, since the two are linearly independent, the vectors U and V form a basis for the space, so that the subspace spanned by them may be thought of as the entire plane (Figure 6.1.11).

If we consider the space of all 1×3 row vectors, and U is a non-zero member of that space, then the subspace spanned by U again may be thought of as the line through the origin containing U (Figure 6.1.12). If V and W are linearly independent vectors, then the subspace

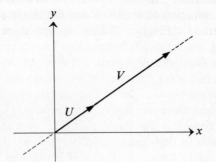

Figure 6.1.10

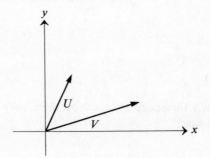

Figure 6.1.11

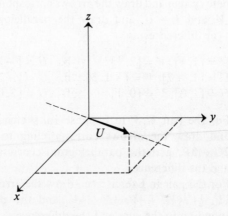

Figure 6.1.12

spanned by them is the plane through the origin containing V and W. If X is a third vector, so that $\{V, W, X\}$ is linearly dependent, then X is a linear combination of V and W and lies in the plane spanned by them (Figure 6.1.13). Finally, if U, V, W are three linearly independent

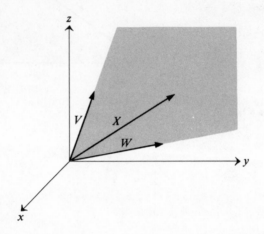

Figure 6.1.13

vectors, then the space spanned by them may be thought of as the whole of 3-space.

Exercises 6.1

1. For the following pairs of vectors U, V in 2-space, sketch a co-ordinate system and draw the arrows corresponding to $U, V, U + V$, $U - V$, and $V - U$, and draw the parallelograms related to the sums (or differences).

   a. $U = [1, 1]$, $V = [2, 1]$ b. $U = [-1, -1]$, $V = [1, 2]$
   c. $U = [1, -2]$, $V = [-1, 3]$ d. $U = [-2, -3]$, $V = [2, -1]$
   e. $U = [1, 3]$, $V = [0, 1]$ f. $U = [2, 0]$, $V = [0, -3]$

2. a. For the pair U, V in Exercise 1a. sketch a coordinate system and draw the arrows corresponding to $2U, 3V, 2U + 3V$, $2U - 3V$, and the parallelograms corresponding to the sum and the difference.

   b. For the pair in Exercise 1c., draw the arrows corresponding to $\frac{1}{3}U, \frac{1}{2}V, \frac{1}{3}U + \frac{1}{2}V, \frac{1}{3}U - \frac{1}{2}V$, and the parallelograms corresponding to the sum and the difference.

3. With coordinate system as in Figure 6.1.1, draw the arrows corresponding to $U = [1, 2, 3]$ and $V = [3, 1, 2]$. Sketch the parallelogram corresponding to the sum $U + V$.

4. In 2-space sketch the vector U and the subspace spanned by U.

   a. $U = [2, 2]$ b. $U = [-1, 2]$ c. $U = [-1, -2]$
   d. $U = [1, -3]$ e. $U = [0, -3]$ f. $U = [2, 0]$

5. In 3-space, sketch the vector U and the space spanned by U.

   a. $U = [2, 1, 3]$ b. $U = [1, 2, 1]$ c. $U = [0, 2, 1]$
   d. $U = [1, 2, 0]$ e. $[1, 1, -1]$

6. In a 3-dimensional coordinate system x, y, z:
   a. Draw the vectors

$$U = \begin{bmatrix} 1 \\ 0 \\ 1 \end{bmatrix}, V = \begin{bmatrix} 2 \\ 3 \\ 3 \end{bmatrix}$$

   and sketch a portion of the plane determined by U and V.
   b. Show algebraically that

$$\begin{bmatrix} 1 \\ 1 \\ 4/3 \end{bmatrix}$$

   is in the plane spanned by U and V and that

$$\begin{bmatrix} 1 \\ 1 \\ 1 \end{bmatrix}$$

   is not; that is, show that the former is a linear combination of U and V and that the latter is not. Use your sketch from 6a. to illustrate the situation.

7. Describe in your own words the subspace of 4-space spanned by the following.

   a. $U = [1, 1, 0, 0]$
   b. $U = [1, 0, 0, 0]$ and $V = [0, 1, 0, 0]$
   c. $U = [1, 1, 0, 0]$ and $V = [1, 2, 0, 0]$
   d. $U = [1, 1, 0, 0]$, $V = [1, 2, 0, 0]$ and $W = [1, 1, 1, 0]$

8. In 3-space, sketch the vectors U and V and the subspace spanned by them.

   a. $U = [1, 1, 1]$, $V = [0, 1, 2]$ b. $U = [1, 2, 0]$, $V = [0, 0, 1]$
   c. $U = [3, 1, 1]$, $V = [1, 3, 2]$

New terms

6.2 Change of basis

In this section we shall consider the effects of a change of basis upon the coordinates of a given vector X in 2-space or 3-space. To illustrate the situation we suppose that $\{U_1, U_2\}$ and $\{V_1, V_2\}$ are each bases in $\mathcal{M}_{2,1}$. The problem has two aspects:

1. Given X_U, the coordinate matrix of X with respect to the U-basis, find X_V, the coordinate matrix of X with respect to the V-basis.

2. Given X_V, find X_U.

The key to the solution of both problems is the fact that we can express each element of one basis in terms of the elements of the other basis. For example, since $\{V_1, V_2\}$ is a basis for $\mathcal{M}_{2,1}$ we know that there exist scalars a_{ij} such that

$$U_1 = a_{11} V_1 + a_{21} V_2$$
$$U_2 = a_{12} V_1 + a_{22} V_2.$$

Thus $U_1 = [V_1, V_2]\begin{bmatrix} a_{11} \\ a_{21} \end{bmatrix}$ and $U_2 = [V_1, V_2]\begin{bmatrix} a_{12} \\ a_{22} \end{bmatrix}$. More compactly, denoting the matrix $[V_1, V_2]$ by V, and letting $A_1 = \begin{bmatrix} a_{11} \\ a_{21} \end{bmatrix}$, $A_2 = \begin{bmatrix} a_{12} \\ a_{22} \end{bmatrix}$, we have

$$U_1 = VA_1 \quad \text{and} \quad U_2 = VA_2.$$

Putting U_1 and U_2 together in a matrix U, we have

(1) $$U = [U_1, U_2] = [VA_1, VA_2] = V[A_1, A_2] = VA.$$

This is the result we need to solve our problem.

Consider the first aspect of our problem in which we know $X_U = \begin{bmatrix} u_1 \\ u_2 \end{bmatrix}$ such that

(2) $$X = u_1 U_1 + u_2 U_2,$$

and wish to find $X_V = \begin{bmatrix} v_1 \\ v_2 \end{bmatrix}$ such that

(3) $$X = v_1 V_1 + v_2 V_2.$$

It will be helpful to put (2) and (3) in an equivalent form, namely

(4) $$X = [U_1, U_2]\begin{bmatrix} u_1 \\ u_2 \end{bmatrix} = UX_U$$

and

(5) $$X = [V_1, V_2]\begin{bmatrix} v_1 \\ v_2 \end{bmatrix} = VX_V.$$

Thus we see that

$$UX_U = VX_V$$

and using our earlier result (1) that $U = VA$, we have

$$(VA)X_U = VX_V$$

or

$$V(AX_U) = VX_V.$$

The matrix V is non-singular (see Theorems 4.5.1(3) and 5.4.4) so V^{-1} must exist. Multiplying in our last result by V^{-1} on the left we obtain

$$AX_U = X_V.$$

Example 6.2.1

Let $\{U_1, U_2\} = \left\{ \begin{bmatrix} 2 \\ 0 \end{bmatrix}, \begin{bmatrix} 0 \\ 2 \end{bmatrix} \right\}$ and $\{V_1, V_2\} = \left\{ \begin{bmatrix} 1 \\ -1 \end{bmatrix}, \begin{bmatrix} 1 \\ 1 \end{bmatrix} \right\}$. Then

$$U_1 = \begin{bmatrix} 2 \\ 0 \end{bmatrix} = 1\begin{bmatrix} 1 \\ -1 \end{bmatrix} + 1\begin{bmatrix} 1 \\ 1 \end{bmatrix} = \begin{bmatrix} 1 & 1 \\ -1 & 1 \end{bmatrix}\begin{bmatrix} 1 \\ 1 \end{bmatrix} = VA_1$$

and

$$U_2 = \begin{bmatrix} 0 \\ 2 \end{bmatrix} = -1\begin{bmatrix} 1 \\ -1 \end{bmatrix} + 1\begin{bmatrix} 1 \\ 1 \end{bmatrix} = \begin{bmatrix} 1 & 1 \\ -1 & 1 \end{bmatrix}\begin{bmatrix} -1 \\ 1 \end{bmatrix} = VA_2,$$

so that $A = \begin{bmatrix} 1 & -1 \\ 1 & 1 \end{bmatrix}$. Suppose $X = \begin{bmatrix} 2 \\ 3 \end{bmatrix}$. Then

$$X = \begin{bmatrix} 2 \\ 3 \end{bmatrix} = 1\begin{bmatrix} 2 \\ 0 \end{bmatrix} + (3/2)\begin{bmatrix} 0 \\ 2 \end{bmatrix} = \begin{bmatrix} 2 & 0 \\ 0 & 2 \end{bmatrix}\begin{bmatrix} 1 \\ 3/2 \end{bmatrix} = UX_U,$$

and we see that $X_U = \begin{bmatrix} 1 \\ 3/2 \end{bmatrix}$. Then

$$X_V = AX_U = \begin{bmatrix} 1 & -1 \\ 1 & 1 \end{bmatrix}\begin{bmatrix} 1 \\ 3/2 \end{bmatrix} = \begin{bmatrix} -1/2 \\ 5/2 \end{bmatrix},$$

as we verify by computing

$$(-1/2)\begin{bmatrix} 1 \\ -1 \end{bmatrix} + 5/2\begin{bmatrix} 1 \\ 1 \end{bmatrix} = \begin{bmatrix} 2 \\ 3 \end{bmatrix} = X.$$

Since $U = VA$, and each of V and A is square, we have that $|U| = |V||A|$. Moreover, U is non-singular so that $|U| \neq 0$ and hence $|A| \neq 0$. Therefore A^{-1} exists in general and we can solve for X_U in the formula $AX_U = X_V$. Thus,

$$A^{-1}(AX_U) = A^{-1}X_V$$

so that

$$X_U = A^{-1}X_V.$$

Example 6.2.2

In the previous example, $A = \begin{bmatrix} 1 & -1 \\ 1 & 1 \end{bmatrix}$ and $A^{-1} = \begin{bmatrix} 1/2 & 1/2 \\ -1/2 & 1/2 \end{bmatrix}$.

For $X = \begin{bmatrix} 2 \\ 3 \end{bmatrix}$, the coordinate matrix $X_V = \begin{bmatrix} -1/2 \\ 5/2 \end{bmatrix}$, and

$$X_U = A^{-1}X_V = \begin{bmatrix} 1/2 & 1/2 \\ -1/2 & 1/2 \end{bmatrix} \begin{bmatrix} -1/2 \\ 5/2 \end{bmatrix} = \begin{bmatrix} 1 \\ 3/2 \end{bmatrix},$$

as we expected. Letting $Y = \begin{bmatrix} 1 \\ 3 \end{bmatrix} = -1 \begin{bmatrix} 1 \\ -1 \end{bmatrix} + 2 \begin{bmatrix} 1 \\ 1 \end{bmatrix}$, we have $Y_V = \begin{bmatrix} -1 \\ 2 \end{bmatrix}$. Thus

$$Y_U = A^{-1}Y_V = \begin{bmatrix} 1/2 & 1/2 \\ -1/2 & 1/2 \end{bmatrix} \begin{bmatrix} -1 \\ 2 \end{bmatrix} = \begin{bmatrix} 1/2 \\ 3/2 \end{bmatrix}.$$

We verify that $1/2 \begin{bmatrix} 2 \\ 0 \end{bmatrix} + (3/2) \begin{bmatrix} 0 \\ 2 \end{bmatrix} = \begin{bmatrix} 1 \\ 3 \end{bmatrix} = Y$.

Example 6.2.3

For the moment imagine yourself in command of a lunar-bound space vehicle. Consider the situation at a certain instant in time when the spacecraft is 1000 miles from the moon's surface. Much of the information that you need to properly control your craft to its proposed landing site may be available only in terms of vectors expressed in a local coordinate system (with the spacecraft as origin). It is important for ground control, at Houston, Texas, to know what these vectors are in terms of the directions that have been used to establish a Houston coordinate system. Let us say that the Houston system has basis $\{V_1, V_2, V_3\}$ where

$$V_1 = \begin{bmatrix} 1 \\ 0 \\ 0 \end{bmatrix}, \qquad V_2 = \begin{bmatrix} 0 \\ 1 \\ 0 \end{bmatrix}, \qquad V_3 = \begin{bmatrix} 0 \\ 0 \\ 1 \end{bmatrix},$$

and that the spacecraft system has basis $\{U_1, U_2, U_3\}$. We imagine that the origin of the spacecraft coordinate system is translated to the Houston origin so that the two systems appear as in Figure 6.2.1.

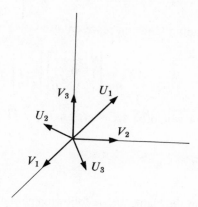

Figure 6.2.1

Further, at the instant in time of which we speak, the spacecraft basis vectors are known in terms of the Houston system to be

$$U_1 = \qquad V_2 + V_3$$
$$U_2 = V_1 \qquad + V_3$$
$$U_3 = V_1 + V_2.$$

Thus,

$$U_1 = [V_1 \quad V_2 \quad V_3] \begin{bmatrix} 0 \\ 1 \\ 1 \end{bmatrix},$$

$$U_2 = [V_1 \quad V_2 \quad V_3] \begin{bmatrix} 1 \\ 0 \\ 1 \end{bmatrix},$$

and

$$U_3 = [V_1 \quad V_2 \quad V_3] \begin{bmatrix} 1 \\ 1 \\ 0 \end{bmatrix}.$$

Then

$$[U_1 \quad U_2 \quad U_3] = [V_1 \quad V_2 \quad V_3] \begin{bmatrix} 0 & 1 & 1 \\ 1 & 0 & 1 \\ 1 & 1 & 0 \end{bmatrix}$$

or

$$U = VA.$$

If you observe the coordinate matrix $X_U = \begin{bmatrix} 1 \\ -1 \\ 2 \end{bmatrix}$ of a vector X, then

the corresponding Houston representation of X would be

$$X_V = AX_U = \begin{bmatrix} 0 & 1 & 1 \\ 1 & 0 & 1 \\ 1 & 1 & 0 \end{bmatrix} \begin{bmatrix} 1 \\ -1 \\ 2 \end{bmatrix} = \begin{bmatrix} 1 \\ 3 \\ 0 \end{bmatrix},$$

and the vector would be deciphered as $V_1 + 3V_2$.

Exercises 6.2

1. a. Fill in the blanks in the following paragraph: Let $\{U_1, U_2\}$ and $\{V_1, V_2\}$ be bases for $\mathcal{M}_{2,1}$ with corresponding basis matrices U, V. If X is in $\mathcal{M}_{2,1}$ then there exist coordinate matrices _____, _____ such that $X = U$_____ and $X = V$_____. If A is the square matrix with the property that $U = VA$, then $X = VA$_____ $=$ _____X_V, from which we deduce that $AX_U =$ _____.

   b. Let $A = \begin{bmatrix} 1 & 2 \\ -1 & 3 \end{bmatrix}$ and $X_U = \begin{bmatrix} 1 \\ 2 \end{bmatrix}$. Find X_V.

   c. With A as in b. above, let $X_V = \begin{bmatrix} 3 \\ -2 \end{bmatrix}$ and find X_U.

   d. By looking at A we know that $U_1 =$ _____$V_1 +$ _____V_2, and $U_2 =$ _____$V_1 +$ _____V_2. Express $2U_1 + U_2$ in terms of the V basis vectors.

2. How do we know that a basis matrix U or V in equation (1) of this section is non-singular?

3. Let $\{U_1, U_2\} = \left\{ \begin{bmatrix} 1 \\ 1 \end{bmatrix}, \begin{bmatrix} 2 \\ 1 \end{bmatrix} \right\}$ and $\{V_1, V_2\} = \left\{ \begin{bmatrix} 1 \\ -2 \end{bmatrix}, \begin{bmatrix} -1 \\ 3 \end{bmatrix} \right\}$.

   a. Find A such that $U = VA$.

   b. Let $X = \begin{bmatrix} 3 \\ 2 \end{bmatrix}$. Find X_U by observation and use it and A to compute X_V. Verify your result by checking to see that $VX_V = X$.

   c. Let $X = \begin{bmatrix} 0 \\ 1 \end{bmatrix}$. Find X_V by observation and use it and A^{-1} to compute X_U. Verify your result.

4. Let $\{U_1, U_2\} = \left\{ \begin{bmatrix} 1 \\ 2 \end{bmatrix}, \begin{bmatrix} 2 \\ 1 \end{bmatrix} \right\}$ and $\{V_1, V_2\} = \left\{ \begin{bmatrix} 1 \\ 0 \end{bmatrix}, \begin{bmatrix} 0 \\ 1 \end{bmatrix} \right\}$.

   a. Find A such that $U = VA$.

   b. Let $X = \begin{bmatrix} 3 \\ 3 \end{bmatrix}$. Find X_U by observation and use it to compute X_V. Verify your result by observation.

   c. Let $X = \begin{bmatrix} 5 \\ 4 \end{bmatrix}$. Find X_V by observation and use to compute X_U. Verify your result.

5. Let $\{U_1, U_2, U_3\} = \left\{ \begin{bmatrix} 1 \\ 0 \\ 1 \end{bmatrix}, \begin{bmatrix} 2 \\ 1 \\ 1 \end{bmatrix}, \begin{bmatrix} 1 \\ 1 \\ 2 \end{bmatrix} \right\}$

   and $\{V_1, V_2, V_3\} = \left\{ \begin{bmatrix} 1 \\ 0 \\ 0 \end{bmatrix}, \begin{bmatrix} 0 \\ 1 \\ 0 \end{bmatrix}, \begin{bmatrix} 0 \\ 0 \\ 1 \end{bmatrix} \right\}$.

   a. Find A such that $U = AV$

   b. Find X such that $X_U = \begin{bmatrix} 1 \\ 1 \\ 1 \end{bmatrix}$.

   c. Find X_V by two methods.

6.3   Linear transformations

In Chapter 1, we discussed the notion of a function and gave a variety of examples of functions from one set S into another set W. The main topic of this chapter is a special type of function T from a vector space $\mathscr{V}$ into itself; that is, T associates with each vector X in $\mathscr{V}$ another vector Y in $\mathscr{V}$, and, in our usual functional notation, we write

$$Y = T(X).$$

As before, we shall often describe Y as the image of X under the function T.

   The type of function T which we wish to describe is called a **linear transformation** (*transformation* being a synonym for *function*). T is linear in the following sense:

   A linear transformation T from a vector space $\mathscr{V}$ into the space $\mathscr{V}$ is a function which associates with each vector X in $\mathscr{V}$ an image vector Y in $\mathscr{V}$ in such a way that for any vectors, X_1 and X_2, and any scalars, a_1 and a_2,

   $$T(a_1 X_1 + a_2 X_2) = a_1 T(X_1) + a_2 T(X_2).$$

There is an alternate definition of linear transformation as follows:

T is said to be a linear transformation provided that for any vectors X_1, X_2, and any scalar a,

1. $T(X_1 + X_2) = T(X_1) + T(X_2)$

2. $T(aX_1) = aT(X_1)$.

In Exercise 6, the reader is asked to show that these two definitions are equivalent. We shall use the first formulation for most of our development.

Thus a linear transformation T is linear in that the image of any linear combination $a_1 X_1 + a_2 X_2$ of vectors in V is that same linear combination $a_1 T(X_1) + a_2 T(X_2)$ of the images of X_1 and X_2.

Example 6.3.1

Let T be the transformation on the space of all 2×1 vectors defined as

$$T\left(\begin{bmatrix} c \\ d \end{bmatrix}\right) = \begin{bmatrix} 2c \\ d \end{bmatrix}.$$

Then in particular, we have $T\left(\begin{bmatrix} 3 \\ 2 \end{bmatrix}\right) = \begin{bmatrix} 6 \\ 2 \end{bmatrix}$; and $T\left(\begin{bmatrix} -4 \\ 7 \end{bmatrix}\right) = \begin{bmatrix} -8 \\ 7 \end{bmatrix}$;

and $T\left(3\begin{bmatrix} 3 \\ 2 \end{bmatrix} + 2\begin{bmatrix} -4 \\ 7 \end{bmatrix}\right) = T\left(\begin{bmatrix} 1 \\ 20 \end{bmatrix}\right) = \begin{bmatrix} 2 \\ 20 \end{bmatrix}$. On the other hand,

$3T\left(\begin{bmatrix} 3 \\ 2 \end{bmatrix}\right) + 2T\left(\begin{bmatrix} -4 \\ 7 \end{bmatrix}\right) = 3\begin{bmatrix} 6 \\ 2 \end{bmatrix} + 2\begin{bmatrix} -8 \\ 7 \end{bmatrix} = \begin{bmatrix} 2 \\ 20 \end{bmatrix}$, so that we have in this instance

$$T\left(3\begin{bmatrix} 3 \\ 2 \end{bmatrix} + 2\begin{bmatrix} -4 \\ 7 \end{bmatrix}\right) = 3T\left(\begin{bmatrix} 3 \\ 2 \end{bmatrix}\right) + 2T\left(\begin{bmatrix} -4 \\ 7 \end{bmatrix}\right).$$

In general for this transformation T, we have, for any scalars a and b, and any vectors $\begin{bmatrix} c \\ d \end{bmatrix}$ and $\begin{bmatrix} e \\ f \end{bmatrix}$, that

$$T\left(a\begin{bmatrix} c \\ d \end{bmatrix} + b\begin{bmatrix} e \\ f \end{bmatrix}\right) = T\left(\begin{bmatrix} ac + be \\ ad + bf \end{bmatrix}\right) = \begin{bmatrix} 2(ac + be) \\ ad + bf \end{bmatrix} = \begin{bmatrix} 2ac \\ ad \end{bmatrix} + \begin{bmatrix} 2be \\ bf \end{bmatrix}$$

$$= a\begin{bmatrix} 2c \\ d \end{bmatrix} + b\begin{bmatrix} 2e \\ f \end{bmatrix} = aT\left(\begin{bmatrix} c \\ d \end{bmatrix}\right) + bT\left(\begin{bmatrix} e \\ f \end{bmatrix}\right).$$

Thus T is linear.

Example 6.3.2

Let T be the transformation defined on the space of all 3×1 matrices as follows:

$$T\left(\begin{bmatrix} a \\ b \\ c \end{bmatrix}\right) = \begin{bmatrix} a \\ 0 \\ 0 \end{bmatrix}.$$

Then, for any scalars x and y, and any vectors

$$\begin{bmatrix} a \\ b \\ c \end{bmatrix} \quad \text{and} \quad \begin{bmatrix} d \\ e \\ f \end{bmatrix},$$

we have

$$T\left(x\begin{bmatrix} a \\ b \\ c \end{bmatrix} + y\begin{bmatrix} d \\ e \\ f \end{bmatrix} \right) = T\left(\begin{bmatrix} xa + yd \\ xb + ye \\ xc + yf \end{bmatrix} \right) = \begin{bmatrix} xa + yd \\ 0 \\ 0 \end{bmatrix} = x\begin{bmatrix} a \\ 0 \\ 0 \end{bmatrix} + y\begin{bmatrix} d \\ 0 \\ 0 \end{bmatrix}$$

$$= xT\left(\begin{bmatrix} a \\ b \\ c \end{bmatrix} \right) + yT\left(\begin{bmatrix} d \\ e \\ f \end{bmatrix} \right).$$

Thus T is a linear transformation.

Example 6.3.3

The following is an example of a function from the space of all 2×1 matrices into itself which is *not* linear. Let N be defined by:

$$N\left(\begin{bmatrix} a \\ b \end{bmatrix} \right) = \begin{bmatrix} 2a \\ b \end{bmatrix} + \begin{bmatrix} 1 \\ 1 \end{bmatrix}.$$

Then it is not true in general that $N(aX + bY) = aN(X) + bN(Y)$, for consider, with $a = b = 1$, and $X = \begin{bmatrix} 1 \\ 0 \end{bmatrix}$, $Y = \begin{bmatrix} 0 \\ 1 \end{bmatrix}$, that

$$N\left(\begin{bmatrix} 1 \\ 0 \end{bmatrix} + \begin{bmatrix} 0 \\ 1 \end{bmatrix} \right) = N\left(\begin{bmatrix} 1 \\ 1 \end{bmatrix} \right) = \begin{bmatrix} 2 \\ 1 \end{bmatrix} + \begin{bmatrix} 1 \\ 1 \end{bmatrix} = \begin{bmatrix} 3 \\ 2 \end{bmatrix},$$

while

$$N\left(\begin{bmatrix} 1 \\ 0 \end{bmatrix} \right) + N\left(\begin{bmatrix} 0 \\ 1 \end{bmatrix} \right) = \left(\begin{bmatrix} 2 \\ 0 \end{bmatrix} + \begin{bmatrix} 1 \\ 1 \end{bmatrix} \right) + \left(\begin{bmatrix} 0 \\ 1 \end{bmatrix} + \begin{bmatrix} 1 \\ 1 \end{bmatrix} \right)$$

$$= \begin{bmatrix} 3 \\ 1 \end{bmatrix} + \begin{bmatrix} 1 \\ 2 \end{bmatrix} = \begin{bmatrix} 4 \\ 3 \end{bmatrix}.$$

Hence N is not linear, since $N\left(\begin{bmatrix} 1 \\ 0 \end{bmatrix} + \begin{bmatrix} 0 \\ 1 \end{bmatrix} \right) \neq N\left(\begin{bmatrix} 1 \\ 0 \end{bmatrix} \right) + N\left(\begin{bmatrix} 0 \\ 1 \end{bmatrix} \right).$

There are two very important linear transformations defined for every vector space $\mathscr{V}$ which require special mention. One is the transformation E which maps every vector to itself:

$$E(X) = X \quad \text{for each } X \text{ in } \mathscr{V}.$$

E is called the **identity transformation**. The other special transformation we want to mention is usually denoted by 0, and is such that

$$0(X) = 0;$$

that is, 0 maps each vector in $\mathscr{V}$ to the zero vector in $\mathscr{V}$. 0 is called the **zero transformation**. We leave it as an exercise to verify that these transformations are indeed linear.

Finally, one may generalize from the definition of a linear transformation T that, for any linear combination

$$V = a_1 V_1 + a_2 V_2 + \cdots + a_n V_n$$

of vectors $V_1, \ldots, V_n$, it is true that

$$T(V) = T(a_1 V_1 + \cdots + a_n V_n) = a_1 T(V_1) + \cdots + a_n T(V_n).$$

It is in this sense that one says, "a linear transformation preserves linear combinations"—meaning that the image of a linear combination of vectors is that same combination of the images of the separate vectors. We shall not present the general induction proof of the above assertion. It is, however, easily verified for three vectors. Thus,

$$
\begin{aligned}
T(a_1 V_1 + a_2 V_2 + a_3 V_3) &= T((a_1 V_1 + a_2 V_2) + a_3 V_3) \\
&= T(a_1 V_1 + a_2 V_2) + a_3 T(V_3) \\
&= a_1 T(V_1) + a_2 T(V_2) + a_3 T(V_3).
\end{aligned}
$$

We are now ready to develop a simple but fundamental property of linear transformations. Let $I = \begin{bmatrix} 1 \\ 0 \end{bmatrix}$ and $J = \begin{bmatrix} 0 \\ 1 \end{bmatrix}$ be a basis for the space of all 2×1 matrices. Let T denote any linear transformation defined on that space. We note that any 2×1 matrix

$$\begin{bmatrix} a \\ b \end{bmatrix} = a \begin{bmatrix} 1 \\ 0 \end{bmatrix} + b \begin{bmatrix} 0 \\ 1 \end{bmatrix},$$

so that

$$T\left(\begin{bmatrix} a \\ b \end{bmatrix}\right) = T\left(a \begin{bmatrix} 1 \\ 0 \end{bmatrix} + b \begin{bmatrix} 0 \\ 1 \end{bmatrix}\right) = aT\left(\begin{bmatrix} 1 \\ 0 \end{bmatrix}\right) + bT\left(\begin{bmatrix} 0 \\ 1 \end{bmatrix}\right),$$

since T is linear. Thus, if we are told what $T\left(\begin{bmatrix} 1 \\ 0 \end{bmatrix}\right)$ and $T\left(\begin{bmatrix} 0 \\ 1 \end{bmatrix}\right)$ are, then we know what $T\left(\begin{bmatrix} a \\ b \end{bmatrix}\right)$ is for any $\begin{bmatrix} a \\ b \end{bmatrix}$.

More generally, if $\{U, V\}$ is any basis for 2-space, then a linear transformation T is completely determined when we know $T(U)$ and $T(V)$; since if X is any vector, then for some scalars a and b we can write $X = aU + bV$, so that $T(X) = T(aU + bV) = aT(U) + bT(V)$.

In even more general terms, let $\mathscr{V}$ be a vector space with basis $\{B_1, B_2, \ldots, B_m\}$. If T is a linear transformation on $\mathscr{V}$, then the value of T at any X in $\mathscr{V}$ is known when we know $T(B_1), \ldots, T(B_m)$. Thus if $X = a_1 B_1 + a_2 B_2 + \cdots + a_m B_m$, then

$$T(X) = T(a_1 B_1 + \cdots + a_m B_m) = a_1 T(B_1) + \cdots + a_m T(B_m).$$

Example 6.3.4

Let T be the linear transformation which takes $\begin{bmatrix} 1 \\ 0 \end{bmatrix}$ into $\begin{bmatrix} 2 \\ 0 \end{bmatrix}$ and takes $\begin{bmatrix} 0 \\ 1 \end{bmatrix}$ to $\begin{bmatrix} 0 \\ 1 \end{bmatrix}$; that is,

$$T\left(\begin{bmatrix} 1 \\ 0 \end{bmatrix}\right) = \begin{bmatrix} 2 \\ 0 \end{bmatrix} \quad \text{and} \quad T\left(\begin{bmatrix} 0 \\ 1 \end{bmatrix}\right) = \begin{bmatrix} 0 \\ 1 \end{bmatrix}.$$

Then for any $\begin{bmatrix} a \\ b \end{bmatrix}$, we first write $\begin{bmatrix} a \\ b \end{bmatrix} = a\begin{bmatrix} 1 \\ 0 \end{bmatrix} + b\begin{bmatrix} 0 \\ 1 \end{bmatrix}$; then, since T is linear,

$$T\left(\begin{bmatrix} a \\ b \end{bmatrix}\right) = T\left(a\begin{bmatrix} 1 \\ 0 \end{bmatrix} + b\begin{bmatrix} 0 \\ 1 \end{bmatrix}\right) = aT\left(\begin{bmatrix} 1 \\ 0 \end{bmatrix}\right) + bT\left(\begin{bmatrix} 0 \\ 1 \end{bmatrix}\right)$$

$$= a\begin{bmatrix} 2 \\ 0 \end{bmatrix} + b\begin{bmatrix} 0 \\ 1 \end{bmatrix} = \begin{bmatrix} 2a \\ b \end{bmatrix}.$$

Thus T is the same transformation as that in Example 6.3.1.

Finally, we note that the set of all images of elements of $\mathscr{V}$ under a linear transformation T is a *subspace* of $\mathscr{V}$. This is easily proved by showing that the set of all images, denoted by $T(\mathscr{V})$ and defined as

$$T(\mathscr{V}) = \{Y \mid Y = T(X) \text{ for some } X \text{ in } \mathscr{V}\},$$

is closed under vector addition and scalar multiplication. Thus, if Y_1 and Y_2 are in $T(\mathscr{V})$, then there are X_1 and X_2 in $\mathscr{V}$ such that $T(X_1) = Y_1$ and $T(X_2) = Y_2$. Then

$$Y_1 + Y_2 = T(X_1) + T(X_2) = T(X_1 + X_2),$$

so that the sum $Y_1 + Y_2$ is in $T(\mathscr{V})$ since it is the image of $X_1 + X_2$, which must be in $\mathscr{V}$ since $\mathscr{V}$ is closed under addition. Similarly, a scalar multiple aY of any Y in $T(\mathscr{V})$ is also in $T(\mathscr{V})$—since for some X in $\mathscr{V}$, $Y = T(X)$ so that $aY = aT(X) = T(aX)$. (Why is aX in $\mathscr{V}$?)

The set $T(\mathscr{V})$ is called the **range space** of the transformation T, or, more briefly, just the range of T. Moreover, if $\{B_1, \ldots, B_m\}$ is a basis for $\mathscr{V}$ then the set $S = \{T(B_1), T(B_2), \ldots, T(B_m)\}$ spans $T(\mathscr{V})$. Thus we claim that if Y is in $T(\mathscr{V})$ then Y is a linear combination of the elements of $\{T(B_1), T(B_2), \ldots, T(B_m)\}$. That this is so may be seen from the following argument. If Y is in $T(\mathscr{V})$, then Y is the T-image of some vector X; that is, $Y = T(X)$. Since X is in $\mathscr{V}$, it is a linear combination of the basis vectors $B_1, \ldots, B_m$; let us say

$$X = a_1 B_1 + \cdots + a_m B_m.$$

Then

$$Y = T(X) = T(a_1 B_1 + a_2 B_2 + \cdots + a_m B_m)$$
$$= a_1 T(B_1) + a_2 T(B_2) + \cdots + a_m T(B_m),$$

and Y is indeed a linear combination of elements of S. Thus, S spans $T(\mathscr{V})$.

Example 6.3.5

Let $T\left(\begin{bmatrix} a \\ b \\ c \end{bmatrix}\right) = \begin{bmatrix} a \\ 0 \\ 0 \end{bmatrix}$, as in Example 6.3.2. With basis

$$\left\{ I = \begin{bmatrix} 1 \\ 0 \\ 0 \end{bmatrix}, \quad J = \begin{bmatrix} 0 \\ 1 \\ 0 \end{bmatrix}, \quad \text{and} \quad K = \begin{bmatrix} 0 \\ 0 \\ 1 \end{bmatrix} \right\},$$

we have $T(I) = \begin{bmatrix} 1 \\ 0 \\ 0 \end{bmatrix}$, and $T(J) = \begin{bmatrix} 0 \\ 0 \\ 0 \end{bmatrix}$, and $T(K) = \begin{bmatrix} 0 \\ 0 \\ 0 \end{bmatrix}$. Thus the set of

images $\left\{ \begin{bmatrix} 1 \\ 0 \\ 0 \end{bmatrix}, \begin{bmatrix} 0 \\ 0 \\ 0 \end{bmatrix}, \begin{bmatrix} 0 \\ 0 \\ 0 \end{bmatrix} \right\}$ of the basis $\{I, J, K\}$ is easily seen to span

$T(\mathscr{V})$. But the set of images is certainly not a basis for $T(\mathscr{V})$, since it is not a linearly independent set. Of course, a basis for $T(\mathscr{V})$ could be extracted from this spanning set. Thus we observe that

$$\left\{ \begin{bmatrix} 1 \\ 0 \\ 0 \end{bmatrix} \right\}$$

is a basis for the range space of T. Thus the range space of T is the

space of all scalar multiples of $\begin{bmatrix} 1 \\ 0 \\ 0 \end{bmatrix}$ and may be thought of as the line

containing the vector $\begin{bmatrix} 1 \\ 0 \\ 0 \end{bmatrix}$.

Example 6.6.6

If $T\left(\begin{bmatrix} a \\ b \end{bmatrix}\right) = \begin{bmatrix} 2a \\ b \end{bmatrix}$, as in Example 6.3.1, then $T\left(\begin{bmatrix} 1 \\ 0 \end{bmatrix}\right) = \begin{bmatrix} 2 \\ 0 \end{bmatrix}$ and

$T\left(\begin{bmatrix} 0 \\ 1 \end{bmatrix}\right) = \begin{bmatrix} 0 \\ 1 \end{bmatrix}$, so that $T(\mathscr{V})$ is spanned in this case by $\begin{bmatrix} 2 \\ 0 \end{bmatrix}$ and $\begin{bmatrix} 0 \\ 1 \end{bmatrix}$.

But these vectors are linearly independent, so that they also form a basis for the range space of T. Thus, for this particular transformation, the range space $T(\mathscr{V})$ is $\mathscr{V}$ itself.

Exercises 6.3

In Exercises 1–5, decide which of the defined transformations are linear and which are non-linear.

1. $T\left(\begin{bmatrix} a \\ b \end{bmatrix}\right) = \begin{bmatrix} a + b \\ 0 \end{bmatrix}$

2. $T\left(\begin{bmatrix} a \\ b \end{bmatrix}\right) = \begin{bmatrix} ab \\ 0 \end{bmatrix}$

3. $T\left(\begin{bmatrix} a \\ b \\ c \end{bmatrix}\right) = \begin{bmatrix} a + 1 \\ b \\ c \end{bmatrix}$

4. $T\left(\begin{bmatrix} a \\ b \\ c \end{bmatrix}\right) = \begin{bmatrix} a + b \\ a - b \\ 2a \end{bmatrix}$

5. $T\left(\begin{bmatrix} a \\ b \\ c \end{bmatrix}\right) = \begin{bmatrix} a \\ b \\ abc \end{bmatrix}$

6. Show that the two definitions of *linear transformation* given in this section are equivalent.

7. If T is a linear transformation from the space $\mathscr{V}$ into itself, prove that $T(0) = 0$; that is, any linear transformation maps the zero vector to the zero vector.

8. Prove that if T is a linear transformation from the vector space $\mathscr{V}$ into itself, then for each vector X in $\mathscr{V}$, $T(-X) = -T(X)$; that is, T maps the additive inverse of each X into the additive inverse of $T(X)$.

9. Let $X = \begin{bmatrix} 1 \\ 1 \\ 1 \end{bmatrix}$ and define the transformation T on $\mathscr{M}_{3,1}$ as

$$T\left(\begin{bmatrix} a \\ b \\ c \end{bmatrix}\right) = (a + b + c)X.$$

Is T a linear transformation? Why?

10. Let $T\left(\begin{bmatrix} x_1 \\ x_2 \end{bmatrix}\right) = \begin{bmatrix} x_1 + x_2 \\ x_1 - x_2 \end{bmatrix} = T(X)$. By solving the appropriate set of homogeneous linear equations find $\{X \mid T(X) = 0\}$. This set is called the **null space** of the linear transformation T.

11. Let

$$T\left(\begin{bmatrix} x_1 \\ x_2 \\ x_3 \end{bmatrix}\right) = \begin{bmatrix} x_1 + x_2 - x_3 \\ 3x_1 + 2x_2 - x_3 \\ 2x_1 + x_2 \end{bmatrix}.$$

Find the null space of T (see Exercise 10).

12. a. Prove that the null space of a linear transformation T is a vector space.

b. From the results of Exercise 11, can you formulate a conjecture about the relationship between the dimension of the null space of T and the rank of the coefficient matrix of the set of homogeneous equations?

New terms

linear transformation, 181   zero transformation, 184   null space, 187
identity transformation, 183   range space, 185

6.4 Linear transformations and matrices

Let us consider the space $\mathcal{M}_{2,1}$ of all 2×1 matrices. We now show how one may use a matrix to define a linear transformation T. We first choose some 2×2 matrix, say $\begin{bmatrix} 1 & 2 \\ 3 & 4 \end{bmatrix}$. Then we *define* the transformation T on $\mathcal{M}_{2,1}$ by showing how to find the image of each vector $\begin{bmatrix} a \\ b \end{bmatrix}$. Thus

$$T\left(\begin{bmatrix} a \\ b \end{bmatrix}\right) = \begin{bmatrix} 1 & 2 \\ 3 & 4 \end{bmatrix}\begin{bmatrix} a \\ b \end{bmatrix} = \begin{bmatrix} a + 2b \\ 3a + 4b \end{bmatrix}.$$

T associates with each vector in $\mathcal{M}_{2,1}$ another vector in $\mathcal{M}_{2,1}$. Moreover, this association is linear in that, because of the distributive property of matrix multiplication and the properties of scalar multiplication,

$$T\left(x\begin{bmatrix} a \\ b \end{bmatrix} + y\begin{bmatrix} c \\ d \end{bmatrix}\right) = \begin{bmatrix} 1 & 2 \\ 3 & 4 \end{bmatrix}\left(x\begin{bmatrix} a \\ b \end{bmatrix} + y\begin{bmatrix} c \\ d \end{bmatrix}\right)$$

$$= x\begin{bmatrix} 1 & 2 \\ 3 & 4 \end{bmatrix}\begin{bmatrix} a \\ b \end{bmatrix} + y\begin{bmatrix} 1 & 2 \\ 3 & 4 \end{bmatrix}\begin{bmatrix} c \\ d \end{bmatrix}$$

$$= xT\left(\begin{bmatrix} a \\ b \end{bmatrix}\right) + yT\left(\begin{bmatrix} c \\ d \end{bmatrix}\right).$$

In a similar manner, we may use a 3×3 matrix to define a linear transformation T as

$$T\left(\begin{bmatrix} a \\ b \\ c \end{bmatrix}\right) = \begin{bmatrix} 1 & 0 & 2 \\ 2 & 0 & 4 \\ 1 & 1 & 2 \end{bmatrix}\begin{bmatrix} a \\ b \\ c \end{bmatrix} = \begin{bmatrix} a + 2c \\ 2a + 4c \\ a + b + 2c \end{bmatrix}.$$

Indeed, there is no reason to stop with 3. We can, in general, define a linear transformation on $\mathscr{M}_{n,1}$ by using an $n \times n$ matrix.

Now the foregoing comments are not so remarkable at this point, for they are really a restatement of the distributive property of matrix multiplication and the properties of scalar multiplication of a matrix. The remarkable connection between linear transformations and matrices is that every linear transformation T on, say, $\mathscr{M}_{2,1}$ can be associated with a matrix $\begin{bmatrix} a_{11} & a_{12} \\ a_{21} & a_{22} \end{bmatrix}$ such that $T(X) = AX$ for each X in $\mathscr{M}_{2,1}$.

We now make precise how we may associate a matrix with a given linear transformation. We consider this problem first in

Example 6.4.1

Let the transformation T be defined as $T(X) = T\left(\begin{bmatrix} a \\ b \end{bmatrix}\right) = \begin{bmatrix} a + 2b \\ 3a + 4b \end{bmatrix}$. We then choose a basis for $\mathscr{M}_{2,1}$ and the basis which we select is $\left\{ \begin{bmatrix} 1 \\ 0 \end{bmatrix}, \begin{bmatrix} 0 \\ 1 \end{bmatrix} \right\}$. We recall that T is completely determined by its action on a basis, so we write down the T-images of our chosen basis elements, and we further express these images in the chosen basis. Thus

$$T\left(\begin{bmatrix} 1 \\ 0 \end{bmatrix}\right) = \begin{bmatrix} 1 \\ 3 \end{bmatrix} = 1\begin{bmatrix} 1 \\ 0 \end{bmatrix} + 3\begin{bmatrix} 0 \\ 1 \end{bmatrix}$$

$$T\left(\begin{bmatrix} 0 \\ 1 \end{bmatrix}\right) = \begin{bmatrix} 2 \\ 4 \end{bmatrix} = 2\begin{bmatrix} 1 \\ 0 \end{bmatrix} + 4\begin{bmatrix} 0 \\ 1 \end{bmatrix}.$$

We now write down the matrix $A = \begin{bmatrix} 1 & 2 \\ 3 & 4 \end{bmatrix}$, whose columns are respectively the coordinates of $T\left(\begin{bmatrix} 1 \\ 0 \end{bmatrix}\right)$ and the coordinates of $T\left(\begin{bmatrix} 0 \\ 1 \end{bmatrix}\right)$ in the chosen basis, as indicated. Now note that the transformation S such that $S(X) = AX$ is the same as the transformation T since each has the same effect upon a basis; indeed, for any $X = \begin{bmatrix} a \\ b \end{bmatrix}$, we have

$$S(X) = \begin{bmatrix} 1 & 2 \\ 3 & 4 \end{bmatrix} \begin{bmatrix} a \\ b \end{bmatrix} = \begin{bmatrix} a + 2b \\ 3a + 4b \end{bmatrix} = T(X). \text{ This relationship, we note,}$$
is a property of the special basis chosen.

Let us consider another example.

Example 6.4.2

Let T be defined so that $T\left(\begin{bmatrix} a \\ b \end{bmatrix}\right) = \begin{bmatrix} 2a - b \\ a + b \end{bmatrix}$. Still using the basis of the previous example, we write

$$T\left(\begin{bmatrix} 1 \\ 0 \end{bmatrix}\right) = \begin{bmatrix} 2 \\ 1 \end{bmatrix} = 2\begin{bmatrix} 1 \\ 0 \end{bmatrix} + 1\begin{bmatrix} 0 \\ 1 \end{bmatrix}$$

$$T\left(\begin{bmatrix} 0 \\ 1 \end{bmatrix}\right) = \begin{bmatrix} -1 \\ 1 \end{bmatrix} = -1\begin{bmatrix} 1 \\ 0 \end{bmatrix} + 1\begin{bmatrix} 0 \\ 1 \end{bmatrix}.$$

Our associated matrix is then $\begin{bmatrix} 2 & -1 \\ 1 & 1 \end{bmatrix}$. Let us consider a particular vector $\begin{bmatrix} 3 \\ 4 \end{bmatrix}$ and see how we use matrix multiplication to find $T\left(\begin{bmatrix} 3 \\ 4 \end{bmatrix}\right)$. We note from our defining equation for T that $T\left(\begin{bmatrix} 3 \\ 4 \end{bmatrix}\right) = \begin{bmatrix} 2 \\ 7 \end{bmatrix}$. We first express $\begin{bmatrix} 3 \\ 4 \end{bmatrix}$ in terms of the chosen basis, so that $\begin{bmatrix} 3 \\ 4 \end{bmatrix} = 3\begin{bmatrix} 1 \\ 0 \end{bmatrix} + 4\begin{bmatrix} 0 \\ 1 \end{bmatrix}$. If we multiply the matrix of coordinates $\begin{bmatrix} 3 \\ 4 \end{bmatrix}$, which, because of the basis we chose, is the vector $\begin{bmatrix} 3 \\ 4 \end{bmatrix}$, by the matrix $\begin{bmatrix} 2 & -1 \\ 1 & 1 \end{bmatrix}$ we obtain $\begin{bmatrix} 2 & -1 \\ 1 & 1 \end{bmatrix}\begin{bmatrix} 3 \\ 4 \end{bmatrix} = \begin{bmatrix} 2 \\ 7 \end{bmatrix}$ which is the matrix of coordinates of the image vector. Again, the matrix of coordinates of the image is the same as the image vector $\begin{bmatrix} 2 \\ 7 \end{bmatrix}$ because of the particular basis used. In general, in this example, $\begin{bmatrix} 2 & -1 \\ 1 & 1 \end{bmatrix}\begin{bmatrix} a \\ b \end{bmatrix} = \begin{bmatrix} 2a - b \\ a + b \end{bmatrix}$.

The same procedure used in the preceding examples may be used to associate with each linear transformation T on $\mathcal{M}_{3,1}$ a certain matrix A such that

$$T\left(\begin{bmatrix} a \\ b \\ c \end{bmatrix}\right) = A\begin{bmatrix} a \\ b \\ c \end{bmatrix},$$

if we use the usual I, J, K basis to construct the matrix.

Example 6.4.3

Let T be the transformation defined as

$$T\left(\begin{bmatrix} a \\ b \\ c \end{bmatrix}\right) = \begin{bmatrix} 2a - b + c \\ b + c \\ a - b \end{bmatrix}.$$

We use the basis

$$I = \begin{bmatrix} 1 \\ 0 \\ 0 \end{bmatrix}, \qquad J = \begin{bmatrix} 0 \\ 1 \\ 0 \end{bmatrix}, \qquad K = \begin{bmatrix} 0 \\ 0 \\ 1 \end{bmatrix},$$

and write

$$T\left(\begin{bmatrix} 1 \\ 0 \\ 0 \end{bmatrix}\right) = \begin{bmatrix} 2 \\ 0 \\ 1 \end{bmatrix} = 2\begin{bmatrix} 1 \\ 0 \\ 0 \end{bmatrix} + (0)\begin{bmatrix} 0 \\ 1 \\ 0 \end{bmatrix} + 1\begin{bmatrix} 0 \\ 0 \\ 1 \end{bmatrix}$$

$$T\left(\begin{bmatrix} 0 \\ 1 \\ 0 \end{bmatrix}\right) = \begin{bmatrix} -1 \\ 1 \\ -1 \end{bmatrix} = -1\begin{bmatrix} 1 \\ 0 \\ 0 \end{bmatrix} + 1\begin{bmatrix} 0 \\ 1 \\ 0 \end{bmatrix} - 1\begin{bmatrix} 0 \\ 0 \\ 1 \end{bmatrix}$$

$$T\left(\begin{bmatrix} 0 \\ 0 \\ 1 \end{bmatrix}\right) = \begin{bmatrix} 1 \\ 1 \\ 0 \end{bmatrix} = 1\begin{bmatrix} 1 \\ 0 \\ 0 \end{bmatrix} + 1\begin{bmatrix} 0 \\ 1 \\ 0 \end{bmatrix} + (0)\begin{bmatrix} 0 \\ 0 \\ 1 \end{bmatrix}.$$

Forming the matrix as before, we obtain

$$A = \begin{bmatrix} 2 & -1 & 1 \\ 0 & 1 & 1 \\ 1 & -1 & 0 \end{bmatrix}.$$

Using the results of the above example, suppose that we wish to find

$$T\left(\begin{bmatrix} 1 \\ 2 \\ -1 \end{bmatrix}\right).$$

We first express

$$\begin{bmatrix} 1 \\ 2 \\ -1 \end{bmatrix}$$

in the chosen basis $\{I, J, K\}$ and find that the coordinate matrix is

$$\begin{bmatrix} 1 \\ 2 \\ -1 \end{bmatrix}$$

also. We then find

$$A\begin{bmatrix} 1 \\ 2 \\ -1 \end{bmatrix} = \begin{bmatrix} 2 & -1 & 1 \\ 0 & 1 & 1 \\ 1 & -1 & 0 \end{bmatrix}\begin{bmatrix} 1 \\ 2 \\ -1 \end{bmatrix} = \begin{bmatrix} -1 \\ 1 \\ -1 \end{bmatrix}$$

which is the coordinate matrix for

$$T\left(\begin{bmatrix} 1 \\ 2 \\ -1 \end{bmatrix}\right).$$

Thus

$$T\left(\begin{bmatrix} 1 \\ 2 \\ -1 \end{bmatrix}\right) = -1\begin{bmatrix} 1 \\ 0 \\ 0 \end{bmatrix} + 1\begin{bmatrix} 0 \\ 1 \\ 0 \end{bmatrix} - 1\begin{bmatrix} 0 \\ 0 \\ 1 \end{bmatrix}.$$

The method may be extended, of course, to obtain a matrix-multiplication representation for a linear transformation on $\mathcal{M}_{n,1}$. The reader interested in the situation that arises when a basis other than the simple ones we have chosen is used is encouraged to work through Exercises 13–15 below.

Exercises 6.4

In Exercises 1–6, use the basis $\left\{\begin{bmatrix} 1 \\ 0 \end{bmatrix}, \begin{bmatrix} 0 \\ 1 \end{bmatrix}\right\}$ and construct the matrix A of the given linear transformation on $\mathcal{M}_{2,1}$ relative to this basis. Use the matrix to find $T\left(\begin{bmatrix} 2 \\ 3 \end{bmatrix}\right)$ in each case.

1. $T\left(\begin{bmatrix} a \\ b \end{bmatrix}\right) = \begin{bmatrix} a \\ b \end{bmatrix}$

2. $T\left(\begin{bmatrix} a \\ b \end{bmatrix}\right) = \begin{bmatrix} b \\ a \end{bmatrix}$

3. $T\left(\begin{bmatrix} a \\ b \end{bmatrix}\right) = \begin{bmatrix} 2a + b \\ a + 2b \end{bmatrix}$

4. $T\left(\begin{bmatrix} a \\ b \end{bmatrix}\right) = \begin{bmatrix} 0 \\ 3b - a \end{bmatrix}$

5. $T\left(\begin{bmatrix} a \\ b \end{bmatrix}\right) = \begin{bmatrix} a + 2b \\ -2a \end{bmatrix}$

6. $T\left(\begin{bmatrix} a \\ b \end{bmatrix}\right) = \begin{bmatrix} b - a \\ b + a \end{bmatrix}$

In Exercises 7–12, use the basis

$$\left\{\begin{bmatrix} 1 \\ 0 \\ 0 \end{bmatrix}, \begin{bmatrix} 0 \\ 1 \\ 0 \end{bmatrix}, \begin{bmatrix} 0 \\ 0 \\ 1 \end{bmatrix}\right\}$$

and construct the matrix of the given transformation T on $\mathcal{M}_{3,1}$ relative to this basis. Use the matrix to find

$$T\left(\begin{bmatrix} -1 \\ 2 \\ 3 \end{bmatrix}\right)$$

in each case.

7. $T\left(\begin{bmatrix} a \\ b \\ c \end{bmatrix}\right) = \begin{bmatrix} a \\ b \\ c \end{bmatrix}$

8. $T\left(\begin{bmatrix} a \\ b \\ c \end{bmatrix}\right) = \begin{bmatrix} c \\ a \\ b \end{bmatrix}$

9. $T\left(\begin{bmatrix} a \\ b \\ c \end{bmatrix}\right) = \begin{bmatrix} a \\ b \\ a+b+c \end{bmatrix}$

10. $T\left(\begin{bmatrix} a \\ b \\ c \end{bmatrix}\right) = \begin{bmatrix} b+c \\ a+c \\ a+b \end{bmatrix}$

11. $T\left(\begin{bmatrix} a \\ b \\ c \end{bmatrix}\right) = \begin{bmatrix} a+b+c \\ a-b-c \\ a+b-c \end{bmatrix}$

12. $T\left(\begin{bmatrix} a \\ b \\ c \end{bmatrix}\right) = \begin{bmatrix} 3a \\ 2b \\ c \end{bmatrix}$

13. In the text of this section we have hinted that the matrix associated with a transformation depends upon the basis chosen. To illustrate what happens, use the basis $\left\{ U = \begin{bmatrix} 1 \\ 2 \end{bmatrix}, V = \begin{bmatrix} 2 \\ 1 \end{bmatrix} \right\}$ and the transformation T of Example 6.4.1 above and:

   a. Express the T-images of $\begin{bmatrix} 1 \\ 2 \end{bmatrix}$ and of $\begin{bmatrix} 2 \\ 1 \end{bmatrix}$ in the U, V basis.

   b. Construct the matrix B which represents T in the basis $\{U, V\}$. B is the matrix whose columns are the coordinates of $T(U)$ and $T(V)$ found in a.

   c. Find the coordinates of $\begin{bmatrix} 3 \\ 4 \end{bmatrix}$ in the U, V basis.

   d. By matrix multiplication find the U, V coordinates of $T\left(\begin{bmatrix} 3 \\ 4 \end{bmatrix}\right)$ by multiplying the matrix found in b. above by the coordinate matrix found in c. above.

   e. Using the coordinate matrix of $T\left(\begin{bmatrix} 3 \\ 4 \end{bmatrix}\right)$, construct $T\left(\begin{bmatrix} 3 \\ 4 \end{bmatrix}\right)$.

14. a. Find the matrices A of the transformations of Exercises 7–12 relative to the basis

$$\left\{ U = \begin{bmatrix} 0 \\ 1 \\ 1 \end{bmatrix}, V = \begin{bmatrix} 1 \\ 0 \\ 1 \end{bmatrix}, W = \begin{bmatrix} 1 \\ 1 \\ 0 \end{bmatrix} \right\}.$$

   b. Express $X = \begin{bmatrix} -1 \\ 2 \\ 3 \end{bmatrix}$ in terms of the U, V, W basis. Call the coordinate matrix C.

   c. Find the U, V, W coordinates of $T(X)$ by finding AC.

   d. Find $T(X)$ by using its coordinate matrix and the basis vectors.

15. a. Find the matrix A which represents the linear transformation T of Exercise 5 with respect to the basis $\left\{ U = \begin{bmatrix} 1 \\ 2 \end{bmatrix}, V = \begin{bmatrix} 2 \\ 1 \end{bmatrix} \right\}.$

b. Express $\begin{bmatrix} 3 \\ 3 \end{bmatrix} = X$ in terms of the U, V basis. The coordinate matrix C of X is _____.

c. Find the U, V coordinates of $T(X)$ by computing AC.

d. Find $T(X)$ by the formula in Exercise 5 and by using the co-ordinates in c.

6.5 Dot product, length, angle in 2-space

In this section we wish to give a definition for length of a vector and for the angle between two vectors. The setting of our discussion is the 2-dimensional space $\mathscr{M}_{1,2}$ (or $\mathscr{M}_{2,1}$) which we use for the sake of simplicity. The ideas and results presented here may be generalized to 3-space or 30-space or to any n-dimensional space. The interested reader is encouraged to consult the references at the end of this section for a more general outlook.

Let $U = [a, b]$ and $V = [c, d]$ be two vectors in $\mathscr{M}_{1,2}$. We define the **dot product** $U \cdot V$ to be the matrix UV^T. Thus $U \cdot V = [a, b]\begin{bmatrix} c \\ d \end{bmatrix} = [ac + bd]$. (For vectors U, V in $\mathscr{M}_{2,1}$ we define $U \cdot V = U^T V$.) The reader should note that the dot product of two vectors is a 1×1 matrix which has the same properties as a scalar. For this reason we shall not use the matrix symbolism and shall treat $U \cdot V$ as a scalar. Thus the dot product of $[2, -3]$ and $[-3, 1]$ is $2(-3) + (-3)(1) = -9$.

For any vector $U = [a, b]$ we have $U \cdot U \geqslant 0$, and $U \cdot U = 0$ only in case $U = [0, 0]$. To prove this, we simply note that $U \cdot U = UU^T = a^2 + b^2$ and that $a^2 + b^2 > 0$ except when both a and b are 0. The reader should now use the definition of dot product and the familiar matrix properties to prove (see Exercise 3) the first three parts of

THEOREM 6.5.1

For any vectors U, V, W in $\mathscr{M}_{1,2}$ and any scalar c, the dot product satisfies the following properties:

1. $U \cdot V = V \cdot U$;
2. $U \cdot (V + W) = U \cdot V + U \cdot W$;
3. $U \cdot (cV) = c(U \cdot V)$;
4. $U \cdot U \geqslant 0$ and $U \cdot U = 0$ only in case $U = 0$.

We are now prepared to define the **length of a vector** $U = [a, b]$ as

$$(U \cdot U)^{1/2},$$

and will use the symbol $\|U\|$ to stand for the length of U. The reader should note that, by property 4. of Theorem 6.5.1, the length of a vector $U \neq 0$ is always defined and is the (positive) square root of $U \cdot U$. For $U = 0$, we have $\|U\| = 0$. And he should further note that this definition of length is consistent with our representation of vectors as arrows, described in Section 6.1. Thus the arrow corresponding to the vector $[a, b]$ is the arrow from the origin to the point whose horizontal and vertical coordinates are a and b, respectively (Figure 6.5.1).

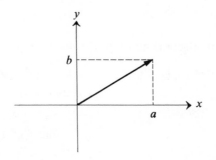

Figure 6.5.1

The length of the arrow representing $[a, b]$ is $(a^2 + b^2)^{1/2}$. We say that a vector of length 1 is a **unit vector** and note that, among many examples, $[1, 0]$, $[0, 1]$, $[1/\sqrt{2}, 1/\sqrt{2}]$ are unit vectors.

Now let us consider two non-zero vectors $U = [a, b]$ and $V = [c, d]$. We define the **angle** between U and V to be the angle θ such that $0° \leqslant \theta \leqslant 180°$ and

$$\cos \theta = \frac{U \cdot V}{\|U\| \, \|V\|}.$$

That this definition of angle between two vectors is consistent with the arrow representation of vectors may be seen as follows. We represent U, V, and θ as in Figure 6.5.2.

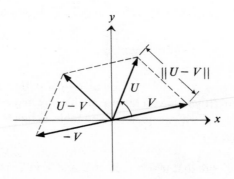

Figure 6.5.2

Note that the length of one dotted line segment is the length of the vector $U - V$. Considering the triangle two sides of which are U and V, we can find from the Law of Cosines that

$$\|U - V\|^2 = \|U\|^2 + \|V\|^2 - 2\|U\|\,\|V\| \cos \theta.$$

Solving this for $\cos \theta$ we have

$$\cos \theta = \frac{\|U\|^2 + \|V\|^2 - \|U - V\|^2}{2\|U\|\,\|V\|} .$$

Now, a little algebra applied to the numerator of this fraction shows that

$$
\begin{aligned}
\|U\|^2 + \|V\|^2 - \|U - V\|^2 &= (a^2 + b^2) + (c^2 + d^2) \\
&\quad - ((a - c)^2 + (b - d)^2) \\
&= a^2 + b^2 + c^2 + d^2 \\
&\quad - (a^2 - 2ac + c^2 + b^2 - 2bd + d^2) \\
&= 2(ac + bd) \\
&= 2(U \cdot V).
\end{aligned}
$$

Thus we may write

$$\cos \theta = \frac{2U \cdot V}{2\,\|U\|\,\|V\|} = \frac{U \cdot V}{\|U\|\,\|V\|} .$$

We shall find this relationship between dot product and angle useful in the next section where we describe some special types of linear transformations.

Example 6.5.1

Find the cosine of the angle θ between the vectors $U = [-1, 2]$ and $V = [1, -1]$. We have $U \cdot V = [-1, 2] \cdot [1, -1] = -1 - 2 = -3$; and $\|U\| = (U \cdot U)^{1/2} = ((-1)^2 + (2)^2)^{1/2} = \sqrt{5}$; and $\|V\| = (V \cdot V)^{1/2} = ((1)^2 + (-1)^2)^{1/2} = \sqrt{2}$. Thus we see that

$$\cos \theta = \frac{U \cdot V}{\|U\|\,\|V\|} = \frac{-3}{\sqrt{5}\sqrt{2}} = -0.9487.$$

The angle θ can now be found by consulting a table of the cosine function. (If you have a table available you may verify that θ is approximately $161.5°$; if you do not have a table, sketch the vectors and measure the angle θ.)

We note that if two vectors U and V in 2-space are at right angles (Figure 6.5.3) then the cosine of the angle between them is 0. Thus we

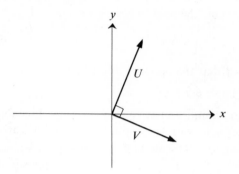

Figure 6.5.3

must have $U \cdot V = 0$. Conversely, if $U \cdot V = 0$, and neither U nor V is
0, so that $\|U\| \neq 0$ and $\|V\| \neq 0$, then the cosine of the angle between
them is 0 and the vectors are at right angles. In this case we use the
terminology that U and V are **perpendicular** or that they are **orthogonal**
to each other. The zero vector is considered to be orthogonal to every
vector.

Example 6.5.2

Consider the vector $U = [1, 2]$. Find a unit vector V which is
orthogonal to U. We first find a vector W which is orthogonal to U as
follows. If $W = [a, b]$, then W is orthogonal to U if and only if $U \cdot W$
$= 0$. Thus we require that $1a + 2b = 0$, and thus we may choose any
values of a and b (other than $a = b = 0$) which satisfy this equation;
for example, we may take $a = 2$, and $b = -1$. Then $W = [2, -1]$ is
orthogonal to U. Now to obtain a vector of unit length which is
orthogonal to U, we simply divide W by $\|W\|$ to obtain

$$V = \frac{1}{\|W\|} W = \frac{1}{\sqrt{5}} W = \left[\frac{2}{\sqrt{5}}, -\frac{1}{\sqrt{5}} \right].$$

Thus V has unit length $\left(\text{since } \|V\| = \left\| \frac{1}{\|W\|} W \right\| = \frac{1}{\|W\|} \|W\| = 1\right)$, and
V is orthogonal to U since by our properties for dot product,

$$V \cdot U = \left(\frac{1}{\|W\|} W \right) \cdot U = \frac{1}{\|W\|} \left(W \cdot U \right) = \frac{1}{\|W\|} (0) = 0.$$

Finally, we say that two vectors $U = [a, b]$ and $V = [c, d]$ have the
same direction if the angle between them is $0°$, and have **opposite
direction** if the angle between them is $180°$. Now the angle between any
vector U and itself is $0°$, so that U has the same direction as U. Since

$\|-U\| = ((-U) \cdot (-U))^{1/2} = ((-1)^2 U \cdot U)^{1/2} = (U \cdot U)^{1/2} = \|U\|$, we may compute the angle θ between U and $-U$ as $180°$ since

$$\cos \theta = \frac{U \cdot (-U)}{\|U\| \|U\|} = \frac{-U \cdot U}{U \cdot U} = -1.$$

Thus $-U$ has the opposite direction to U.

Example 6.5.3

Find a unit vector V_1 with the same direction as $U = [1, 2]$ and a unit vector V_2 with the opposite direction. Clearly, $[1, 2]$ has the same direction as itself, so that we take $V_1 = U/\|U\| = [1, 2]/\|[1, 2]\| = [1/\sqrt{5}, 2/\sqrt{5}]$. Moreover $-[1, 2]$ has opposite direction to $[1, 2]$ so that $V_2 = [-1/\sqrt{5}, -2/\sqrt{5}]$ will suffice. (Are these unique?)

Exercises 6.5

1. Sketch the vectors and find their dot product:
   a. $[1, 0], [0, 2]$ b. $[1, 1], [1, 3]$
   c. $[-1, 2], [1, 1/2]$ d. $[2, 1], [-1, 3]$
   e. $[1, 2], [2, 4]$ f. $[1, 2], [-3, -6]$

2. Find the length of
   a. $[1, 0]$ b. $[2, 1]$
   c. $[-2, 3]$ d. $[3, 4]$
   e. $[-5, 12]$ f. $2[1, 2]$

3. Sketch the vector $U = [3, 4]$ and find a unit vector in the direction of U.

4. Prove Theorem 6.5.1.

5. Find the cosine of the angle between the two vectors in each part of Exercise 1.

6. a. Show that if $[x, y]$ has the same direction as $[1, 2]$ then $[x, y]$ is a scalar multiple of $[1, 2]$.
   b. Show that if $[x, y]$ has the same direction as $[a, b]$ then $[x, y]$ is a scalar multiple of $[a, b]$

7. Find a unit vector which is orthogonal to $[3, 4]$.

Suggested reading

D. Finkbeiner, *Introduction to Matrices and Linear Transformations*, 2nd Ed., W. H. Freeman Co., San Francisco (1966).

R. Johnson, *Linear Algebra*, Prindle, Weber & Schmidt, Boston (1967).

New terms

6.6   Some special linear transformations in 2-space

There are several types of linear transformations which have a special geometric interest. We investigate these in the familiar setting of 2-space.

1. *Stretching or Shrinking Transformations.* If each vector in 2-space is multiplied by a fixed scalar c, then we call the related transformation S a **stretching transformation** if $|c| > 1$ and a **shrinking transformation** if $|c| < 1$. Here $S(U) = cU$, and it is immediate that S is linear, since

$$S(a_1 U_1 + a_2 U_2) = c(a_1 U_1 + a_2 U_2)$$
$$= a_1(cU_1) + a_2(cU_2)$$
$$= a_1 S(U_1) + a_2 S(U_2).$$

The reader may easily verify that the matrix of such a transformation with respect to the usual basis is $\begin{bmatrix} c & 0 \\ 0 & c \end{bmatrix} = c\begin{bmatrix} 1 & 0 \\ 0 & 1 \end{bmatrix}$.

2. *Projection on a Line.* Consider a line L through the origin in 2-space as in Figure 6.6.1, and a vector U. By the **projection** of U on the line L we mean (Figure 6.6.2) a vector V such that the head of V is

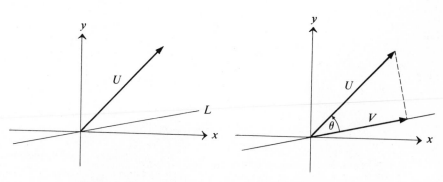

Figure 6.6.1   Figure 6.6.2

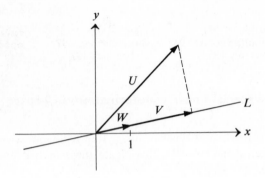

Figure 6.6.3

the foot of the perpendicular to L from the head of U. If we let W be a unit vector in the line L (Figure 6.6.3) then we require that V be a scalar multiple of W, say $V = kW$. Thus the length $\|V\|$ of V must be $|k|$. But from the figure, assuming $\theta \leqslant 90°$, we see that $\|V\| = \|U\| \cos \theta$. Thus we have $V = (\|U\| \cos \theta)W$. But, since $\|W\| = 1$,

$$\cos \theta = \frac{U \cdot W}{\|U\| \, \|W\|} = \frac{U \cdot W}{\|U\|}$$

so that $\|U\| \cos \theta = U \cdot W$. Hence

$$V = (U \cdot W)W.$$

The reader should note that the final formulation is valid also in the case that $90° \leqslant \theta \leqslant 180°$; in that case $\cos \theta$ is negative and the projection V is thus a negative multiple of W, which is as it should be (Figure 6.6.4).

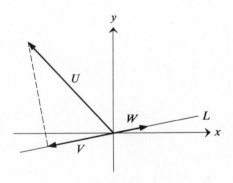

Figure 6.6.4

The transformation P which projects each vector in 2-space on the line L is a linear transformation since, if W is a unit vector in the line L, P is defined as $P(U) = (U \cdot W)W$, a scalar multiple of W. Now let a_1, a_2 be scalars and U_1, U_2 any two vectors. From the definition of P and the properties of the dot product,

$$P(a_1 U_1 + a_2 U_2) = ((a_1 U_1 + a_2 U_2) \cdot W)W$$
$$= (a_1 U_1 \cdot W + a_2 U_2 \cdot W)W$$
$$= (a_1 U_1 \cdot W)W + (a_2 U_2 \cdot W)W$$
$$= a_1((U_1 \cdot W)W) + a_2((U_2 \cdot W)W)$$
$$= a_1 P(U_1) + a_2 P(U_2).$$

Thus P preserves linear combinations and is a linear transformation on 2-space.

Example 6.6.1

Let P be the projection (Figure 6.6.5) on the line L containing the vector $\begin{bmatrix} 1 \\ 1 \end{bmatrix}$.

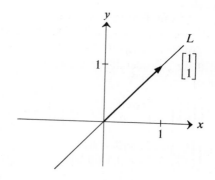

Figure 6.6.5

We should like to find the matrix of P in the usual basis. We take $W = \begin{bmatrix} 1/\sqrt{2} \\ 1/\sqrt{2} \end{bmatrix}$ which is a unit vector in the line L, and compute the effect of P on the basis vectors.

$$P\left(\begin{bmatrix} 1 \\ 0 \end{bmatrix}\right) = \left(\begin{bmatrix} 1 \\ 0 \end{bmatrix} \cdot W\right)W = (1/\sqrt{2})W = \begin{bmatrix} 1/2 \\ 1/2 \end{bmatrix} = 1/2\begin{bmatrix} 1 \\ 0 \end{bmatrix} + 1/2\begin{bmatrix} 0 \\ 1 \end{bmatrix}$$

$$P\left(\begin{bmatrix} 0 \\ 1 \end{bmatrix}\right) = \left(\begin{bmatrix} 0 \\ 1 \end{bmatrix} \cdot W\right)W = (1/\sqrt{2})W = \begin{bmatrix} 1/2 \\ 1/2 \end{bmatrix} = 1/2\begin{bmatrix} 1 \\ 0 \end{bmatrix} + 1/2\begin{bmatrix} 0 \\ 1 \end{bmatrix}.$$

Thus the required matrix is $\begin{bmatrix} 1/2 & 1/2 \\ 1/2 & 1/2 \end{bmatrix}$.

3. *Rotation Through a Fixed Angle.* Suppose that T denotes the transformation that rotates each vector counterclockwise through a fixed angle θ (Figure 6.6.6).

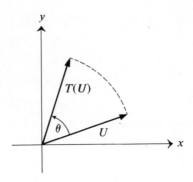

Figure 6.6.6

From Figure 6.6.7, it is clear that T preserves scalar multiples so that $T(cU) = cT(U)$.

Similarly, from Figure 6.6.8, we see that T preserves addition. Now since T preserves sums and scalar products, $T(a_1 U_1 + a_2 U_2) = T(a_1 U_1) + T(a_2 U_2) = a_1 T(U_1) + a_2 T(U_2)$, so that T is linear. Moreover, if we consider the effect of T on the usual basis, we have (Figure 6.6.9)

$$T\left(\begin{bmatrix} 1 \\ 0 \end{bmatrix}\right) = \begin{bmatrix} \cos\theta \\ \sin\theta \end{bmatrix} = \cos\theta \begin{bmatrix} 1 \\ 0 \end{bmatrix} + \sin\theta \begin{bmatrix} 0 \\ 1 \end{bmatrix}$$

$$T\left(\begin{bmatrix} 0 \\ 1 \end{bmatrix}\right) = \begin{bmatrix} \cos(\theta + 90°) \\ \sin(\theta + 90°) \end{bmatrix} = -\sin\theta \begin{bmatrix} 1 \\ 0 \end{bmatrix} + \cos\theta \begin{bmatrix} 0 \\ 1 \end{bmatrix}.$$

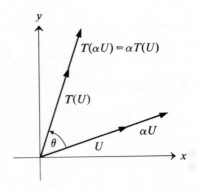

Figure 6.6.7

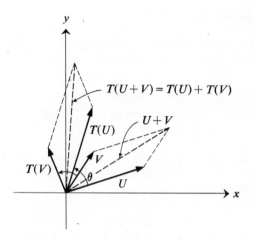

Figure 6.6.8

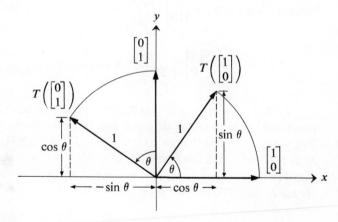

Figure 6.6.9

Thus the matrix of T in the usual basis is

$$\begin{bmatrix} \cos \theta & -\sin \theta \\ \sin \theta & \cos \theta \end{bmatrix}.$$

Such a transformation is called a **rotation transformation,** or simply a **rotation.**

Example 6.6.2

Find, in the usual basis, the matrix of the rotation transformation through the angle $\theta = 60°$. From the foregoing discussion, the matrix is

$$\begin{bmatrix} \cos 60° & -\sin 60° \\ \sin 60° & \cos 60° \end{bmatrix} = \begin{bmatrix} 1/2 & -\sqrt{3}/2 \\ \sqrt{3}/2 & 1/2 \end{bmatrix}.$$

Thus for a typical vector $\begin{bmatrix} a \\ b \end{bmatrix}$ the coordinates of the image of $\begin{bmatrix} a \\ b \end{bmatrix}$ under this rotation are

$$\begin{bmatrix} 1/2 & -\sqrt{3}/2 \\ \sqrt{3}/2 & 1/2 \end{bmatrix}\begin{bmatrix} a \\ b \end{bmatrix} = \begin{bmatrix} a/2 - \sqrt{3}b/2 \\ \sqrt{3}a/2 + b/2 \end{bmatrix}.$$

Since we use the basis $\left\{ \begin{bmatrix} 1 \\ 0 \end{bmatrix}, \begin{bmatrix} 0 \\ 1 \end{bmatrix} \right\}$, the T-image of $\begin{bmatrix} a \\ b \end{bmatrix}$ is

$$(a/2 - \sqrt{3}b/2)\begin{bmatrix} 1 \\ 0 \end{bmatrix} + (\sqrt{3}a/2 + b/2)\begin{bmatrix} 0 \\ 1 \end{bmatrix} = \begin{bmatrix} a/2 - \sqrt{3}b/2 \\ \sqrt{3}a/2 + b/2 \end{bmatrix}.$$

4. *Reflection in a Line.* Let T be the transformation (Figure 6.6.10) which reflects each vector U in the line L. From the figure we see that $T(U)$ has the same length as U. From Figure 6.6.11, we see that $U + T(U)$ lies in the line L; indeed, $U + T(U)$ is just 2 times the projection $P(U)$ on the line L. Thus, if we take W as a unit vector in the line L we have, since $P(U) = (U \cdot W)W$,

$$U + T(U) = 2(U \cdot W)W$$

Hence, solving for $T(U)$, we have the result

$$T(U) = 2(U \cdot W)W - U.$$

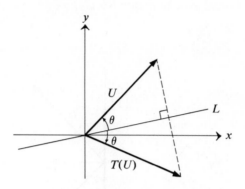

Figure 6.6.10

We may verify from this last result that T is linear. Thus

$$T(a_1 U_1 + a_2 U_2) = 2((a_1 U_1 \cdot W) + (a_2 U_2 \cdot W))W - (a_1 U_1 + a_2 U_2)$$
$$= 2(a_1 U_1 \cdot W)W + 2(a_2 U_2 \cdot W)W - (a_1 U_1 + a_2 U_2)$$
$$= (2(a_1 U_1 \cdot W)W - a_1 U_1)$$
$$+ (2(a_2 U_2 \cdot W)W - a_2 U_2)$$
$$= a_1(2(U_1 \cdot W)W - U_1) + a_2(2(U_2 \cdot W)W - U_2)$$
$$= a_1 T(U_1) + a_2 T(U_2).$$

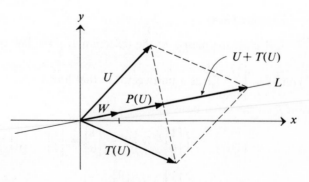

Figure 6.6.11

Example 6.6.3

Calculate the matrix (in the usual basis) of the reflection T in the horizontal axis. In Figure 6.6.12

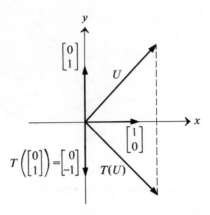

Figure 6.6.12

we see that

$$T\left(\begin{bmatrix}1\\0\end{bmatrix}\right) = \begin{bmatrix}1\\0\end{bmatrix} = 1\begin{bmatrix}1\\0\end{bmatrix} + 0\begin{bmatrix}0\\1\end{bmatrix},$$

$$T\left(\begin{bmatrix}0\\1\end{bmatrix}\right) = \begin{bmatrix}0\\-1\end{bmatrix} = 0\begin{bmatrix}1\\0\end{bmatrix} - 1\begin{bmatrix}0\\1\end{bmatrix}.$$

Thus the matrix of T is $\begin{bmatrix}1 & 0\\0 & -1\end{bmatrix}$. Hence the coordinate matrix of the image of any vector $\begin{bmatrix}a\\b\end{bmatrix}$ is $\begin{bmatrix}1 & 0\\0 & -1\end{bmatrix}\begin{bmatrix}a\\b\end{bmatrix} = \begin{bmatrix}a\\-b\end{bmatrix}$.

Example 6.6.4

Calculate the matrix of the reflection T in the line containing $\begin{bmatrix}1\\1\end{bmatrix}$.

With $W = \begin{bmatrix}1/\sqrt{2}\\1/\sqrt{2}\end{bmatrix}$ as a unit vector in that line, the effect of the reflection T on the usual basis is

$$T\left(\begin{bmatrix}1\\0\end{bmatrix}\right) = 2\left(\begin{bmatrix}1\\0\end{bmatrix} \cdot W\right)W - \begin{bmatrix}1\\0\end{bmatrix} = \begin{bmatrix}1\\1\end{bmatrix} - \begin{bmatrix}1\\0\end{bmatrix} = \begin{bmatrix}0\\1\end{bmatrix}$$

$$= (0)\begin{bmatrix}1\\0\end{bmatrix} + (1)\begin{bmatrix}0\\1\end{bmatrix},$$

$$T\left(\begin{bmatrix} 0 \\ 1 \end{bmatrix}\right) = 2\left(\begin{bmatrix} 0 \\ 1 \end{bmatrix} \cdot W\right)W - \begin{bmatrix} 0 \\ 1 \end{bmatrix} = \begin{bmatrix} 1 \\ 1 \end{bmatrix} - \begin{bmatrix} 0 \\ 1 \end{bmatrix} = \begin{bmatrix} 1 \\ 0 \end{bmatrix}$$

$$= (1)\begin{bmatrix} 1 \\ 0 \end{bmatrix} + (0)\begin{bmatrix} 0 \\ 1 \end{bmatrix}.$$

Thus the matrix of T in the usual basis is $\begin{bmatrix} 0 & 1 \\ 1 & 0 \end{bmatrix}$. Hence the coordinate

matrix of the T-image of any vector $\begin{bmatrix} a \\ b \end{bmatrix}$ is

$$\begin{bmatrix} 0 & 1 \\ 1 & 0 \end{bmatrix}\begin{bmatrix} a \\ b \end{bmatrix} = \begin{bmatrix} b \\ a \end{bmatrix}.$$

Exercises 6.6

1. Let T be the stretching transformation such that $T(V) = 2V$ for each V. Find the matrix A of T in the usual basis $\left\{\begin{bmatrix} 1 \\ 0 \end{bmatrix}, \begin{bmatrix} 0 \\ 1 \end{bmatrix}\right\}$.

2. Let T be the stretching (or shrinking) transformation such that $T(V) = cV$ for each V. Find the matrix A of T in the usual basis.

3. Find the matrix A (with respect to the usual basis) of the projection P on the line L containing the given vector. In each case find the image of a typical vector $\begin{bmatrix} a \\ b \end{bmatrix}$.

   a. $\begin{bmatrix} 1 \\ 0 \end{bmatrix}$ b. $\begin{bmatrix} 0 \\ 1 \end{bmatrix}$ c. $\begin{bmatrix} -1 \\ 1 \end{bmatrix}$

   d. $\begin{bmatrix} -1 \\ -1 \end{bmatrix}$ e. $\begin{bmatrix} 1 \\ 2 \end{bmatrix}$ f. $\begin{bmatrix} 2 \\ 1 \end{bmatrix}$

4. The projection P on the line containing $\begin{bmatrix} 1 \\ 2 \end{bmatrix}$ is a function from 2-space into 2-space. Is P onto 2-space? Is P one-to-one?

5. Find the matrix A of the rotation transformation through the given angle θ and calculate the image of the vector $\begin{bmatrix} 1 \\ 1 \end{bmatrix}$.

   a. $\theta = 30°$ b. $\theta = 45°$ c. $\theta = 240°$
   d. $\theta = 60°$ e. $\theta = 225°$ f. $\theta = 720°$

6. Calculate the matrix A of the rotation through $\theta = 180°$. Is this particular rotational transformation also another kind of transformation?

7. Calculate the matrix A (in the usual basis, of course) of the reflection in the line containing the given vector. In each case find the image under the reflection of a typical vector $\begin{bmatrix} a \\ b \end{bmatrix}$ and the specific vector $\begin{bmatrix} 1 \\ 1 \end{bmatrix}$.

a. $\begin{bmatrix} 0 \\ 1 \end{bmatrix}$ b. $\begin{bmatrix} -1 \\ 1 \end{bmatrix}$ c. $\begin{bmatrix} 1 \\ -1 \end{bmatrix}$

d. $\begin{bmatrix} 1 \\ 2 \end{bmatrix}$ e. $\begin{bmatrix} 3 \\ 1 \end{bmatrix}$ f. $\begin{bmatrix} -1 \\ -1 \end{bmatrix}$.

New terms

stretching transformation, 199   projection, 199   reflection, 204
shrinking transformation, 199   rotation, 204

6.7 Eigenvectors and eigenvalues

Suppose that we are given a linear transformation T on, say, $\mathcal{M}_{3,1}$. We pose the following question: "Which vectors are only stretched or shrunk (in the same or opposite direction) by T?" That is, are there vectors U and scalars c such that $T(U) = cU$? To answer this question let us suppose that the given transformation T is represented in the usual I, J, K basis by the matrix

$$\begin{bmatrix} a_{11} & a_{12} & a_{13} \\ a_{21} & a_{22} & a_{23} \\ a_{31} & a_{32} & a_{33} \end{bmatrix}.$$

Our question may be restated, "Does there exist a scalar c and a vector U, with coordinate matrix

$$\begin{bmatrix} x_1 \\ x_2 \\ x_3 \end{bmatrix},$$

relative to the I, J, K basis, such that

$$\begin{bmatrix} a_{11} & a_{12} & a_{13} \\ a_{21} & a_{22} & a_{23} \\ a_{31} & a_{32} & a_{33} \end{bmatrix} \begin{bmatrix} x_1 \\ x_2 \\ x_3 \end{bmatrix} = c \begin{bmatrix} x_1 \\ x_2 \\ x_3 \end{bmatrix} ?$$

The foregoing matrix equation may be rewritten, using our matrix algebra, as

$$\begin{bmatrix} a_{11} - c & a_{12} & a_{13} \\ a_{21} & a_{22} - c & a_{23} \\ a_{31} & a_{32} & a_{33} - c \end{bmatrix} \begin{bmatrix} x_1 \\ x_2 \\ x_3 \end{bmatrix} = \begin{bmatrix} 0 \\ 0 \\ 0 \end{bmatrix}$$

or more simply as

$$(A - cI_3)X = 0.$$

In this form, the problem may be restated as, "Are there any values of c and any matrices X which satisfy the homogeneous system $(A - cI_3)X = 0$?" Recalling our study of homogeneous linear equations, the answer is that the zero matrix 0 is always such a matrix X, and further, for any scalar c such that the rank of

$$(A - cI_3) = \begin{bmatrix} a_{11} - c & a_{12} & a_{13} \\ a_{21} & a_{22} - c & a_{23} \\ a_{31} & a_{32} & a_{33} - c \end{bmatrix}$$

is less than $n = 3$, there will always be such a non-zero X. On the other hand, if there is a non-zero X satisfying the homogeneous equations, then the corresponding c must be such that the rank of $(A - cI_3)$ is less than 3.

Now, one way of saying that the rank of $(A - cI_3)$ is less than 3, is to say that $\det(A - cI_3) = 0$. If we expand $\det(A - cI_3)$ we obtain a polynomial of degree 3 in the unknown c, and the real roots of this polynomial (remember that we are only working with real numbers here) are the values for which $\det(A - cI_3) = 0$. The polynomial $|A - cI_3|$ is called the **characteristic polynomial** of the matrix A and the equation $|A - cI_3| = 0$ is called the **characteristic equation** of A. The real roots, if any, are called the **eigenvalues** (or characteristic values) of A, or of the original transformation T, represented by A in the I, J, K basis. For any such eigenvalue c_1 the homogeneous system $(A - c_1 I_3)X = 0$ has non-zero solution vectors X, which are called **eigenvectors** (or characteristic vectors) of A corresponding to the eigenvalue c_1. Such eigenvectors may be found, of course, by our standard technique of solving systems of linear equations, once c_1 is known.

Example 6.7.1

Let T be the transformation whose matrix in the usual I, J, K basis is

$$A = \begin{bmatrix} 1 & 1 & 0 \\ 0 & 2 & 1 \\ 0 \cdot & 0 & 3 \end{bmatrix}.$$

Then the characteristic equation of A is

$$\begin{vmatrix} 1-c & 1 & 0 \\ 0 & 2-c & 1 \\ 0 & 0 & 3-c \end{vmatrix} = 0.$$

We expand this determinant by the elements and cofactors of the first row to obtain

$$(1-c)\begin{vmatrix} 2-c & 1 \\ 0 & 3-c \end{vmatrix} - 1\begin{vmatrix} 0 & 1 \\ 0 & 3-c \end{vmatrix} + 0\begin{vmatrix} 0 & 2-c \\ 0 & 0 \end{vmatrix}$$
$$= (1-c)(2-c)(3-c) = 0.$$

Thus the eigenvalues of A are 1, 2, and 3. Corresponding to the eigenvalue 1, we find the eigenvectors by solving the homogeneous system $(A - 1I_3) = 0$. Thus we solve

$$\begin{bmatrix} 0 & 1 & 0 \\ 0 & 1 & 1 \\ 0 & 0 & 2 \end{bmatrix} \begin{bmatrix} x_1 \\ x_2 \\ x_3 \end{bmatrix} = \begin{bmatrix} 0 \\ 0 \\ 0 \end{bmatrix}$$

and find that $x_3 = 0$, $x_2 = 0$, and $x_1 = a$, for any choice of a. Thus the eigenvectors corresponding to the eigenvalue 1 are all those vectors of the form

$$a\begin{bmatrix} 1 \\ 0 \\ 0 \end{bmatrix}.$$

The reader may now easily verify (by matrix multiplication) that

$$A\left(a\begin{bmatrix} 1 \\ 0 \\ 0 \end{bmatrix}\right) = a\begin{bmatrix} 1 \\ 0 \\ 0 \end{bmatrix}.$$

To find the eigenvectors corresponding to the eigenvalue 2, we solve the system $(A - 2I_3)X = 0$ which is

$$\begin{bmatrix} -1 & 1 & 0 \\ 0 & 0 & 1 \\ 0 & 0 & 1 \end{bmatrix} \begin{bmatrix} x_1 \\ x_2 \\ x_3 \end{bmatrix} = \begin{bmatrix} 0 \\ 0 \\ 0 \end{bmatrix}.$$

We find that in this case $x_3 = 0$, $x_2 = a$, $x_1 = a$ for any a. Thus the eigenvectors corresponding to the eigenvalue 2 are of the form

$$a\begin{bmatrix} 1 \\ 1 \\ 0 \end{bmatrix}.$$

Again the reader may now verify that for any a,

$$A\left(a\begin{bmatrix}1\\1\\0\end{bmatrix}\right) = 2a\begin{bmatrix}1\\1\\0\end{bmatrix}.$$

Finally, we leave it to the reader to verify that the eigenvectors corresponding to the eigenvalue 3 are of the form

$$a\begin{bmatrix}1/2\\1\\1\end{bmatrix}.$$

Example 6.7.2

Let A be the transformation whose matrix in the usual basis is $\begin{bmatrix}0 & 2\\-3 & 5\end{bmatrix}$. Then the characteristic polynomial of A is $\begin{vmatrix}-c & 2\\-3 & 5-c\end{vmatrix} = c^2 - 5c + 6$. Hence the eigenvalues of A are 2, 3. To find the eigenvectors corresponding to the eigenvalue 2, we solve

$$\begin{bmatrix}-2 & 2\\-3 & 3\end{bmatrix}\begin{bmatrix}x_1\\x_2\end{bmatrix} = \begin{bmatrix}0\\0\end{bmatrix}$$

and obtain the eigenvectors of the form $a\begin{bmatrix}1\\1\end{bmatrix}$. To find the eigenvectors corresponding to the eigenvalue 3, we solve

$$\begin{bmatrix}-3 & 2\\-3 & 2\end{bmatrix}\begin{bmatrix}x_1\\x_2\end{bmatrix} = \begin{bmatrix}0\\0\end{bmatrix}$$

to obtain eigenvectors of the form $a\begin{bmatrix}2/3\\1\end{bmatrix}$. The reader should verify that the vectors U found above are really eigenvectors by verifying that $AU = cU$.

Example 6.7.3

Let A be the transformation whose matrix in the usual I, J, K basis is

$$\begin{bmatrix}1 & 0 & 0\\0 & 1 & 0\\0 & 0 & 2\end{bmatrix}.$$

Then the characteristic polynomial of A is $(1 - c)(1 - c)(2 - c)$ and its eigenvalues are 1, 1, 2 with 1 as a root of multiplicity 2, or a double root. The eigenvectors corresponding to the eigenvalue 2 are of the form

$$a\begin{bmatrix}0\\0\\1\end{bmatrix}.$$

To find the eigenvectors corresponding to the eigenvalue 1, we solve $(A - 1I_3)X = 0$

$$\begin{bmatrix} 0 & 0 & 0 \\ 0 & 0 & 0 \\ 0 & 0 & 1 \end{bmatrix} \begin{bmatrix} x_1 \\ x_2 \\ x_3 \end{bmatrix} = \begin{bmatrix} 0 \\ 0 \\ 0 \end{bmatrix}$$

to find eigenvectors which are of the form

$$\begin{bmatrix} a \\ b \\ 0 \end{bmatrix}$$

for any choices of a and b. Thus the set of all eigenvectors corresponding to 1 is the set of all linear combinations of

$$\begin{bmatrix} 1 \\ 0 \\ 0 \end{bmatrix} \quad \text{and} \quad \begin{bmatrix} 0 \\ 1 \\ 0 \end{bmatrix},$$

and is thus a subspace of $\mathcal{M}_{3,1}$ of dimension 2.

The concluding remark of the foregoing example is not really so strange. For if E_1 and E_2 are eigenvectors of A corresponding to the eigenvalue c so that $AE_1 = cE_1$ and $AE_2 = cE_2$, then for any scalars a_1 and a_2, $A(a_1 E_1 + a_2 E_2) = a_1 AE_1 + a_2 AE_2 = a_1(cE_1) + a_2(cE_2) = c(a_1 E_1 + a_2 E_2)$ so that $a_1 E_1 + a_2 E_2$ is also an eigenvector of A corresponding to c. Thus the set of all eigenvectors corresponding to a particular eigenvalue is a subspace of the space on which the transformation T, represented by the matrix A, is defined.

Example 6.7.4

Let A be the transformation whose matrix in the usual basis is $\begin{bmatrix} 0 & -1 \\ 1 & 0 \end{bmatrix}$. Then the characteristic polynomial of A is $\begin{vmatrix} -c & -1 \\ 1 & -c \end{vmatrix} = c^2 + 1$. But, fortunately or otherwise, $c^2 + 1$ has no roots (we are only working with real numbers). Thus, no vectors are mapped by A into scalar multiples of themselves (other than the zero vector, which is always mapped to itself). Had our underlying number system (field of scalars) been the complex numbers, then the transformation represented by A would have eigenvalues i and $-i$ (where $i^2 = -1$) and the corresponding eigenvectors are found to be of the forms

$$a\begin{bmatrix} i \\ 1 \end{bmatrix} \quad \text{and} \quad a\begin{bmatrix} -i \\ 1 \end{bmatrix}.$$

The point of our example is, however, that in our discussion, where the scalars are real numbers, some linear transformations simply do not have eigenvectors; thus some transformations alter the direction of every non-zero vector.

We close this section with the statement (but *not* the proof) of a curious theorem, and the application of that theorem to the calculation of the inverse of a matrix.

THEOREM (Hamilton-Cayley)

If A is the $n \times n$ matrix of some transformation T in the usual basis, then A satisfies the characteristic polynomial of A in the following sense: If $a_0 + a_1 c + a_2 c^2 + \cdots + a_n c^n$ is the characteristic polynomial of A, then $a_0 I_n + a_1 A + a_2 A^2 + \cdots + a_n A^n = 0$. (The 0 on the right-hand side of this matrix equation is, of course, the symbol for the $n \times n$ matrix, all of whose elements are zero.).

Example 6.7.5

Let A be the matrix of Example 6.7.2, $\begin{bmatrix} 0 & 2 \\ -3 & 5 \end{bmatrix}$, whose characteristic polynomial is $6 - 5c + c^2$. Then

$$6I_2 - 5A + A^2 = 6\begin{bmatrix} 1 & 0 \\ 0 & 1 \end{bmatrix} - 5\begin{bmatrix} 0 & 2 \\ -3 & 5 \end{bmatrix} + \begin{bmatrix} 0 & 2 \\ -3 & 5 \end{bmatrix}\begin{bmatrix} 0 & 2 \\ -3 & 5 \end{bmatrix}$$

$$= \begin{bmatrix} 6 & 0 \\ 0 & 6 \end{bmatrix} + \begin{bmatrix} 0 & -10 \\ 15 & -25 \end{bmatrix} + \begin{bmatrix} -6 & 10 \\ -15 & 19 \end{bmatrix}$$

$$= \begin{bmatrix} 0 & 0 \\ 0 & 0 \end{bmatrix}.$$

Example 6.7.6

Let T be the transformation whose matrix in the usual basis is $\begin{bmatrix} 1 & 2 \\ 3 & 4 \end{bmatrix}$. The characteristic polynomial is $\begin{vmatrix} 1 - c & 2 \\ 3 & 4 - c \end{vmatrix} = c^2 - 5c - 2$. Then $\begin{bmatrix} 1 & 2 \\ 3 & 4 \end{bmatrix}$ satisfies this polynomial in that

$$A^2 - 5A - 2I_2 = \begin{bmatrix} 1 & 2 \\ 3 & 4 \end{bmatrix}\begin{bmatrix} 1 & 2 \\ 3 & 4 \end{bmatrix} - 5\begin{bmatrix} 1 & 2 \\ 3 & 4 \end{bmatrix} - 2\begin{bmatrix} 1 & 0 \\ 0 & 1 \end{bmatrix}$$

$$= \begin{bmatrix} 7 & 10 \\ 15 & 22 \end{bmatrix} + \begin{bmatrix} -5 & -10 \\ -15 & -20 \end{bmatrix} + \begin{bmatrix} -2 & 0 \\ 0 & -2 \end{bmatrix}$$

$$= \begin{bmatrix} 0 & 0 \\ 0 & 0 \end{bmatrix}.$$

In order to apply this theorem to the calculation of the inverse of a matrix, we make one observation which the reader may verify in the examples presented so far; namely, the constant term a_0 in the characteristic polynomial of A is the determinant of A. That this is true in general is seen from considering that the constant term of any polynomial in c is the value of the polynomial when $c = 0$. The characteristic polynomial of A is $|A - cI_n|$ and its value for $c = 0$ is simply $|A|$.

With this in mind, suppose that A is a matrix which has an inverse (so that $|A| \neq 0$). By the Hamilton-Cayley Theorem, A satisfies its characteristic polynomial, which is, let us say, $a_0 + a_1 c + \cdots + a_n c^n$. Thus

$$a_0 I_n + a_1 A + a_2 A^2 + \cdots + a_n A^n = 0.$$

Multiplying each side of the equation on the left by A^{-1} we obtain

$$a_0 A^{-1} + a_1 I_n + a_2 A + \cdots + a_n A^{n-1} = 0.$$

Since $a_0 = |A| \neq 0$, we solve for A^{-1} and obtain

$$A^{-1} = \frac{-1}{a_0} (a_1 I_n + a_2 A + a_3 A^2 + \cdots + a_n A^{n-1}).$$

Example 6.7.7

For the matrix $A = \begin{bmatrix} 1 & 2 \\ 3 & 4 \end{bmatrix}$, the characteristic polynomial is $c^2 - 5c - 2$. Thus

$$\begin{bmatrix} 1 & 2 \\ 3 & 4 \end{bmatrix}^{-1} = \frac{-1}{-2}\left(-5\begin{bmatrix} 1 & 0 \\ 0 & 1 \end{bmatrix} + \begin{bmatrix} 1 & 2 \\ 3 & 4 \end{bmatrix}\right)$$

$$= \begin{bmatrix} -2 & 1 \\ 3/2 & -1/2 \end{bmatrix}.$$

Exercises 6.7

1. Each of the following matrices is considered as the matrix of a certain linear transformation in the usual $\begin{bmatrix} 1 \\ 0 \end{bmatrix}, \begin{bmatrix} 0 \\ 1 \end{bmatrix}$ basis. Calculate the eigenvalues (if any) and the form of the corresponding eigenvectors.

a. $\begin{bmatrix} 1 & 0 \\ 0 & 0 \end{bmatrix}$ b. $\begin{bmatrix} 1 & 1 \\ 2 & 2 \end{bmatrix}$ c. $\begin{bmatrix} 2 & 0 \\ 0 & 2 \end{bmatrix}$ d. $\begin{bmatrix} 2 & -4 \\ 1 & -3 \end{bmatrix}$

2. Each of the following matrices is considered as the matrix of a linear transformation in the usual

$$\left\{ \begin{bmatrix} 1 \\ 0 \\ 0 \end{bmatrix}, \begin{bmatrix} 0 \\ 1 \\ 0 \end{bmatrix}, \begin{bmatrix} 0 \\ 0 \\ 1 \end{bmatrix} \right\}$$

basis. Calculate the eigenvalues (if any) and the general form for the eigenvectors corresponding to each eigenvalue.

a. $\begin{bmatrix} 1 & 2 & 3 \\ 0 & 2 & 3 \\ 0 & 0 & 3 \end{bmatrix}$
b. $\begin{bmatrix} 4 & 2 & -1 \\ -5 & -3 & 1 \\ 3 & 2 & 0 \end{bmatrix}$

c. $\begin{bmatrix} 1 & 1 & 1 \\ 1 & 1 & 1 \\ 1 & 1 & 1 \end{bmatrix}$
d. $\begin{bmatrix} 5 & -3 & -2 \\ 1 & 1 & -2 \\ 1 & -3 & 2 \end{bmatrix}$

3. Verify the Hamilton-Cayley Theorem for each matrix in Exercise 1.

4. Verify the Hamilton-Cayley Theorem for each matrix in Exercise 2.

5. Find the characteristic polynomial for each of the following matrices and calculate the inverse of each matrix using the Hamilton-Cayley Theorem.

a. $\begin{bmatrix} 1 & 2 \\ 0 & 3 \end{bmatrix}$
b. $\begin{bmatrix} 1 & 2 & 1 \\ 1 & 3 & 1 \\ 2 & 1 & 4 \end{bmatrix}$
c. $\begin{bmatrix} 0 & 1 & 2 \\ 0 & 0 & 2 \\ 2 & 1 & 3 \end{bmatrix}$

New terms

characteristic polynomial, 209   eigenvalues, 209
characteristic equation, 209   eigenvectors, 209

6.8   Quadratic forms

Consider the function f from $R \times R$ into R such that

$$f(x_1, x_2) = a_{11}x_1^2 + a_{12}x_1x_2 + a_{21}x_2x_1 + a_{22}x_2^2.$$

Such a function is said to be a **quadratic function** and the sum on the right-hand side of the equation is called a **quadratic form** in the variables x_1, x_2. Such functions occur frequently in the study of statistics, economics and in several other mathematical applications.

Example 6.8.1

Let

$$f_1(x_1, x_2) = x_1^2 + x_2^2, \qquad f_2(x_1, x_2) = 2x_1^2 - x_1x_2 + 3x_2x_1 + 5x_2^2,$$
$$f_3(x_1, x_2) = -3x_1^2 + x_2x_1 + 4x_2^2$$

and

$$f_4(x_1, x_2) = x_1^2 + 2x_1x_2 + 4x_2x_1 + 9x_2^2.$$

Each of the f_i in Example 6.8.1 is a quadratic function. The significance for us of these functions and their associated forms lies in the fact that these functions can be conveniently represented by matrices. Consider f_1, above, for example. If we let $A_1 = \begin{bmatrix} 1 & 0 \\ 0 & 1 \end{bmatrix}$ and $X = \begin{bmatrix} x_1 \\ x_2 \end{bmatrix}$ and form the matrix product $X^T A_1 X$ we have

$$f_1(X) = X^T A_1 X = [x_1, x_2] \begin{bmatrix} 1 & 0 \\ 0 & 1 \end{bmatrix} \begin{bmatrix} x_1 \\ x_2 \end{bmatrix} = x_1^2 + x_2^2$$

—if we regard the 1×1 matrix $[x_1^2 + x_2^2]$ as the scalar $x_1^2 + x_2^2$. Similarly for f_2,

$$f_2(X) = [x_1, x_2] \begin{bmatrix} 2 & -1 \\ 3 & 5 \end{bmatrix} \begin{bmatrix} x_1 \\ x_2 \end{bmatrix} = X^T A_2 X$$

$$= [2x_1 + 3x_2, -x_1 + 5x_2] \begin{bmatrix} x_1 \\ x_2 \end{bmatrix}$$

$$= (2x_1^2 + 3x_2 x_1) + (-x_1 x_2 + 5x_2^2)$$

$$= 2x_1^2 - x_1 x_2 + 3x_2 x_1 + 5x_2^2,$$

since addition is commutative for the real numbers. The reader should verify that the matrices $A_3 = \begin{bmatrix} -3 & 0 \\ 1 & 4 \end{bmatrix}$ and $A_4 = \begin{bmatrix} 1 & 2 \\ 4 & 9 \end{bmatrix}$ will serve to represent f_3 and f_4. In general, then, the matrix

$$A = \begin{bmatrix} a_{11} & a_{12} \\ a_{21} & a_{22} \end{bmatrix}$$

will serve to represent the quadratic form

$$f(x_1, x_2) = a_{11}x_1^2 + a_{12}x_1 x_2 + a_{21}x_2 x_1 + a_{22}x_2^2$$

in that

$$f(x_1, x_2) = X^T A X.$$

Many terms which we have used for matrices may also be applied to quadratic forms. For example, we speak of the **rank of the quadratic form** $X^T A X$ as being the rank of any symmetric matrix A such that $f(X) = X^T A X$.

It turns out, as you may have suspected, that the matrix which represents a given quadratic form is *not* unique. Consider $f_2(x_1, x_2)$ defined above. We found that $A_2 = \begin{bmatrix} 2 & -1 \\ 3 & 5 \end{bmatrix}$ represented f_2. However,

$B_2 = \begin{bmatrix} 2 & 1 \\ 1 & 5 \end{bmatrix}$ also represents f_2 since

$$X^T B_2 X = [x_1, x_2] \begin{bmatrix} 2 & 1 \\ 1 & 5 \end{bmatrix} \begin{bmatrix} x_1 \\ x_2 \end{bmatrix} = 2x_1^2 + x_2 x_1 + x_1 x_2 + 5x_2^2$$

$$= 2x_1^2 + 2x_1 x_2 + 5x_2^2$$

$$= 2x_1^2 - x_1 x_2 + 3x_2 x_1 + 5x_2^2,$$

a phenomenon which occurs only because of commutativity of multiplication for the real numbers. B_2 is a symmetric matrix. For a given quadratic function f such that

$$f(x_1, x_2) = a_{11}x_1{}^2 + a_{12}x_1x_2 + a_{21}x_2x_1 + a_{22}x_2{}^2,$$

it is always possible to find a symmetric matrix B to represent f. We merely let $b_{11} = a_{11}, b_{22} = a_{22}$ and then average the coefficients of the cross-product terms $x_i x_j$ to let $b_{12} = b_{21} = (a_{12} + a_{21})/2$.

Example 6.8.2

For $f_3(x_1, x_2) = -3x_1{}^2 + x_2 x_1 + 4x_2{}^2$ we have $B_3 = \begin{bmatrix} -3 & 1/2 \\ 1/2 & 4 \end{bmatrix}$.

For $f_4(x_1, x_2) = x_1{}^2 + 2x_1x_2 + 4x_2 x_1 + 9x_2{}^2$, take $B_4 = \begin{bmatrix} 1 & 3 \\ 3 & 9 \end{bmatrix}$.

The rank of B_4 is the rank of the form.

The quadratic function f, the quadratic form $X^T A X$, and any associated matrix A which represents f are said to be **positive definite** if $f(x_1, x_2) \geqslant 0$ for each pair (x_1, x_2) and $f(x_1, x_2) = 0$ only if $x_1 = x_2 = 0$.

Example 6.8.3

$f_1(x_1, x_2) = x_1{}^2 + x_2{}^2$ has the associated symmetric matrix $\begin{bmatrix} 1 & 0 \\ 0 & 1 \end{bmatrix} = A$. Since $f_1 \geqslant 0$ for each pair (x_1, x_2) and $f_1 = 0$ only if $x_1 = x_2 = 0$, then f_1, $X^T A X$, and A are each said to be positive definite.

Example 6.8.4

$f_4(x_1, x_2) = x_1{}^2 + 2x_1x_2 + 4x_2 x_1 + 9x_2{}^2$ has the associated symmetric matrix $A = \begin{bmatrix} 1 & 3 \\ 3 & 9 \end{bmatrix}$. Since we may write $f_4(x_1, x_2) = (x_1 + 3x_2)^2$ it is clear that $f_4 \geqslant 0$. However, it is not true that $f_4 = 0$ implies that $x_1 = x_2 = 0$. For example, $f_4(3, -1) = 0$. Thus f_4 is not positive definite.

The quadratic function f, the quadratic form $X^T A X$, and the associated matrix A are said to be **positive semi-definite** if $f(x_1, x_2) \geqslant 0$ for each pair (x_1, x_2), and there is at least one pair $(x_1, x_2) \neq (0, 0)$ such that $f(x_1, x_2) = 0$. Thus, f_4 above is seen to be positive semi-definite.

Example 6.8.5

$f_3(x_1, x_2) = -3x_1{}^2 + x_2 x_1 + 4x_2{}^2$ is neither positive definite nor positive semi-definite since $f_3(1, 0) = -3 < 0$.

We could just as well have defined the terms **negative definite** and **negative semi-definite** above. To obtain these definitions we merely reverse the inequalities.

Exercises 6.8

1. Find a non-symmetric matrix representation for the following quadratic forms.

   a. $f(x_1, x_2) = x_1^2 + 2x_1x_2 + 3x_2x_1 + 5x_2^2$
   b. $f(x_1, x_2) = 2x_1^2 + x_1x_2 - x_2^2$
   c. $f(x_1, x_2) = 3x_1^2 + x_1x_2 - x_2x_1 + x_2^2$

2. Find a symmetric matrix representation of the functions in Exercise 1.

3. Show that $(X^T A X)^T = X^T A^T X$

4. Find the quadratic form represented by the matrices listed below.

   a. $\begin{bmatrix} 1 & 2 \\ 3 & 4 \end{bmatrix}$
   b. $\begin{bmatrix} 1 & 0 \\ 0 & 2 \end{bmatrix}$
   c. $\begin{bmatrix} -1 & 0 \\ -2 & -3 \end{bmatrix}$

   d. $\begin{bmatrix} 1 & 3 \\ 3 & 1 \end{bmatrix}$
   e. $\begin{bmatrix} 1 & 0 \\ 0 & -2 \end{bmatrix}$

5. State whether the following quadratic forms are positive definite, positive semi-definite, or neither. Justify your answer if f is not positive definite by finding points required by the definition.

   a. $x_1^2 + 3x_2^2$
   b. $x_1^2 + 2x_1x_2 + x_2^2$
   c. $x_1^2 - 2x_2^2$
   d. $-x_1^2 + 2x_2^2$
   e. $x_1^2 - 3x_1x_2 - x_2x_1 + 4x_2^2$

6. On a graph in the plane, draw several of the level curves of the quadratic function $f(x_1, x_2) = x_1^2 + x_2^2$. That is, let $f(x_1, x_2) = 1, 4, 9$, say, and connect the points which satisfy the various equations with a smooth curve.

7. Refer to Exercise 6 and draw level curves for the quadratic function $f(x_1, x_2) = x_1^2 + 2x_2^2$.

New terms

quadratic function, 215
quadratic form, 215
rank of a quadratic form, 216
positive definite, 217

positive semi-definite, 217
negative definite, 218
negative semi-definite, 218

$\begin{bmatrix} 7 \end{bmatrix}$ Linear Programming

7.1 Introduction

One of the most useful applications of the concepts and techniques which we have developed is called **linear programming** (henceforth abbreviated *LP*). Contrary to what you may be thinking, the term "programming", as used here, does not refer to the programming of a computer. The term is used in the economic sense of "allocation" or "programming" of scarce resources as the examples in this section will show. The adjective "linear" refers to the linear equations and functions which arise in the study of many such problems. We should not, however, play down the importance of the computer as it pertains to LP. It was the advent of high-speed computing systems that kindled the great interest in this subject that has arisen in the past 25 years or so. Although much of the underlying theory has been known for some time, it was not until 1947 that George B. Dantzig, working on a United States Air Force project, introduced an efficient computational algorithm for the solution of a large class of these problems. This technique, known as the simplex algorithm, still requires the use of the computer to solve meaningful business, industrial, and military problems.

In this section we shall formulate several problems which are classified as LP problems. In succeeding sections we shall investigate the geometry of LP problems and develop the simplex algorithm in some detail. We shall show why it is so important that the problems be "linear" in nature.

Example 7.1.1

Suppose that a university wishes to charter a sufficient number of aircraft to transport 500 students to an athletic event. Two types of aircraft are available. A_1 carries 50 passengers, has a crew of 6 including 3 hostesses, and will cost \$2000 for the trip. A_2 carries 100 passengers, has a crew of 8 with 4 hostesses, and will cost \$5000 for the trip. On the day in question, only 24 hostesses are available. How many of each type of aircraft should be chartered to perform the airlift at the minimum cost?

The data may be compactly portrayed as in Table 7.1.1.

	Totals	A_1	A_2
Cost	minimize	\$2000	\$5000
Passengers	500	50	100
Hostesses	24	3	4

Table 7.1.1

If we let x_i denote the number of aircraft of type i to be chartered, then we may describe the problem algebraically as follows:

Find x_1, x_2 such that

1. $x_i \geqslant 0, i = 1, 2$
2. $50x_1 + 100x_2 \geqslant 500$ (students)
3. $3x_1 + 4x_2 \leqslant 24$ (hostesses) and
4. $2000x_1 + 5000x_2 = f(x_1, x_2) = z$ is minimized.

As is the case in most allocation problems, negative values of the variables do not make sense, so **non-negativity restrictions** of the form $x_i \geqslant 0$ are included. Constraint 2 is included to insure that the number of aircraft chartered is sufficient to carry the required number of students. Constraint 3 prevents the number of hostesses required from being greater than the number available. $z = f(x_1, x_2)$ is called the **ob-**

jective function or criterion function or cost function which is to be minimized.

Example 7.1.2

Consider the following problem—also one of interest to charter airlines.

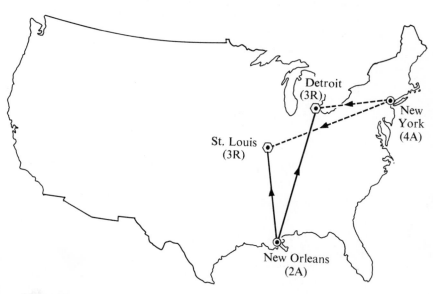

Figure 7.1.1

XYZ Airline has 6 aircraft, 2 of which are at New Orleans and the other 4 at New York. 6 charter loads are to be picked up—3 at St Louis and 3 at Detroit. Each charter load is to be picked up by a different aircraft. Find the number of aircraft which should be sent to each pick-up site in order to minimize the total flight time involved in the pick-up deployment. The various flight times, available aircraft, and required aircraft are depicted in Table 7.1.2.

Flight Time	Detroit	St. Louis	Aircraft Available
New York	2	3	4
New Orleans	3	2	2
Aircraft Required	3	3	

Table 7.1.2

If we let x_1 denote the number of aircraft to be sent from New York to Detroit, x_2 the number to be sent from New York to St. Louis, x_3 the number from New Orleans to Detroit and x_4 the number to be sent from New Orleans to St. Louis, then we may phrase the problem as follows:

Find x_1, x_2, x_3, x_4, each greater than or equal to zero, such that

1. $x_1 + x_2 \qquad\qquad = 4$

2. $\qquad\qquad x_3 + x_4 = 2$

3. $x_1 \qquad + x_3 \qquad = 3$

4. $\qquad x_2 \qquad + x_4 = 3$ and

$z = f(x_1, x_2, x_3, x_4) = 2x_1 + 3x_2 + 3x_3 + 2x_4$ is a minimum.

In Example 7.1.2, $f(x_1, x_2, x_3, x_4) = 2x_1 + 3x_2 + 3x_3 + 2x_4$ is the objective or criterion function. It represents the total flight time involved in the deployment. Equation 1 represents a constraint on the choices available for the x_i and simply restricts us to choices of values for these variables that require the total number of aircraft sent from New York to be 4, since all four are needed to complete the deployment. Similarly, constraint 2 reflects a requirement on the number of aircraft departing New Orleans. Constraints 3 and 4 are equations which insure that the number of aircraft arriving at Detroit and St. Louis, respectively, are sufficient to handle the requirements there. Negative values of the variables do not make sense, so the non-negativity restrictions are included.

If we let $C = [2, 3, 3, 2]$,

$$A = \begin{bmatrix} 1 & 1 & 0 & 0 \\ 0 & 0 & 1 & 1 \\ 1 & 0 & 1 & 0 \\ 0 & 1 & 0 & 1 \end{bmatrix}, \qquad X = \begin{bmatrix} x_1 \\ x_2 \\ x_3 \\ x_4 \end{bmatrix}, \qquad \text{and} \qquad R = \begin{bmatrix} 4 \\ 2 \\ 3 \\ 3 \end{bmatrix},$$

then we may phrase the problem of Example 7.1.2 in matrix notation:

Minimize $z = CX$ such that

$AX = R$ and

$X \geqslant 0$.

Here we have used the notational device $X \geqslant 0$ to mean that each component of X is non-negative. For any two matrices A and B, we shall say that $A \leqslant B$ or $B \geqslant A$ if and only if $a_{ij} \leqslant b_{ij}$ for all i and j.

We now consider an industrial problem which falls into the LP category.

Example 7.1.3

Company Z blends two grades of gasoline, grade A and grade B, to make two intermediate types of gasoline, regular and premium. Each gallon of regular gasoline requires 0.2 gallons of grade A and 0.8 gallons of grade B. Each gallon of premium gasoline requires 0.8 gallons of grade A and 0.2 gallons of grade B. The company makes 2 cents profit on each gallon of regular gasoline and 3 cents on each gallon of premium gasoline that it sells. If it has only 1000 gallons of each basic grade of gasoline, how much of each type of gasoline should be blended in order to maximize the company's profit, assuming that all can be sold?

In this case we let x_1 denote the amount of regular gasoline and x_2 denote the amount of premium gasoline to be blended from the basic grades on hand. Then we formulate the problem as follows:

Find x_1, x_2 such that $x_i \geqslant 0$ and

$$0.2x_1 + 0.8x_2 \leqslant 1000 \qquad \text{(grade } A)$$
$$0.8x_1 + 0.2x_2 \leqslant 1000 \qquad \text{(grade } B)$$

and

$$z = f(x_1, x_2) = 2x_1 + 3x_2 \qquad \text{is maximized.}$$

In matrix format, letting

$$C = [2, 3], \qquad X = \begin{bmatrix} x_1 \\ x_2 \end{bmatrix}, \qquad A = \begin{bmatrix} 0.2 & 0.8 \\ 0.8 & 0.2 \end{bmatrix}, \qquad R = \begin{bmatrix} 1000 \\ 1000 \end{bmatrix}$$

we wish to

Find $X \geqslant 0$ such that $AX \leqslant R$ and $z = f(x_1, x_2) = CX$ is maximized.

In this problem the first constraint insures that the total amount of grade A base to be utilized is not greater than the amount available. The second constraint performs the same function for the grade B base. $f(x_1, x_2) = CX$ represents the company's profit for a given allocation of the available basic gasolines.

　　The following, a small example of a problem historically called the "diet problem," provides another example of an allocation problem which may easily be put into LP form.

Example 7.1.4

　　The dining hall dietician wishes to provide at least 3 units of vitamin A and 4 units of vitamin B per serving. She has two choices of foods, F_1 and F_2, which contain vitamins A and B in the amounts shown in the table below.

Vitamin

Food	A	B
F_1	1 unit/oz.	1 unit/oz.
F_2	1 unit/oz.	2 unit/oz.

Table 7.1.3

　　If we let x_1 denote the number of ounces of F_1 per serving to be used and x_2 denote the number of ounces of F_2 per serving, then

$$1x_1 + 1x_2 \geqslant 3$$

is a constraint guaranteeing a sufficient amount of vitamin A per serving, and

$$1x_1 + 2x_2 \geqslant 4$$

is a constraint insuring a sufficient amount of vitamin B.

　　As in most dining halls, the manager wishes to provide this portion of the meal for as low a cost as possible. Suppose that F_1 costs 4 cents an ounce and that F_2 costs 5 cents an ounce. What is the price of the minimum cost serving satisfying the minimum vitamin requirements? The cost of serving x_1 ounces of F_1 and x_2 ounces of F_2 is

$$z = f(x_1, x_2) = 4x_1 + 5x_2.$$

We thus have another type of linear programming problem:

Find x_1, x_2, each non-negative, such that

$$1x_1 + 1x_2 \geqslant 3 \quad \text{and}$$
$$1x_1 + 2x_2 \geqslant 4 \quad \text{and}$$
$$z = f(x_1, x_2) = 4x_1 + 5x_2 \quad \text{is minimized.}$$

In matrix format we wish to

Find $X \geq 0$ such that $AX \geq R$ and $z = CX$ is minimized.

Here

$$A = \begin{bmatrix} 1 & 1 \\ 1 & 2 \end{bmatrix}, \quad X = \begin{bmatrix} x_1 \\ x_2 \end{bmatrix}, \quad R = \begin{bmatrix} 3 \\ 4 \end{bmatrix}, \quad \text{and} \quad C = [4, 5].$$

These examples should be sufficient to acquaint the reader with some of the types of problems which lend themselves to LP formulation. Examples 7.1.1 and 7.1.2 are of special interest. For practical purposes, the only values for the variables which would make sense would have to be non-negative *integers*. A solution in Example 7.1.2 of the form $X^T = [x_1, x_2, x_3, x_4] = [3/2, 5/2, 3/2, 1/2]$, calling for 3/2 aircraft to be sent from New York to Detroit would not be of much help to the operations officer in charge. Problems of this nature are called **Integer Programming** (IP) problems. Some IP problems can be solved by special algorithms requiring even less time than the "**continuous**" or non-integer problems. The general IP problem, although one of outstanding practical significance, still presents computational difficulties that researchers are trying to overcome. As recently as 1958 and 1960, Dr. Ralph Gomory presented two very interesting and intellectually satisfying algorithms for the solution of such problems (see Suggested Reading). Computer programs utilizing these algorithms have met with varying degrees of success. While some problems have been very readily solved, others take inordinate amounts of expensive computer time. For this reason, researchers have been looking at the problem from other points of view in an attempt to find methods of greater computational reliability.

The problems of Examples 7.1.3 and 7.1.4 are "*continuous*" LP problems; that is, they are of a type such that any non-negative values of the variables will suffice. Except when we note otherwise, this is the type of problem in which we will be interested.

Exercises 7.1

Formulate Exercises 1—6 as LP problems.
1. A company makes two products—P_1 and P_2. The manufacturing process for P_1 requires 5 minutes on machine M_1, 10 minutes on machine M_2, and 3 minutes on machine M_3. Product P_2, however,

requires 4 minutes on M_1, 8 minutes on M_2, and 6 minutes on M_3. The net profit on each unit of P_1 is \$4.00 while each unit of P_2 nets \$3.00. If there are 480 minutes of machine time available on M_1, 960 minutes on M_2, and 480 on M_3, how many units of each of P_1, P_2 should be made in order to maximize the firm's profit over the time period involved?

2. A furniture manufacturer makes chairs of types F_1, F_2 and tables of types F_3, F_4, F_5. Each item must pass through the wood-working shop and then go to the finishing department. The time unit requirements for each piece and the time available in each department are shown below, along with the unit profit on each piece. Assuming that orders which must be filled are on hand for $10F_1$ and $6F_4$, how many of each should be produced in order to maximize the firm's profit?

Furniture Dept.	F_1	F_2	F_3	F_4	F_5	Time Available
Woodworking	2	3	2	4	5	200
Finishing	1	2	3	4	3	160
Profit/unit	10	20	25	30	30	

3. A supervisor wishes to assign each of his 3 men to one of 3 jobs in order to make the time required to accomplish all 3 jobs as small as possible. The time required for each man to complete each job is known and is recorded below.

Job Man	1	2	3
1	3	5	4
2	4	4	4
3	4	6	5

Let $x_{ij} = 1$ if man i is assigned to job j, and 0 otherwise. Express the problem as an LP problem with 6 constraints (not including non-negativity restrictions). You should have 1 constraint for each man (to insure that he has a job) and 1 constraint for each job.

4. A truck is to be loaded with cases of products P_1, P_2 which it carries for c_1, c_2 dollars per case. A case of P_i has volume v_i and weight w_i. The truck limitations on freight weight and volume are

W and V, respectively. Find the number of cases of each type which should be carried in order to maximize net revenue.

5. A pharmaceutical firm makes 4 types of capsules, c_1, c_2, c_3, c_4. Each of the capsules uses ingredients D_1, D_2. The amounts of each of the ingredients required to make 1 unit of each type of capsule are shown in the table, along with the unit profit for each type of capsule, and the ingredient availability.

Ingredient \ Capsule	c_1	c_2	c_3	c_4	Units Available
D_1	3	6	7	8	10,000
D_2	2	5	8	10	14,000
Unit Profit	3	4	6	8	

Assuming that at least 250 units of c_2 and 500 units of c_3 must be produced, find the production plan which will maximize the firm's profit.

6. A chemical manufacturer has 3 warehouses (W_i) and 4 retail outlets (S_j) in a given district. A certain chemical is shipped by rail at a cost of C dollars per pound-mile. The amount of the chemical on hand at the various warehouses and that required at the various outlets is shown in the table, along with the distances between the various points. Find the amounts which should be shipped from W_i to S_j in order to minimize the total shipping cost.

W_i \ S_j	S_1	S_2	S_3	S_4	Available
W_1	d_{11}	d_{12}	d_{13}	d_{14}	a_1
W_2	d_{21}	d_{22}	d_{23}	d_{24}	a_2
W_3	d_{31}	d_{32}	d_{33}	d_{34}	a_3
Required	b_1	b_2	b_3	b_4	

7. Express the LP problem of Exercise 1 in matrix format.

8. Express the LP problem of Exercise 3 in matrix format.

9. A men's shop wishes to purchase the following quantities of two types of men's suits.

Type	1	2
Number	200	300

Bids have been received from 3 different wholesalers, W_1, W_2, W_3 who have agreed to supply not more than the number of suits indicated below

$$
\begin{array}{ll}
W_1 & 200 \\
W_2 & 250 \\
W_3 & 150
\end{array}
$$

The owner has estimated that his profit/suit sold from each of the W_i is given by the following table.

| | Suit | |
Wholesaler	1	2
W_1	30	40
W_2	38	35
W_3	40	36

Let x_{ij} denote the number of suits of type i to be bought from wholesaler j and set up an LP problem to maximize the owner's profit.

10. A charter outfit has two types of aircraft, A_1 and A_2 available. A firm wishes to rent a sufficient number of aircraft to transport 200 tons of equipment. A_1 can carry 20 tons while A_2 can carry only 10. A_1 rents for \$400 and needs 4000 gallons of fuel for the round trip. A_2 rents for \$300 and needs 1000 gallons of fuel for the trip. Assuming that each aircraft makes only 1 round-trip and that only 30,000 gallons of fuel are available, set up an LP problem to perform the move at minimum rental cost.

Suggested reading

M. M. Balinksi, "Integer Programming: Methods, Uses, Computation," *Management Science*, Vol. 12, No. 3 (November, 1965) pp. 253–312.

C. R. Carr, and C. W. Howe, *Quantitative Decision Procedures in Management and Economics*, McGraw-Hill, New York (1964).

A. Charnes, and W. W. Cooper, *Management Models and Industrial Applications of Linear Programming*, Vols. I–II, John Wiley & Sons, New York (1961).

G. B. Dantzig, *Linear Programming and Extensions*, Princeton University Press, Princeton, N.J. (1963).

S. I. Gass, *Linear Programming*, McGraw-Hill, New York (1964).

R. E. Gomory, "An Algorithm for Integer Solutions to Linear Programs," Princeton-IBM Mathematics Research Project, Technical Report No. 1 (November 17, 1958).

R. E. Gomory, "All-Integer Integer Programming Algorithm" Report RC-189, IBM Research Center, Yorktown Heights, N.Y. (January 29, 1960).

G. Hadley, *Linear Programming*, Addison-Wesley, Reading, Mass. (1962).

New terms

linear programming, 219
non-negativity restrictions, 220
objective function, 220–221
criterion function, 221

cost function, 221
integer programming, 225
continuous LP problem, 225

7.2   Geometrical solution of an LP problem

We now examine a problem that is algebraically similar to Example 7.1.3. We shall call this problem "problem P" and shall refer to it many times throughout the remainder of this chapter. Here, we solve it geometrically and use it as a vehicle to illustrate some of the special properties of LP problems. We depend upon your intuitive understanding of the terms which we introduce in this section. In later sections we shall obtain a general formulation of the LP problem and define the terms more precisely.

Problem P: Find x_1, x_2 such that

1. $x_i \geqslant 0, i = 1, 2$
2. $\begin{cases} 2x_1 + x_2 \leqslant 6 \\ x_1 + x_2 \leqslant 4 \end{cases}$
3. $z = f(x_1, x_2) = 5x_1 + 3x_2$ is maximized.

We solve problem P in 3 steps.

1. Out of all points (x_1, x_2) in the x_1, x_2-plane, we find those which have the property that $x_1 \geqslant 0$ and $x_2 \geqslant 0$, and call this set S_1.

2. We then determine S_2, the set of all points (x_1, x_2) in the x_1, x_2-plane that satisfy the remaining inequality constraints.

3. Out of $S_3 = S_1 \cap S_2$ we pick that point $(\bar{x}_1, \bar{x}_2)$, or points, at which $f(x_1, x_2)$ takes on its largest value, if there is one.

Let us first consider the x_1, x_2-plane as shown in Figure 7.2.1.

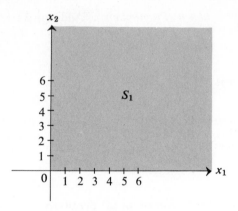

Figure 7.2.1

We see that $x_1 \geqslant 0$ for all points lying on or to the right of the x_2 axis. Similarly $x_2 \geqslant 0$ for all points lying above or on the x_1 axis. Therefore, the set of points $S_1 = \{(x_1, x_2) \mid x_1 \geqslant 0, x_2 \geqslant 0\}$ is the set of points in the shaded first quadrant as shown, including the points on the non-negative x_1 and x_2 axes.

In step 2 we need to determine S_2, the set of points which satisfy both $2x_1 + x_2 \leqslant 6$ and $x_1 + x_2 \leqslant 4$. Let us first determine $\{(x_1, x_2) \mid 2x_1 + x_2 \leqslant 6\}$. We know (Figure 7.2.2) that $\{(x_1, x_2) \mid 2x_1 + x_2 = 6\}$

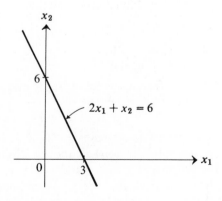

Figure 7.2.2

forms a straight line in the x_1, x_2-plane. This straight line divides the x_1, x_2-plane into two separate or disjoint subsets, namely $P_1 = \{(x_1, x_2) \mid 2x_1 + x_2 < 6\}$ and $P_2 = \{(x_1, x_2) \mid 2x_1 + x_2 > 6\}$. Our only problem is to decide which side of the line is P_1 and which is P_2. The answer is quickly provided, however, by picking any point not on the line and testing it to see in which set it belongs. The origin $(0, 0)$ is usually a good point to test. Since $2(0) + 1(0) = 0 < 6$, $(0, 0)$ lies in P_1, so we know that P_1 is the shaded half-plane in Figure 7.2.3.

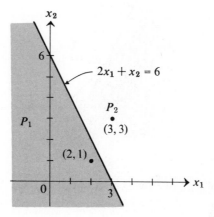

Figure 7.2.3

Similarly we use the line $x_1 + x_2 = 4$ to determine $P_3 = \{(x_1, x_2) \mid x_1 + x_2 \leqslant 4\}$, and find that P_3 is the shaded portion of Figure 7.2.4.

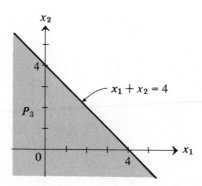

Figure 7.2.4

$S_2 = \{(x_1, x_2) \mid 2x_1 + x_2 \leqslant 6 \text{ and } x_1 + x_2 \leqslant 4\}$ is thus the intersection of P_1 and P_3. In Figure 7.2.5, we show $S_2 = P_1 \cap P_3$ geometrically by exhibiting both lines on the same plane. The darkly-shaded region represents $S_2 = P_1 \cap P_3$ while the lightly-shaded regions represent

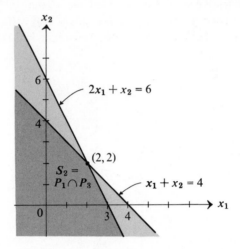

Figure 7.2.5

portions of P_1 and P_3 which do not lie in both. We obtain the point of intersection of the two lines by solving the two equations by Gauss-Jordan reduction.

In step 3, we first find $S_1 \cap S_2$ by eliminating all points of S_2 not in S_1, the first quadrant, and obtain S_3 in Figure 7.2.6. S_3 is the set of all allowable or feasible points for an answer to our problem. Any point (x_1, x_2) in S_3 has the property that it satisfies both the non-

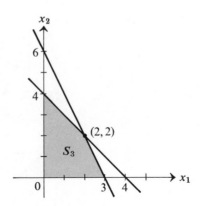

Figure 7.2.6

negativity restrictions and the other inequality constraints. The remaining problem is to pick that point $(\bar{x}_1, \bar{x}_2)$ or points in S_3 which provides the *best* answer; that is, that point which maximizes the function $f(x_1, x_2) = 5x_1 + 3x_2$.

Let us arbitrarily pick some points in S_3 and compute their functional values. The results of such a computation are shown in Table 7.2.1 below where, for example, we computed $f(1, 0) = 5(1) + 3(0) = 5$ and $f(1, 1) = 5(1) + 3(1) = 8$.

x_1	0	1	2	3	0	0	0	0	2	1	2	1
x_2	0	0	0	0	1	2	3	4	2	1	1	3
$f(x_1, x_2)$	0	5	10	15	3	6	9	12	16	8	13	14

Table 7.2.1

It would clearly be a never-ending process to try to compute the maximum value of f by computing $f(x_1, x_2)$ for every point in S_3. Another method equivalent to such an enumeration must be found.

We begin to develop an equivalent procedure by examining the objective function f. For each value of the constant a, the function $f(x_1, x_2) = 5x_1 + 3x_2 = a$ represents a straight line in the x_1, x_2-plane. At each point on this fixed line, $f(x_1, x_2) = a$. Such lines for $a = 0$, 5, 10, 16, 18 are shown superimposed on S_3 in Figure 7.2.7.

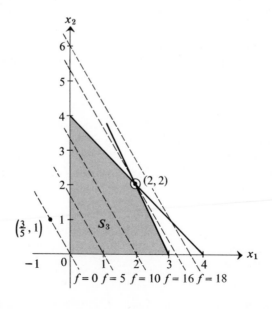

Figure 7.2.7

To draw the line $z = f(x_1, x_2) = 5x_1 + 3x_2 = 0$, we find two points on the line, say $(0, 0)$ and $(-3/5, 1)$, for example, by choosing a simple value for one of the variables and solving for the other. We know from our previous table that $(1, 0)$ is on the line $z = 5x_1 + 3x_2 = 5$. Letting $x_1 = 0$ we find that $(0, 5/3)$ is also on this line. Similarly, $(2, 0)$ and $(0, 10/3)$ are on the line $z = 5x_1 + 3x_2 = 10$; $(2, 2)$ and $(0, 16/3)$ are on the line $z = 5x_1 + 3x_2 = 16$; and $(18/5, 0)$ and $(0, 6)$ are on the line $z = 5x_1 + 3x_2 = 18$. We use these points to plot the graphs of the lines. The figure shows that each of these lines has the same slope which we compute as $-5/3$ by putting the equation in the so-called slope-intercept form:

$$x_2 = \frac{-5x_1 + a}{3} = \frac{-5}{3}x_1 + \frac{a}{3}.$$

In this form we see that $-5/3$ is the slope of each of the lines and that for any particular value of a, the x_2 intercept is $a/3$, which we obtain by letting $x_1 = 0$.

Examination of the same graph shows that $z = f(x_1, x_2)$ takes on its maximum value in S_3 at a unique point, namely $(2, 2)$, and that the maximum value of z within S_3 is 16. (We shall refer to this result many times in the sequel.) To establish the latter, it may be helpful to think of taking a movable line through the origin with slope $-5/3$ and moving it, parallel to itself, in the direction of increasing z as far as one can go while still encountering points within S_3. When you are forced to stop, you have found the optimum point (or points). In a minimization problem you would merely move as far as possible in the direction of decreasing z.

Having obtained the solution point for our problem, let us consider some ideas which will prove to be of interest later on.

1. The optimum value of z occurred at a point on the boundary of S_3.

2. Even more specifically, the optimum value of z occurred at a corner point of the boundary of S_3.

3. S_3 has the interesting geometrical property that if you choose any two points in S_3, the entire line segment connecting the two points lies in S_3.

To show that not all functions and plane point sets have these properties, consider the following examples.

Example 7.2.1

Suppose that we have S_3 as shown in Figure 7.2.8 and that we wish to find the point $(\bar{x}_1, \bar{x}_2)$ in S_3 which minimizes the so-called quadratic function

$$z = f(x_1, x_2) = (x_1 - 1)^2 + (x_2 - 1)^2.$$

As a sum of squares, this function can never be negative. $f(1, 1) = 0$,

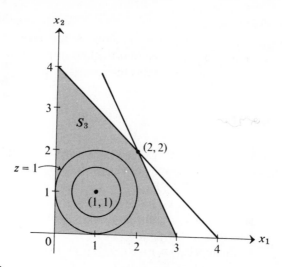

Figure 7.2.8

and $f(x_1, x_2) > 0$ at any other point in the plane. Two of the equal-value circles of z are shown. An equal-value circle has the property that z is the same value at each point on it. For example, $z = 1$ at each point on the outer circle. The function takes on its minimum value 0 at $(1, 1)$, an interior point of S_3—not a boundary point. Thus, for this non-linear function, we could not claim that any optimal solution, or even that at least one optimal solution, had to lie on the boundary of the region determined by the constraints.

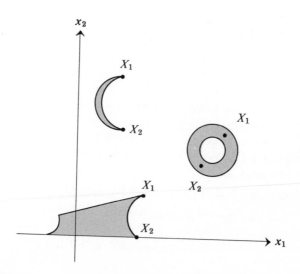

Figure 7.2.9

Example 7.2.2

Figure 7.2.9 shows three regions in the plane, each of which contains 2 points X_1, X_2 such that the line segments joining the points do not lie entirely in the regions themselves.

Exercises 7.2

1. a. Let $P_1 = \{(x_1, x_2) \mid x_1 + x_2 \leqslant 6\}$. Draw a graph to show P_1.
   b. On the same graph show $P_2 = \{(x_1, x_2) \mid 2x_1 + x_2 \leqslant 8\}$.
   c. Show $S_2 = P_1 \cap P_2$.
   d. Let $S_1 = \{(x_1, x_2) \mid x_1 \geqslant 0$ and $x_2 \geqslant 0\}$. Show $S_1 \cap S_2 = S_3$.
   e. By solving the appropriate equations simultaneously determine the corner points of S_3.
   f. Evaluate $f(x_1, x_2) = x_1 + 2x_2$ at each corner point, going clockwise from the origin.
   g. Evaluate f at interior points $(1, 1)$, $(1, 3)$, $(3, 1)$, and at the boundary point $(1, 5)$.

2. For each value of a, the equation $f(x_1, x_2) = 3x_1 + 2x_2 = a$ represents a _____ _____ in the plane. As a varies we generate a family of _____ straight lines in the plane. If we desire to move to one of these lines with a higher value of f we move in a direction _____ to that in which we would move if we desired to decrease f.

3. Consider the following LP problem: Find x_1, x_2 such that $x_i \geqslant 0$ and
   $$2x_1 + \ x_2 \leqslant 6$$
   $$x_1 + 2x_2 \leqslant 6$$
   and $f(x_1, x_2) = x_1 + x_2$ is maximized.
   a. Find $S_1 = \{(x_1, x_2) \mid x_1 \geqslant 0$ and $x_2 \geqslant 0\}$ graphically.
   b. Find $S_2 = \{(x_1, x_2) \mid 2x_1 + x_2 \leqslant 6$ and $x_1 + 2x_2 \leqslant 6\}$.
   c. Find $S_3 = S_1 \cap S_2$.
   d. On your graph show $\{(x_1, x_2) \mid f(x_1, x_2) = x_1 + x_2 = 2\}$.
   e. Find the point in S_3 at which f is a maximum.
   f. Find the point in S_3 at which f is a minimum.
   g. Find the point or points in S_3 at which $g(x_1, x_2) = x_1 + 2x_2$ is maximized.

4. Solve Exercise 1 of Section 7.1 graphically.

5. Consider the LP problem:

Find x_1, x_2 such that $x_i \geqslant 0$ and
$$x_1 + 2x_2 \geqslant 3$$

$$2x_1 + x_2 \geqslant 3$$
$$-x_1 + x_2 \leqslant 1$$
and $f(x_1, x_2) = x_1 + x_2$ is minimized.

a. Show, on a graph, the set of points S which satisfy the non-negativity restrictions and all of the constraints.
b. S is an infinite or unbounded region, the corner points of which are _____, _____, and _____.
c. Evaluate f at the corner points of S.
d. Show $\{(x_1, x_2) \,|\, f(x_1, x_2) = 3\}$ graphically.
e. The "best" point in S is _____ at which $f =$ _____.
f. At what point in S does f take on its maximum?
g. Let $g(x_1, x_2) = -f(x_1, x_2)$ and find the maximum of g over S. At which point of S does it occur? What about the minimum value of g over S?

6. a. Solve the following LP problem graphically:

Find x_1, x_2 such that $x_i \geqslant 0$ and
$$-x_1 + 2x_2 \leqslant 2$$
while $f(x_1, x_2) = -2x_1 + 4x_2$ is maximized.

b. How many points are there for which $f(x_1, x_2)$ is maximized?
c. Is there at least one corner point at which the maximum value is achieved?

7. a. Solve the following LP problem graphically:

Find x_1, x_2 such that $x_i \geqslant 0$ and
$$x_1 + x_2 \leqslant 2$$
$$2x_1 + x_2 \leqslant 4$$
and $f(x_1, x_2) = 2x_1 + 3x_2$ is maximized.

b. What part did the second constraint play in the solution?

8. a. Find the plane region which satisfies the following constraints graphically:
$$x_i \geqslant 0, \quad i = 1, 2$$
$$x_1 + x_2 \leqslant 6$$
$$x_1 - x_2 \leqslant 1$$
$$2x_1 + x_2 \geqslant 6$$
$$-x_1 + 2x_2 \leqslant 8.$$

b. Let $f(x_1, x_2) = (x_1 - 2)^2 + (x_2 - 3)^2$. Show that the minimum value of f over the region in a. does not occur at a corner point of the region.

9. Company Z makes products A and B. Each product requires an operation to be performed by machine M_1 and machine M_2. Product A requires 1 minute on M_1 and 3 minutes on M_2. Product B requires 2 minutes on M_1 and 1 minute on M_2. There are 480 minutes available on each of M_1 and M_2. The profit on each unit of A is 5 cents while the profit on each unit of B is 4 cents.
   a. Set up an LP problem to maximize profit. Let x_1 denote the number of units of A and x_2 the number of units of B to be produced.
   b. Evaluate f at each corner point, found graphically.
   c. Solve the LP problem graphically.

10. Solve the diet problem of Example 7.1.4 graphically.

11. Solve the aircraft charter problem of Example 7.1.1 graphically.

12. Solve the aircraft charter problem of Exercise 10, Section 7.1 graphically.

Suggested reading

G. B. Dantzig, *Linear Programming and Extensions*, Princeton University Press, Princeton, N.J., (1963).

G. Hadley, *Linear Programming*, Addison-Wesley, Reading, Mass. (1962).

7.3 The general linear programming problem

Any problem of the form:

Find $x_1, x_2, \ldots, x_r$ such that

1. $x_i \geqslant 0, \quad i = 1, 2, \ldots, r$

2. $a_{11}x_1 + a_{12}x_2 + \cdots + a_{1r}x_r \lessgtr r_1$
   $a_{21}x_1 + a_{22}x_2 + \cdots + a_{2r}x_r \lessgtr r_2$
   $\cdots$
   $a_{p1}x_1 + a_{p2}x_2 + \cdots + a_{pr}x_r \lessgtr r_p$

3. $z = c_1x_1 + c_2x_2 + \cdots + c_rx_r = f(x_1, x_2, \ldots, x_r)$ is optimized.

---

is called a **linear programming problem**. By **optimized** we mean either maximized or minimized. Our earlier LP examples fit into this general format in which we have used the symbol $\lesseqgtr$ to indicate that any one of the symbols $\leqslant$, $=$, or $\geqslant$ may be present. As we have previously mentioned, the inequalities of the form $x_i \geqslant 0$ are called **non-negativity restrictions** after G. Hadley (see Suggested Reading). The remaining equations and/or inequalities are called **constraints**. The function f is the **criterion** or **objective** function to be optimized. The coefficients c_i of the x_i in f are called **criterion, objective function, or cost coefficients**.

Recalling that we have built up a great deal of machinery to deal with equations rather than inequalities, we shall now demonstrate that, for any given LP problem, it is possible to formulate an equivalent version with only equality constraints. The non-negativity restrictions on the variables will remain, however, and will be dealt with separately in the final solution algorithm. The two versions of the LP problem are equivalent in the sense that a final solution for either one will provide a final solution for the other.

To make the method of constructing the equivalent problem clear, consider problem P:

Find x_1, x_2 such that

1. $x_i \geqslant 0$, $i = 1, 2$
2. $2x_1 + x_2 \leqslant 6$

   $x_1 + x_2 \leqslant 4$

3. $z = f(x_1, x_2) = 5x_1 + 3x_2$ is maximized.

We replace the first inequality constraint $2x_1 + x_2 \leqslant 6$ by an equality constraint

$$2x_1 + x_2 + x_3 = 6$$

obtained by adding a new variable, x_3, also required to be non-negative. As long as x_3 is non-negative, the original inequality constraint will be satisfied whenever the new equality is satisfied. For example, when $x_3 = 1$ and the equality is satisfied,

$$2x_1 + x_2 = 5,$$

and since $5 \leqslant 6$,

$$2x_1 + x_2 \leqslant 6.$$

When $x_3 = 6$, and the equality is satisfied,

$$2x_1 + x_2 = 0 \leqslant 6,$$

and, similarly, when $x_3 = 0$,

$$2x_1 + x_2 = 6 \leqslant 6.$$

Thus, if we have non-negative values for x_1, x_2, x_3 such that

$$2x_1 + x_2 + x_3 = 6,$$

then

$$x_3 = 6 - 2x_1 - x_2 \geqslant 0,$$

and, from the right-hand inequality we see that

$$2x_1 + x_2 \leqslant 6.$$

On the other hand, if we have non-negative values of x_1, x_2 such that

$$2x_1 + x_2 \leqslant 6$$

and let $x_3 = 6 - 2x_1 - x_2$, then $x_3 \geqslant 0$ and

$$2x_1 + x_2 + x_3 = 6.$$

A variable such as x_3 which is added merely to "take up the slack" between the left-hand side of a $\leqslant$ inequality and the constant term is called a **slack variable**. This slack variable may be thought of as serving as a "guard" for the original inequality constraint, in the sense that whenever it is non-negative, the constraint is satisfied, and whenever it is negative the constraint is not satisfied. Thus, if values of x_1, x_2, x_3 are chosen that satisfy the *equation* but such that $x_3 < 0$, then the values for x_1, x_2 do not satisfy the original inequality constraint.

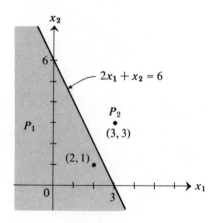

Figure 7.3.1

Here again, a look at the geometry of the situation will help to clarify matters. Consider Figure 7.3.1, which shows $P_1 = \{(x_1, x_2) \mid 2x_1 + x_2 \leqslant 6\}$. Suppose that we add the slack variable x_3 to form the equation

(i) $$2x_1 + x_2 + x_3 = 6.$$

Any point (x_1, x_2, x_3) for which $x_3 = 0$ corresponds to a point (x_1, x_2) in the plane which lies *on* the line, since $2x_1 + x_2 = 6$ if $x_3 = 0$. Any point (x_1, x_2, x_3) which satisfies (i) and for which $x_3 = 1$ corresponds to a point (x_1, x_2) which lies in the interior of P_1 since $2x_1 + x_2 = 5 < 6$. The point $(2, 1, 1)$ in 3-space is such a point and it corresponds to $(2, 1)$ in the plane as shown above. In general then, any point, (x_1, x_2, x_3), for which $x_3 \geqslant 0$, has a corresponding point, (x_1, x_2), which lies in P_1, since if $2x_1 + x_2 + x_3 = 6$ and $x_3 \geqslant 0$, then $2x_1 + x_2 \leqslant 6$ as desired. On the other hand, suppose, for example, that we have the point (x_1, x_2, x_3) such that

$$2x_1 + x_2 + x_3 = 6$$

and $x_3 = -3$, say. Then

$$2x_1 + x_2 = 6 + 3 = 9 > 6,$$

and the original constraint is not satisfied. The point $(3, 3, -3)$ satisfies (i) and we note that the corresponding point $(3, 3)$ lies outside of P_1. The sense in which we say that x_3 *serves as a guard* for the constraint should now be clear. Whenever we have a point (x_1, x_2, x_3) for which the equation is satisfied and $x_3 \geqslant 0$, the original inequality is also satisfied. On the other hand, if we have a point (x_1, x_2, x_3) for which $x_3 < 0$ then the point (x_1, x_2) in the plane lies on the "wrong side" of the line in question and the original inequality constraint is not satisfied.

We have seen that when $x_3 = 0$, $2x_1 + x_2 = 6$, and the point (x_1, x_2) lies on the line. Now, when $x_3 = 1$, we have $2x_1 + x_2 = 5$, also an equation of a straight line, and one with the same slope as the original. In Figure 7.3.2 we show $\{(x_1, x_2) \mid 2x_1 + x_2 = 6 - x_3\}$ for various values of x_3. Those with $x_3 \geqslant 0$ lie in P_1 while the one with $x_3 < 0$ lies outside of P_1.

We now consider the second constraint of problem P, $x_1 + x_2 \leqslant 4$, and add another slack variable x_4 such that

$$x_1 + x_2 + x_4 = 4.$$

x_4 is a non-negative variable which will serve as a guard for the second constraint.

We use these new equations to rephrase our original problem P in an equivalent form:

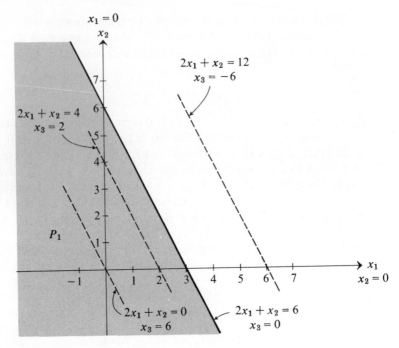

Figure 7.3.2

Find x_1, x_2, x_3, x_4 such that

1. $x_i \geqslant 0$ for $i = 1, 2, 3, 4$
2. $2x_1 + x_2 + x_3 \quad = 6$
   $x_1 + x_2 \quad + x_4 = 4$
3. $z = f(x_1, x_2, x_3, x_4) = 5x_1 + 3x_2$ is maximized.

Since we do not wish the values of these new variables to affect the value of z, they do not enter into the objective function and are assigned objective function coefficients of 0.

Example 7.3.1

We can rephrase Example 7.1.3 in the new format as follows:

Find x_1, x_2, x_3, x_4 such that

1. $x_i \geqslant 0$ for $i = 1, 2, 3, 4$
2. $0.2x_1 + 0.8x_2 + x_3 \quad = 1000$
   $0.8x_1 + 0.2x_2 \quad + x_4 = 1000$
3. $z = f(x_1, x_2, x_3, x_4) = 2x_1 + 3x_2$ is maximized.

In matrix form, we wish to

Find X such that

1. $X \geqslant 0$

2. $AX = R$

3. $z = CX = f(X)$ is maximized

---

where $X^T = [x_1, x_2, x_3, x_4]$, $A = \begin{bmatrix} 0.2 & 0.8 & 1 & 0 \\ 0.8 & 0.2 & 0 & 1 \end{bmatrix}$, $R = \begin{bmatrix} 1000 \\ 1000 \end{bmatrix}$, and $C = [2 \quad 3 \quad 0 \quad 0]$.

Constraints of the $\geqslant$ type may also be replaced by equality constraints. A particularly simple way of accomplishing this would be to multiply both sides of the original inequality by (-1) and changing the $\geqslant$ to $\leqslant$. In so doing we would have really only transferred the variables and the constant terms to opposite sides of the inequality. However, this would have the effect of replacing a positive constant on the right-hand side by a *negative* constant. For example, $x_1 + 2x_2 \geqslant 4$ would be replaced by $-x_1 - 2x_2 \leqslant -4$. Because of the particular way in which we will deal with the non-negativity restrictions on all of the variables, *we wish to have all of the right-hand constants non-negative to start with*. The situation can, however, be handled in a fashion similar to that for the $\leqslant$ constraint.

Consider the constraint

$$1x_1 + 2x_2 \geqslant 4$$

of the diet problem, Example 7.1.4, where the total amount of vitamin B to be served in x_1 ounces of F_1 and x_2 ounces of F_2 was to be at least 4 units. Suppose that a solution with $x_1 = 2$ and $x_2 = 2$ is considered. In this case, the number of units of vitamin B served is

$$1(2) + 2(2) = 6 > 4$$

and there is a surplus of vitamin B provided. If we let

$$x_3 = 1x_1 + 2x_2 - 4,$$

then $x_3 = 6 - 4 = 2$ in the case above and represents the surplus of vitamin B served. Such a variable is called a **surplus variable**. It is subtracted from the left side of the original $\geqslant$ constraint to form an equation. We thus have the equation

$$1x_1 + 2x_2 - x_3 = 4.$$

The logical situation here is analogous to that of the $\leqslant$ constraint previously considered. If we obtain (x_1, x_2, x_3) with $x_3 \geqslant 0$, then the original inequality is satisfied for (x_1, x_2). If, however, we have a pair (x_1, x_2) that does not satisfy the $\geqslant$ inequality, then any point (x_1, x_2, x_3) such that

$$1x_1 + 2x_2 - x_3 = 4$$

must have $x_3 < 0$. Figure 7.3.3 depicts the situation in this case.

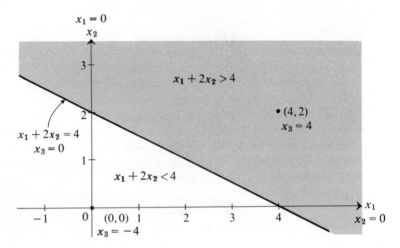

Figure 7.3.3

Consider the point $(0, 0)$. The point is not in the desired region, and from the equation

$$1(0) + 2(0) - x_3 = 4$$

we find that $x_3 = -4$. On the other hand, the point $(4, 2)$ is in the desired region and we find from the equation

$$1(4) + 2(2) - x_3 = 4$$

that $x_3 = 4 \geqslant 0$.

Thus we see that the surplus variable which we subtract to create an equation acts as a "guard" for the $\geqslant$ constraint in the same sense that the slack variable acts as a guard for a $\leqslant$ constraint.

Example 7.3.2

In the problem in which we wish to

Find x_1, x_2 such that

1. $x_i \geqslant 0,$ for $i = 1, 2$
2.1. $x_1 + 2x_2 \geqslant 4$
2.2. $-x_1 + 4x_2 \leqslant 3$
2.3. $3x_1 - 2x_2 \leqslant 6$
3. $f(x_1, x_2) = 2x_1 + 2x_2$ is maximized.

---

we shall add slack variables or subtract surplus variables to obtain a problem with equality constraints. In 2.1 we subtract the surplus variable x_3 to form $x_1 + 2x_2 - x_3 = 4$. In 2.2 and 2.3 we add slack variables x_4 and x_5 to form the equality constraints $-x_1 + 4x_2 + x_4 = 3$ and $3x_1 - 2x_2 + x_5 = 6$. We restrict the three new variables to be non-negative and obtain a new objective function $f'(x_1, x_2, x_3, x_4, x_5) = 2x_1 + 2x_2 = f(x_1, x_2)$ with coefficients of 0 assigned to each of the slack/surplus variables. We therefore have a new but equivalent problem:

Find x_1, x_2, x_3, x_4, x_5 such that

1. $x_i \geqslant 0$ for $i = 1, 2, 3, 4, 5$
2. $\begin{aligned} x_1 + 2x_2 - x_3 &= 4 \\ -x_1 + 4x_2 + x_4 &= 3 \\ 3x_1 - 2x_2 + x_5 &= 6 \end{aligned}$
3. $f(x_1, x_2) = 2x_1 + 2x_2$ is maximized.

It should now be clear that we could in general formulate an equivalent LP problem as follows:

Find $x_1, \ldots, x_n$ such that

1. $x_i \geqslant 0$ for $i = 1, 2, \ldots, n$
2. $a_{11}x_1 + a_{12}x_2 + \cdots + a_{1n}x_n = r_1$
     $a_{21}x_1 + a_{22}x_2 + \cdots + a_{2n}x_n = r_2$
     $\phantom{a_{21}x_1} \cdot \phantom{+ a_{22}x_2} \cdot \cdots \phantom{+ a_{2n}} \cdot \cdot$
     $a_{m1}x_1 + a_{m2}x_2 + \cdots + a_{mn}x_n = r_m$
3. $z = c_1x_1 + c_2x_2 + \cdots + c_nx_n = f(x_1, x_2, \ldots, x_n)$ is optimized.

In matrix format we say that we wish to

Find $X \geqslant 0$

such that $AX = R$

and $z = f(X) = CX$ is optimized.

Henceforth, we shall assume that $m < n$ and that all redundant equations have been removed so that the rank of A is m. If the rank of A were m and $m = n$, then there would only be one vector X satisfying $AX = R$. Thus, no real optimization problem exists. We either use this X or not, depending on whether each component of X is non-negative. Our reformulated problem P,

---

Find x_1, x_2, x_3, x_4 such that

1. $x_i \geqslant 0$ for $i = 1, 2, 3, 4$
2. $2x_1 + x_2 + x_3 \qquad = 6$
   $\quad x_1 + x_2 \qquad + x_4 = 4$
3. $z = f(x_1, x_2, x_3, x_4) = 5x_1 + 3x_2$ is maximized.

---

may now be put into matrix format, with $C = \begin{bmatrix} 5 & 3 & 0 & 0 \end{bmatrix}$, $X^T = \begin{bmatrix} x_1 & x_2 & x_3 & x_4 \end{bmatrix}$, $A = \begin{bmatrix} 2 & 1 & 1 & 0 \\ 1 & 1 & 0 & 1 \end{bmatrix}$ and $R = \begin{bmatrix} 6 \\ 4 \end{bmatrix}$. We now wish to

---

Find $X \geqslant 0$

such that $AX = R$

and $z = f(X) = CX$ is maximized.

In considering the relationship between the general problem with constraints in equality form and the original one, we note that the new problem has at least as many variables as the original, and that there will be an extra variable for each inequality constraint in the original formulation.

One could also start with a problem in equality form and obtain an equivalent problem with inequalities. Consider the equality constraint

$$2x_1 + 3x_2 = 4.$$

If we replace this one constraint with two inequalities, namely

$$2x_1 + 3x_2 \leqslant 4 \quad \text{and} \quad 2x_1 + 3x_2 \geqslant 4,$$

then any $X = [x_1, x_2]^T$ which can satisfy both of these constraints must satisfy the original and vice-versa.

Exercises 7.3

1. To create an equality constraint from $2x_1 + 3x_2 \leqslant 6$ we add the non-_____ variable x_3 to form the equality constraint _____. We say that x_3 serves as a _____ for the constraint in the sense that the inequality constraint is satisfied when x_3 is _____, and the inequality constraint is _____ _____ when x_3 is negative. Because of the fact that x_3 ($= 6 - 2x_1 - 3x_2$) takes up the slack or makes up the difference between 6 and $2x_1 + 3x_2$ we call x_3 a _____ variable.

2. To create an equality constraint from $2x_1 + 3x_2 \geqslant 6$, we _____ the non-negative variable x_3 to form the equality constraint _____. Because of the fact that x_3 ($= 2x_1 + 3x_2 - 6$) _____, we call x_3 a surplus variable.

3. Express the problem of Exercise 3, Section 7.2 in equality constraint form.

4. Describe the objective function, non-negativity restrictions, and constraints of the problem in Exercise 3 above both in inequality and equality constraint form.

5. Express the problem of Exercise 5, Section 7.2 in equality constraint form.

6. For later computational reasons, we wish to keep the constants r_i in our equality constraints _____.

7. Express the problem of Exercise 3, Section 7.2 in matrix format with equality constraints (see Exercise 3 above).

8. Show graphically that

$$\{(x_1, x_2) \mid 2x_1 + x_2 = 3\}$$
$$= \{(x_1, x_2) \mid 2x_1 + x_2 \leqslant 3\} \cap \{(x_1, x_2) \mid 2x_1 + x_2 \geqslant 3\}.$$

9. Express the problem of Exercise 5, Section 7.2 in matrix format with equality constraints (see Exercise 5 above).

10. When we convert from constraints in inequality form to equation form, how many new variables are introduced?

11. Consider $S = \{(x_1, x_2) \,|\, 4x_1 + 3x_2 \leqslant 12\}$.

a. Find the point (x_1, x_2, x_3) corresponding to $(1, 2)$ in the plane. Since x_3 is _____ we know that $(1, 2)$ is in S.

b. Find the point (x_1, x_2, x_3) corresponding to $(2, 2)$ in the plane. Since x_3 is _____ we know that $(2, 2)$ _____ in S.

c. Since $4(2) + 3(1) + 1(1) = 12$, we know that (_____, _____, _____) is the point in 3-space corresponding to the point (_____, _____) in S in 2-space.

12. Express Exercise 8 of Section 7.1 in matrix inequality form.

Suggested reading

G. B. Dantzig, *Linear Programming and Extensions*, Princeton University Press, Princeton, N.J. (1963).

S. I. Gass, *Linear Programming*, McGraw-Hill, New York (1964).

G. Hadley, *Linear Programming*, Addison-Wesley, Reading, Mass. (1962).

New terms

linear programming problem, 239
optimize, 239
non-negativity restriction, 239
constraints, 239
criterion function, 239
objective function, 239

criterion function coefficients, 239
objective function coefficients, 239
cost function coefficients 239
slack variable 240
surplus variable 243

7.4   Basic feasible solutions

From our new formulation of the general LP problem

Find $X \geqslant 0$ such that

$AX = R$

and $z = f(X) = CX$ is optimized.

---

we proceed to define a few more of the terms which we have been using rather intuitively. We shall say that the vector X is a **solution of the**

general LP problem in equality form provided that $AX = R$. Any solution X with the additional property that $X \geqslant 0$ will be called a **feasible solution**. The set of all such feasible solutions will be called the **feasible region**. If X is a feasible solution with the best possible value of the objective function, then X is called an **optimal feasible solution**. For example, in a minimization problem, if $X \geqslant 0$, and $f(X) \leqslant f(Y)$ for all feasible solutions Y, then X is said to be an optimal feasible solution.

Example 7.4.1

Consider problem P in matrix equality form as follows, with

$$C = [5, 3, 0, 0], \ A = \begin{bmatrix} 2 & 1 & 1 & 0 \\ 1 & 1 & 0 & 1 \end{bmatrix}, \ R = \begin{bmatrix} 6 \\ 4 \end{bmatrix},$$

and

$$X^T = [x_1, x_2, x_3, x_4].$$

For $X_1 = [0, 0, 6, 4]^T$ we have

$$AX_1 = \begin{bmatrix} 2 & 1 & 1 & 0 \\ 1 & 1 & 0 & 1 \end{bmatrix} \begin{bmatrix} 0 \\ 0 \\ 6 \\ 4 \end{bmatrix} = \begin{bmatrix} 6 \\ 4 \end{bmatrix} = R.$$

Thus, X_1 is a solution. Since $x_i \geqslant 0$ for each i, X_1 is a feasible solution. Now

$$f(X_1) = CX_1 = [5, 3, 0, 0] \begin{bmatrix} 0 \\ 0 \\ 6 \\ 4 \end{bmatrix} = 0 < 16.$$

Thus X_1 is not an optimal feasible solution. The reader should verify from Figure 7.2.7 and the definitions above, that $X_2 = [2, 2, 0, 0]^T$, $X_3 = [1, 1, 3, 2]^T$, and $X_4 = [0, 6, 0, -2]^T$ are each solutions, that X_4 is not feasible, and that X_2 is optimal and feasible. Recall that the optimum value of z is 16.

Let us continue to use problem P as a vehicle to study the relationship between the geometry and the algebra of a typical LP problem.

In the equivalent new problem in equality form we wish to find a vector X in 4-space. However, we may still portray the situation in two dimensions as before, as depicted in Figure 7.4.1.

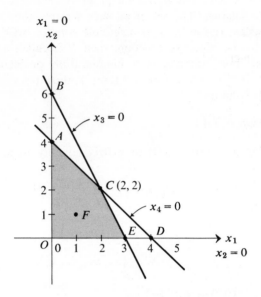

Figure 7.4.1

We point out the particular constraints that x_3 and x_4 are guarding by indicating that $x_3 = 0$ along the appropriate line defining its inequality and that $x_4 = 0$ along the other. Similarly, $x_2 = 0$ is another way of describing the x_1 axis, since $x_2 = 0$ for any point on it.

Each point (x_1, x_2) in this 2-dimensional representation has a corresponding point (x_1, x_2, x_3, x_4) in 4-space that may easily be computed from the equations defining the shaded region. For example, consider the 2-space origin $(0, 0)$. If, in the constraint equations

$$2x_1 + x_2 + x_3 \quad\ = 6$$

$$x_1 + x_2 \quad\ + x_4 = 4$$

we let $x_1 = x_2 = 0$, we find that $x_3 = 6$ and $x_4 = 4$. Thus, in 4-space we have the point $(0, 0, 6, 4)$ which we say corresponds to $(0, 0)$ in 2-space.

Now consider point A in the figure. Point A lies at the intersection of the lines $x_1 = 0$ and $x_4 = 0$. With $x_1 = x_4 = 0$ we have the resulting set of equations

$$x_2 + x_3 = 6$$

$$x_2 \quad\ = 4$$

yielding $x_2 = 4$ and $x_3 = 2$, so that $(0, 4, 2, 0)$ in 4-space corresponds to

A. At point *B*, $x_1 = x_3 = 0$. We thus have

$$x_2 \qquad = 6$$
$$x_2 + x_4 = 4$$

from which we conclude that $x_2 = 6$ and $x_4 = -2$. The corresponding 4-space point is $(0, 6, 0, -2)$. *At any particular corner point of the feasible region, such as A, those variables, n − m in general, which are set equal to 0 are called the* **non-basic variables** *at that point. The remaining m variables, the values of which must be computed, are called the* **basic variables** *at the point in question.*

Proceeding clockwise in the figure, we obtain the information in Table 7.4.1. The reader should carefully verify each of the entries. An understanding of this method is vital in the sequel.

Point	2-Space Solution	Non-Basic Variables	Basic Variables	4-Space Solution X^T
O	$[0, 0]$	x_1, x_2	x_3, x_4	$[0, 0, 6, 4]$
A	$[0, 4]$	x_1, x_4	x_3, x_2	$[0, 4, 2, 0]$
B	$[0, 6]$	x_1, x_3	x_4, x_2	$[0, 6, 0, -2]$
C	$[2, 2]$	x_4, x_3	x_1, x_2	$[2, 2, 0, 0]$
D	$[4, 0]$	x_4, x_2	x_1, x_3	$[4, 0, -2, 0]$
E	$[3, 0]$	x_3, x_2	x_1, x_4	$[3, 0, 0, 1]$
F	$[1, 1]$	none	x_1, x_2, x_3, x_4	$[1, 1, 3, 2]$

Table 7.4.1

Point *F* is a special case. If x_1 and x_2 are each set equal to 1 then the original equations reduce to

$$x_3 = 3$$
$$x_4 = 2,$$

so that $(1, 1, 3, 2)$ is the corresponding 4-space point.

We can learn several important ideas from the graph and the table in conjunction. First of all, each of the points, except *F*, has exactly $m = 2$ of the variables whose values are non-zero. In addition, each of these points which is in the shaded region has no negative components. Furthermore, each such point in the table is an extreme point or a corner point of the feasible region. Finally, the point *F*, an *interior* point of the feasible region, has more than $m = 2$ positive components and it is not a corner point of the feasible region.

Referring to the Figure 7.4.1, Table 7.4.1, our recent definitions, and our earlier results for problem P, we classify the solutions represented by the various points in Table 7.4.2.

Point	Solution	Feasible Solution	Optimal Feasible Solution
O	yes	yes	no
A	yes	yes	no
B	yes	no	no
C	yes	yes	yes
D	yes	no	no
E	yes	yes	no
F	yes	yes	no

Table 7.4.2

It will be helpful to distinguish between feasible solutions like those at the corner points O, A, C, E of the feasible region, and other feasible solutions such as F. We recall that the difference arose because of the number of variables which were set equal to 0, thus causing the number of non-zero variables to be different also. To clarify the situation, we make the following additional definition, recalling that the rank of A is m. We shall say that the solution X is a **basic solution** of $AX = R$ provided that $n - m$ of the variables have been set equal to 0 and the remaining m equations in m unknowns solved simultaneously. The $n - m$ variables are the previously defined non-basic variables while the m variables are the basic variables. If $n = 4$ and $m = 2$ as in problem P then all possible sets of $4 - 2 = 2$ of the variables are set equal to 0 and the remaining sets of 2 equations in 2 unknowns are solved to obtain the various basic solutions.

If X is a basic solution that is also feasible (that is, $X \geqslant 0$) then X is called a **basic feasible solution** (BFS). If, in a basic solution X, some $x_i < 0$, then X is called a **basic infeasible solution**. Points B and D in Figure 7.4.1 represent such solutions in problem P. Points O, A, C, E correspond to the basic feasible solutions of problem P. It is no accident that points O, A, C, E are the corner points of the feasible region. For each such corner point or extreme point of the feasible region of any LP problem it can be proved that there is *at least one* corresponding BFS which can be obtained by choosing the correct set of $n - m$ variables to set equal to 0.* Similarly, it can be proved that for each

* G. Hadley, *Linear Programming*, Addison-Wesley, Reading, Mass., p. 100 ff.

BFS there is a corresponding corner point of the feasible region.

We recall from our earlier study of linear equations of the form $AX = R$, where A is an $m \times n$ matrix of rank m, that we would expect to find $n - m$ free variables, which we are at liberty to set equal to whatever values we like, and to solve for the remaining m variables in terms of these. Perhaps the easiest way to do this is to set $n - m$ of the variables equal to 0. Whenever we do this, and obtain a solution, we obtain a basic solution.

Example 7.4.2

Let us construct all six basic solutions of an LP problem with $A = \begin{bmatrix} 2 & 3 & 1 & 0 \\ 3 & 2 & 0 & 1 \end{bmatrix}$ and $R = \begin{bmatrix} 6 \\ 6 \end{bmatrix}$.

1. For $x_1 = x_2 = 0$ we have $x_3 = x_4 = 6$ and the *BFS* $X^T = [0, 0, 6, 6]$.

2. For $x_1 = x_3 = 0$ we have the remaining set of equations

$$3x_2 \quad\quad = 6$$
$$2x_2 + x_4 = 6$$

from which we obtain $X^T = [0, 2, 0, 2]$ as a *BFS*.

3. For $x_1 = x_4 = 0$ we obtain the augmented matrix

$$\begin{bmatrix} 3 & 1 & | & 6 \\ 2 & 0 & | & 6 \end{bmatrix} \sim \begin{bmatrix} 2 & 0 & | & 6 \\ 3 & 1 & | & 6 \end{bmatrix} \sim \begin{bmatrix} 1 & 0 & | & 3 \\ 0 & 1 & | & -3 \end{bmatrix} \quad \text{and}$$
$$X^T = [0, 3, -3, 0],$$

which is a basic *infeasible* solution.

4. From $x_2 = x_3 = 0$ we obtain $\begin{bmatrix} 2 & 0 & | & 6 \\ 3 & 1 & | & 6 \end{bmatrix}$ and find that $X^T = [3, 0, 0, -3]$ is another basic solution that is not feasible.

5. When $x_2 = x_4 = 0$, we have $\begin{bmatrix} 2 & 1 & | & 6 \\ 3 & 0 & | & 6 \end{bmatrix}$, from which we obtain $X^T = [2, 0, 2, 0]$, a *BFS*.

6. Finally, if $x_3 = x_4 = 0$, we obtain

$$\begin{bmatrix} 2 & 3 & | & 6 \\ 3 & 2 & | & 6 \end{bmatrix} \sim \begin{bmatrix} 1 & 3/2 & | & 3 \\ 0 & -5/2 & | & -3 \end{bmatrix} \sim \begin{bmatrix} 1 & 0 & | & 6/5 \\ 0 & 1 & | & 6/5 \end{bmatrix}$$

and see that $X^T = [6/5, 6/5, 0, 0]$ is a *BFS*.

The reader should sketch the graph of the 2-space feasible region represented by $AX = R$, treating x_3 and x_4 as slack variables, to see that these answers are reasonable.

Exercises 7.4

1. Consider the LP problem with constraints

$$x_1 + 2x_2 \leqslant 3$$
$$2x_1 + x_2 \leqslant 3.$$

   a. Add slack variables to put the constraints in equality form.

   b. Find A, X and R to express the equality constraints in the form $AX = R$.

   c. Sketch the feasible region for this problem (including non-negativity restrictions).

   d. Verify from the algebraic definition of a solution that

$$X_1 = [3/2, 0, 3/2, 0]^T, \; X_2 = [0, 3, -3, 0]^T,$$
$$X_3 = [1/2, 1/2, 3/2, 3/2]^T$$

   are solutions.

   e. Which of the solutions in d. above are feasible?

   f. Which of the solutions in d. above are basic?

   g. Which solutions in d. are basic feasible solutions?

2. Consider the LP problem to maximize $f(X) = CX$, with $X \geqslant 0$ and $AX = R$.

   a. We say that X is a solution provided that _____.

   b. If X is a solution and $X \geqslant 0$ we call X a _____.

   c. We call $\{X \mid AX = R$ and $X \geqslant 0\}$ the _____.

   d. We say that the feasible solution X is an optimal feasible solution provided that if Y is another feasible solution then _____.

3. Consider the feasible region of Exercise 1 as shown in Figure 7.4.2.

   a. At point O, $x_1 = x_2 = 0$, while $x_3 = x_4 = 3$. We call x_1 and x_2 _____ variables at O, while x_3 and x_4 are called _____ variables at that point.

   b. The 4-space coordinates of point F are _____. Is the solution at F feasible? basic?

   c. Fill in the following table in a fashion similar to that of Table 7.4.1.

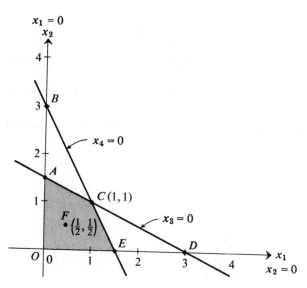

Figure 7.4.2

Point	2-Space Solution	Non-Basic Variables	Basic Variables	4-Space Solution, X^T	Solution Feasible?
O					
A					
B					
C					
D					
E					

Table 7.4.3

4. To obtain all of the basic solutions of the LP problem with constraint set $AX = B$ where A is a 3×7 matrix, we would successively
set _____ of the variables equal to 0 and solve the remaining
_____ equations in _____ variables. We should obtain at most
_____ basic solutions in so doing, not all of which need be _____.

5. Consider the constraint set

$$x_1 + x_2 \leqslant 2$$
$$2x_1 + x_2 \leqslant 4$$

of Exercise 7 of Section 7.2.

a. Add slack variables and put the constraints in the form $AX = R$.

$$A_1 = \begin{bmatrix} \underline{\quad} \\ \underline{\quad} \end{bmatrix} \quad \text{and} \quad A_4 = \begin{bmatrix} \underline{\quad} \\ \underline{\quad} \end{bmatrix}, \quad \text{while} \quad R = \begin{bmatrix} \underline{\quad} \\ \underline{\quad} \end{bmatrix}.$$

b. Using the sketch of the feasible region provided in Figure 7.4.3,

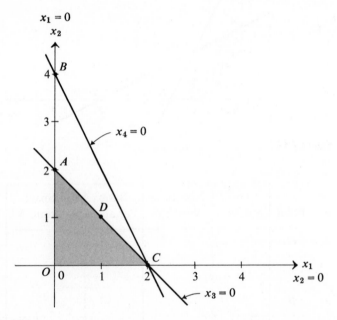

Figure 7.4.3

fill in Table 7.4.4. Note that the 2-space point C has more than one corresponding 4-space point.

c. The 4-space point corresponding to D is _____. The solution at D is non-_____ but _____. Note that D is a boundary point of the feasible region but not a corner point.

Suggested reading

G. B. Dantzig, *Linear Programming and Extensions*, Princeton University Press, Princeton, N.J., (1963).

G. Hadley, *Linear Programming*, Addison-Wesley, Reading, Mass., (1962).

Point	2-Space Solution	Non-Basic Variables	Basic Variables	4-Space Solution, X^T	Solution Feasible?
O	$[0, 0]$			[ ]	
A	$[0, 2]$			[ ]	
B	[ ]	x_1, x_4	x_3, x_2	[ ]	
C	$[2, 0]$	x_2, x_3	x_1, x_4	$[2, 0, 0, 0]$	
C	$[2, 0]$	x_2, x_4	x_3, x_1	$[2, 0, 0, 0]$	
C	$[2, 0]$			[ ]	

Table 7.4.4

New terms

solution of the general LP problem, 248
feasible solution, 249
feasible region, 249
optimal feasible solution, 249
non-basic variables, 251

basic variables, 251
basic solution, 252
basic feasible solution, 252
basic infeasible solution, 252

7.5 A matrix/vector approach to the LP problem

In our equation version of the general LP problem where we wish to

---

Find X such that

1. $X \geqslant 0$
2. $AX = R$ and
3. $z = f(X) = CX$ is optimized.

---

we note that the equality constraints could be written in the alternative form

$$x_1 A_1 + x_2 A_2 + \cdots + x_n A_n = R,$$

where the A_i represent the columns of A and are elements of m-space. We might then think of the LP problem as one asking us to find, in the set of all vectors X in n-space, that subset of vectors with non-negative components which express R as a linear combination of the A_i. Out of this subset we are to pick that vector or set of vectors which provide the best possible value of the objective function.

Let us consider problem P in this light:

Find X such that

1. $X \geqslant 0$

2. $2x_1 + x_2 + x_3 \qquad = 6$

   $x_1 + x_2 \qquad + x_4 = 4$ and

3. $z = f(X) = 5x_1 + 3x_2$ is maximized.

Out of all the vectors in 4-space we wish first to find

$$\left\{ X \mid X = \begin{bmatrix} x_1 \\ x_2 \\ x_3 \\ x_4 \end{bmatrix} \text{ and } x_1 \begin{bmatrix} 2 \\ 1 \end{bmatrix} + x_2 \begin{bmatrix} 1 \\ 1 \end{bmatrix} + x_3 \begin{bmatrix} 1 \\ 0 \end{bmatrix} + x_4 \begin{bmatrix} 0 \\ 1 \end{bmatrix} \right.$$

$$= \begin{bmatrix} 6 \\ 4 \end{bmatrix} \text{ and } x_i \geqslant 0 \Bigg\} .$$

Here, $A_1 = \begin{bmatrix} 2 \\ 1 \end{bmatrix}$, $A_2 = \begin{bmatrix} 1 \\ 1 \end{bmatrix}$, $A_3 = \begin{bmatrix} 1 \\ 0 \end{bmatrix}$, and $A_4 = \begin{bmatrix} 0 \\ 1 \end{bmatrix}$, while $R = \begin{bmatrix} 6 \\ 4 \end{bmatrix}$.

Geometrically, in 2-space, we now portray the situation as shown in Figure 7.5.1.

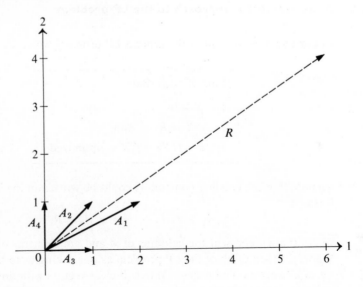

Figure 7.5.1

In the last section we demonstrated the manner in which one could construct all the possible *basic solutions* of this problem by successively choosing $n - m = 4 - 2 = 2$ of the variables to be set equal to 0 and solving the resulting $m = 2$ equations for the remaining $m = 2$ variables. This idea is intimately connected with the idea of a basis for a vector space which we discussed in Chapter 4. Let us reconsider the graph (Figure 7.5.2) and part of the associated table (Table 7.5.1) for problem P.

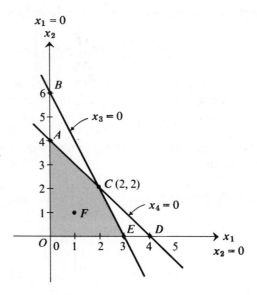

Figure 7.5.2

Point	Basic Variables	Non-Basic Variables	Basic Solution X^T
O	x_3, x_4	x_1, x_2	$[0, 0, 6, 4]$
A	x_3, x_2	x_1, x_4	$[0, 4, 2, 0]$
B	x_4, x_2	x_1, x_3	$[0, 6, 0, -2]$
C	x_1, x_2	x_4, x_3	$[2, 2, 0, 0]$
D	x_1, x_3	x_4, x_2	$[4, 0, -2, 0]$
E	x_1, x_4	x_3, x_2	$[3, 0, 0, 1]$

Table 7.5.1

At point O the basic variables are x_3 and x_4, and the set of equations which must be solved is

$$2(0) + 1(0) + 1x_3 \qquad = 6$$
$$1(0) + 1(0) \qquad + 1x_4 = 4,$$

or

$$x_3 \begin{bmatrix} 1 \\ 0 \end{bmatrix} + x_4 \begin{bmatrix} 0 \\ 1 \end{bmatrix} = \begin{bmatrix} 6 \\ 4 \end{bmatrix}.$$

The vectors $A_3 = \begin{bmatrix} 1 \\ 0 \end{bmatrix}$ and $A_4 = \begin{bmatrix} 0 \\ 1 \end{bmatrix}$ form a basis in 2-space. Thus R is some linear combination of the A_i and in this case it is obvious that

$$R = \begin{bmatrix} 6 \\ 4 \end{bmatrix} = 6 \begin{bmatrix} 1 \\ 0 \end{bmatrix} + 4 \begin{bmatrix} 0 \\ 1 \end{bmatrix},$$

so that $X = [x_1, x_2, x_3, x_4]^T = [0, 0, 6, 4]^T$ is our desired basic solution. Since $x_i \geqslant 0$ for each i, the basic solution is also feasible. In this case, $R = 6A_3 + 4A_4 = [A_3, A_4] \begin{bmatrix} 6 \\ 4 \end{bmatrix} = \begin{bmatrix} 1 & 0 \\ 0 & 1 \end{bmatrix} \begin{bmatrix} 6 \\ 4 \end{bmatrix}$.

Consider the point A. At this point, $x_1 = x_4 = 0$, and we have the set of equations

$$x_2 A_2 + x_3 A_3 = x_2 \begin{bmatrix} 1 \\ 1 \end{bmatrix} + x_3 \begin{bmatrix} 1 \\ 0 \end{bmatrix} = \begin{bmatrix} 1 & 1 \\ 1 & 0 \end{bmatrix} \begin{bmatrix} x_2 \\ x_3 \end{bmatrix} = \begin{bmatrix} 6 \\ 4 \end{bmatrix}$$

to solve, and we already know that

$$R = \begin{bmatrix} 6 \\ 4 \end{bmatrix} = 4 \begin{bmatrix} 1 \\ 1 \end{bmatrix} + 2 \begin{bmatrix} 1 \\ 0 \end{bmatrix} = \begin{bmatrix} 1 & 1 \\ 1 & 0 \end{bmatrix} \begin{bmatrix} 4 \\ 2 \end{bmatrix}.$$

Since $\{A_2, A_3\}$ is a linearly independent subset of 2-space these vectors also form a basis. For this reason the matrix $[A_2, A_3] = \begin{bmatrix} 1 & 1 \\ 1 & 0 \end{bmatrix}$ is a basis matrix.

In an LP problem with matrix A we restrict our previous definition and call any $m \times m$ matrix whose columns are chosen from A and form a linearly independent subset of m-space a **basis matrix***. for A. We will denote such a matrix by B. In the particular case above, $B = \begin{bmatrix} 1 & 1 \\ 1 & 0 \end{bmatrix} = [A_2, A_3]$. We shall find it convenient to use a special notation for the m-component matrix consisting of the values of the m basic variables corresponding to the columns of B. We shall call this

---

* We shall, for the most part, use the notation developed by G. Hadley (see Suggested Reading).

matrix X_B since it does consist of a proper subset of the components of X, namely those corresponding to the m linearly independent columns of A selected to make up B. Thus for

$$B = [A_2, A_3] = \begin{bmatrix} 1 & 1 \\ 1 & 0 \end{bmatrix},$$

$$X_B = \begin{bmatrix} x_2 \\ x_3 \end{bmatrix} = \begin{bmatrix} 4 \\ 2 \end{bmatrix}.$$

The order of the columns in a basis matrix B is important. To keep track of the order of these columns we shall number them as in $B = [B_1, B_2, \ldots, B_m]$. B_1 could be any one of the n columns of A, as could any other B_i, as long as the entire set is linearly independent. (This rules out duplication or scalar multiples.) If $B = [A_2, A_3]$ then $B_1 = A_2$ and $B_2 = A_3$.

We shall further denote the component of X_B that corresponds to column i of B by x_{Bi}, so that in general,

$$x_{B1} B_1 + x_{B2} B_2 + \cdots + x_{Bm} B_m = [B_1, B_2, \ldots, B_m] \begin{bmatrix} x_{B1} \\ x_{B2} \\ \vdots \\ x_{Bm} \end{bmatrix} = R.$$

Above, $4A_2 + 2A_3 = R$. Since $A_2 = B_1$ and $A_3 = B_2$, we have $4B_1 + 2B_2 = R$, so that

$$x_{B1} = 4 \qquad \text{and} \qquad x_{B2} = 2.$$

The entire matrix consisting of such components, namely

$$[x_{B1}, x_{B2}, \ldots, x_{Bm}]^T,$$

is just the matrix X_B. Since

$$[B_1, B_2, \ldots, B_m] \begin{bmatrix} x_{B1} \\ x_{B2} \\ \vdots \\ x_{Bm} \end{bmatrix} = R, \qquad \text{and} \qquad B = [B_1, B_2, \ldots, B_m],$$

we have the following formula:

$$BX_B = R.$$

Let us use points B and C of our graph to exercise our knowledge of the notation just introduced. First consider point B. At this point the corresponding basis consists of A_4 and A_2. Thus

$$B = [B_1, B_2] = [A_4, A_2] \qquad \text{and} \qquad B_1 = A_4 \quad \text{while} \quad B_2 = A_2.$$

Since $R = x_{B1}B_1 + x_{B2}B_2 = -2A_4 + 6A_2$ we find that $x_{B1} = -2$ and $x_{B2} = 6$, and we verify that $BX_B = R$ since

$$\begin{bmatrix} 0 & 1 \\ 1 & 1 \end{bmatrix}\begin{bmatrix} -2 \\ 6 \end{bmatrix} = \begin{bmatrix} 6 \\ 4 \end{bmatrix}.$$

As a matter of fact, since B is a basis matrix, B^{-1} exists, and we see that we could have used B^{-1} to solve for X_B from the following formula:

$$X_B = B^{-1}R.$$

The reader should find B^{-1} in the above example and verify that this is the case.

At point C, the basic variables are x_1, x_2, so that $B = [B_1, B_2] = [A_1, A_2]$. Since $B = \begin{bmatrix} 2 & 1 \\ 1 & 1 \end{bmatrix}$ and $BX_B = R$, we shall use B^{-1} to find X_B.

Now $B^{-1} = \begin{bmatrix} 1 & -1 \\ -1 & 2 \end{bmatrix}$. Therefore $X_B = B^{-1}R = \begin{bmatrix} 1 & -1 \\ -1 & 2 \end{bmatrix}\begin{bmatrix} 6 \\ 4 \end{bmatrix} = \begin{bmatrix} 2 \\ 2 \end{bmatrix} = \begin{bmatrix} x_{B1} \\ x_{B2} \end{bmatrix} = \begin{bmatrix} x_1 \\ x_2 \end{bmatrix}$, as we had found before.

The reader should now verify that Table 7.5.2 has been computed correctly.

Point	Basic Variables	Basis Matrix B	$X_B{}^T$	X^T
O	x_3, x_4	$[A_3, A_4]$	$[6, 4]$	$[0, 0, 6, 4]$
A	x_3, x_2	$[A_3, A_2]$	$[2, 4]$	$[0, 4, 2, 0]$
B	x_4, x_2	$[A_4, A_2]$	$[-2, 6]$	$[0, 6, 0, -2]$
C	x_1, x_2	$[A_1, A_2]$	$[2, 2]$	$[2, 2, 0, 0]$
D	x_1, x_3	$[A_1, A_3]$	$[4, -2]$	$[4, 0, -2, 0]$
E	x_1, x_4	$[A_1, A_4]$	$[3, 1]$	$[3, 0, 0, 1]$

Table 7.5.2

It should be emphasized that the ordering of the columns of B, although important, is quite arbitrary. At the point A, for example, we could have chosen to let $B = [A_2, A_3]$. This would merely have changed the order of the elements in X_B so that X_B would have been $\begin{bmatrix} 4 \\ 2 \end{bmatrix} = \begin{bmatrix} x_{B1} \\ x_{B2} \end{bmatrix} = \begin{bmatrix} x_2 \\ x_3 \end{bmatrix}$.

Example 7.5.1

Consider the problem

Find X such that for $A = \begin{bmatrix} 2 & 1 & 1 & 0 \\ 1 & 1 & 0 & 1 \end{bmatrix}$, $R = \begin{bmatrix} 8 \\ 6 \end{bmatrix}$, $C = [3, 2, 0, 0]$

1. $X \geq 0$
2. $AX = R$ and
3. $z = f(X) = CX$ is maximized.

Fill in the blanks in Table 7.5.3 according to the notation established in Figure 7.5.3. The direction of increasing f is indicated by the arrow

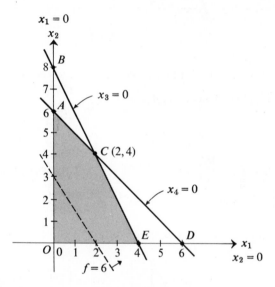

Figure 7.5.3

perpendicular to the line $3x_1 + 2x_2 = 6$. Use the fact that $X_B = B^{-1}R$ to find X_B. The answers, obtained by various methods, are shown in Table 7.5.4. Refer to the steps below only if you need help.

Step 1. At point O the basic variables are x_3, x_4 in that order. So $B = [A_3, A_4]$ and $BX_B = R$. We can either use Gauss-Jordan reduction or find B^{-1}. In the first method we have $[B \,|\, R] = [A_3, A_4 \,|\, R] = \begin{bmatrix} 1 & 0 & | & 8 \\ 0 & 1 & | & 6 \end{bmatrix}$, so that $X_B = \begin{bmatrix} 8 \\ 6 \end{bmatrix}$ and $X^T = [0, 0, 8, 6]$. Using the second method we would have $X_B = B^{-1}R = I_2^{-1}R = I_2 R = R = \begin{bmatrix} 8 \\ 6 \end{bmatrix}$, and $x_{B2} = x_4 = 6$.

Point	Basic Variables	B	$X_B^{\,T}$	X^T	x_{B2}
O	$x_3,$	[ ]	[ ]	[ ]	
A	$, x_2$	[ ]	[ ]	[ ]	
B	$x_4,$	[ ]	[ ]	[ ]	
C	$x_1,$	[ ]	[ ]	[ ]	
D	$, x_3$	[ ]	[ ]	[ ]	
E	$, x_4$	[ ]	[ ]	[ ]	

Table 7.5.3

Step 2. At the point A we have x_3 and x_2 as basic variables since $x_1 = x_4 = 0$. Thus $B = [A_3, A_2] = \begin{bmatrix} 1 & 1 \\ 0 & 1 \end{bmatrix}$.

$$[B \mid R] = [A_3, A_2 \mid R] = \begin{bmatrix} 1 & 1 & | & 8 \\ 0 & 1 & | & 6 \end{bmatrix} \sim \begin{bmatrix} 1 & 0 & | & 2 \\ 0 & 1 & | & 6 \end{bmatrix}$$

so that $X_B = \begin{bmatrix} 2 \\ 6 \end{bmatrix}$ and $X^T = [0, 6, 2, 0]$. We verify that $2\begin{bmatrix} 1 \\ 0 \end{bmatrix} + 6\begin{bmatrix} 1 \\ 1 \end{bmatrix} = \begin{bmatrix} 8 \\ 6 \end{bmatrix} = R$. Here $x_{B2} = x_2 = 6$.

Step 3. At point B, the basis matrix $B = [A_4, A_2] = \begin{bmatrix} 0 & 1 \\ 1 & 1 \end{bmatrix}$.

$$B^{-1} = \frac{\begin{bmatrix} 1 & -1 \\ -1 & 0 \end{bmatrix}}{-1} = \begin{bmatrix} -1 & 1 \\ 1 & 0 \end{bmatrix},$$

and

$$X_B = B^{-1}R = \begin{bmatrix} -1 & 1 \\ 1 & 0 \end{bmatrix}\begin{bmatrix} 8 \\ 6 \end{bmatrix} = \begin{bmatrix} -2 \\ 8 \end{bmatrix}$$

so that $X^T = [0, 8, 0, -2]$ and $x_{B2} = 8$.

Step 4. Point C. $B = [A_1, A_2] = \begin{bmatrix} 2 & 1 \\ 1 & 1 \end{bmatrix}$.

$$[B \mid R] = \begin{bmatrix} 2 & 1 & | & 8 \\ 1 & 1 & | & 6 \end{bmatrix} \sim \begin{bmatrix} 1 & 1/2 & | & 4 \\ 0 & 1/2 & | & 2 \end{bmatrix} \sim \begin{bmatrix} 1 & 0 & | & 2 \\ 0 & 1 & | & 4 \end{bmatrix},$$

so that $X_B = \begin{bmatrix} 2 \\ 4 \end{bmatrix}$ and $X^T = [2, 4, 0, 0]$, while $x_{B2} = 4$.

Step 5. Point D. $B = [A_1, A_3] = \begin{bmatrix} 2 & 1 \\ 1 & 0 \end{bmatrix}$.

$X_B = \begin{bmatrix} 6 \\ -4 \end{bmatrix}$, $X^T = [6, 0, -4, 0]$,   and $x_{B2} = -4$.

Step 6. Point E. $B = [A_1, A_4]$. $X_B = \begin{bmatrix} 4 \\ 2 \end{bmatrix}$, $X^T = [4, 0, 0, 2]$ and $x_{B2} = 2$. This information is gathered together in Table 7.5.4.

Point	Basic Variables	B	$X_B{}^T$	X^T	x_{B2}
O	x_3, x_4	$[A_3, A_4]$	$[8, 6]$	$[0, 0, 8, 6]$	6
A	x_3, x_2	$[A_3, A_2]$	$[2, 6]$	$[0, 6, 2, 0]$	6
B	x_4, x_2	$[A_4, A_2]$	$[-2, 8]$	$[0, 8, 0, -2]$	8
C	x_1, x_2	$[A_1, A_2]$	$[2, 4]$	$[2, 4, 0, 0]$	4
D	x_1, x_3	$[A_1, A_3]$	$[6, -4]$	$[6, 0, -4, 0]$	-4
E	x_1, x_4	$[A_1, A_4]$	$[4, 2]$	$[4, 0, 0, 2]$	2

Table 7.5.4

It should now be apparent that if we are able to represent the feasible region of an LP problem graphically, then it is possible to associate at least one basis with each extreme or corner point. We first determine a set of $n - m$ non-basic variables associated with the corner point. The columns of A associated with the remaining m variables make up B, in some order. When B is known, it is possible to use either Gauss-Jordan elimination or B^{-1} to find X_B, the values of the basic variables at the particular extreme or corner point under examination. Once X_B is known it is a simple matter to fill in the values on the non-basic variables (Why?) to find X.

The discerning reader may be wondering why we have said that it is possible to associate *at least one* basis with each corner point as opposed to *exactly one* basis. Although the latter statement would be true for all of the examples which we have studied so far, consider point C in the so-called degenerate case depicted in Figure 7.5.4. One possible set of non-basic variables associated with C is $\{x_2, x_3\}$. In this case x_1 and x_4 are basic. Thus $B_1 = [A_1, A_4]$ is one basis matrix associated with C. However, $x_4 = 0$ also, so that $\{x_2, x_4\}$ is another possible non-basic set for C. $B_2 = [A_1, A_3]$ is also a legitimate basis matrix for C. Is there another?

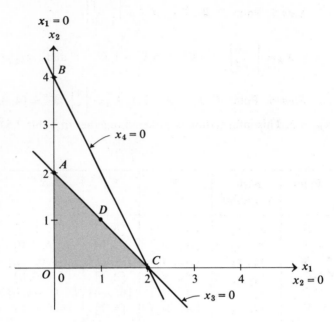

Figure 7.5.4

We should note especially from this example that it is possible for a basic variable to have a value 0. A basic feasible solution X with the property that $x_i = 0$ for some *basic variable* x_i, is called a **degenerate basic feasible solution**. Unless otherwise stated, we shall suppose throughout the remainder of the text that we are discussing a non-degenerate case. Although degeneracy is fairly common in many types of LP problems, it seldom causes serious computational difficulties. The algorithm that will be developed will almost always handle the degenerate case without revision.

Exercises 7.5

1. Let $B^{-1} = \begin{bmatrix} 1 & 1 \\ 5 & 6 \end{bmatrix}$ and $R = \begin{bmatrix} 1 \\ 4 \end{bmatrix}$.
   a. Find X_B.
   b. What is x_{B2}?
   c. Find B.
   d. By solving the appropriate equations, find a, b such that $R = aB_1 + bB_2$, where B_i is column i of B.
   e. Compare $[a, b]$ and $[x_{B1}, x_{B2}]$.

2. With each corner point of the feasible region of an LP problem, we may associate at least one _____ matrix B. From each set of m

linearly independent columns of A we can form a basis _____ and compute $X_B =$ _____. If $X_B \geqslant 0$ then the corresponding solution X is a _____ _____. Otherwise, the corresponding solution is _____. How do we know that we have a solution at all when we pick these m linearly independent vectors arbitrarily?

3. Consider the LP problem with $A = \begin{bmatrix} 1 & 3 & 1 & 0 \\ 3 & 1 & 0 & 1 \end{bmatrix}$, $R = \begin{bmatrix} 4 \\ 4 \end{bmatrix}$.

   a. $A_2 = [\ \ ]$.
   b. Let $B = [A_3, A_4] = B^{-1}$. Find X_B; $x_{B1} = x_{B2} =$ _____.
   c. Let $B = [A_1, A_4]$ and find X_B; $x_{B2} =$ _____.
   d. Let $B = [A_1, A_2]$ and find X_B; $x_{B1} =$ _____.
   e. Find x_{B2} if $B = [A_4, A_1]$. Compare with c. above.

4. If $R = 2B_1 + 3B_2 + 4B_3$ where $B = [B_1, B_2, B_3]$ then $x_{B1} =$ _____, $x_{B2} =$ _____, and $x_{B3} =$ _____. If the columns of B are rearranged to form a new matrix $B' = [B_3, B_1, B_2]$, then the new value of x_{B2} is _____.

5. Consider the constraint set

$$x_1 + 2x_2 + x_3 \qquad = 3$$
$$2x_1 + x_2 \qquad + x_4 = 3$$

of Exercises 1 and 3 of Section 7.4.

   a. Write the constraint equations in the new matrix format described in this section.
   b. Plot the vectors A_i and R as in Figure 7.5.1.
   c. Referring to Figure 7.4.2, fill in Table 7.5.5.

Point	Basic Variables	B	B^{-1}	X_B	X^T	x_{B1}
O	x_3, x_4	$\begin{bmatrix} 1 & 0 \\ 0 & 1 \end{bmatrix}$	$\begin{bmatrix} 1 & 0 \\ 0 & 1 \end{bmatrix}$	$\begin{bmatrix} 3 \\ 3 \end{bmatrix}$	$[0, 0, 3, 3]$	3
A						
B						
C						
D						
E						

Table 7.5.5

6. Consider the constraint set and figure associated with Exercise 5 of Section 7.4.
   a. Write the constraints in the matrix format of this section.
   b. Fill in Table 7.5.6 using appropriate data from Table 7.4.4 and Figure 7.4.3. $R = \begin{bmatrix} 2 \\ 4 \end{bmatrix}$.

Suggested reading

G. B. Dantzig, *Linear Programming and Extensions*, Princeton University Press, Princeton, N.J. (1963).

S. I. Gass, *Linear Programming*, McGraw-Hill, New York (1964).

G. Hadley, *Linear Programming*, Addison-Wesley, Reading, Mass. (1962).

New terms

basis matrix, 260   degenerate basic feasible solution, 266

7.6 A possible solution technique

For our problem P with

$$A = \begin{bmatrix} 2 & 1 & 1 & 0 \\ 1 & 1 & 0 & 1 \end{bmatrix}, \quad X = \begin{bmatrix} x_1 \\ x_2 \\ x_3 \\ x_4 \end{bmatrix}, \quad R = \begin{bmatrix} 6 \\ 4 \end{bmatrix}, \quad C = [5, 3, 0, 0],$$

we have the information shown in Figure 7.6.1 and Table 7.6.1. As before, the direction of increasing f is indicated in Figure 7.6.1 by the arrow. We can evaluate $z = f(X) = CX$ at each of the corner points listed in the table. We could use CX but instead we choose to use the matrix C_B which contains only the objective function coefficients of the basic variables in X_B in the same order. For example, at point O, $X_B = \begin{bmatrix} x_{B1} \\ x_{B2} \end{bmatrix} = \begin{bmatrix} x_3 \\ x_4 \end{bmatrix} = \begin{bmatrix} 6 \\ 4 \end{bmatrix}$. Thus $C_B = [c_{B1}, c_{B2}] = [c_3, c_4] = [0, 0]$. Since, at O, $x_1 = x_2 = 0$, it really does not matter what c_1 and c_2 are. Thus $f(X) = CX = C_B X_B = [0, 0]\begin{bmatrix} 6 \\ 4 \end{bmatrix} = 0$. At A, $C_B = [c_3, c_2] = [0, 3]$, and $f(X) = C_B X_B = [0, 3]\begin{bmatrix} 2 \\ 4 \end{bmatrix} = 12$. Similarly, at C, $f(X) = [5, 3]\begin{bmatrix} 2 \\ 2 \end{bmatrix} = 16$, and at $D, f(X) = [5, 0]\begin{bmatrix} 3 \\ 1 \end{bmatrix} = 15$.

Point	Basic Variables	B	B^{-1}	X_B	X^T	x_{B2}	Solution Degenerate?
O		$[A_3, A_4] = \begin{bmatrix} 1 & 0 \\ 0 & 1 \end{bmatrix}$	$\begin{bmatrix} 1 & 0 \\ 0 & 1 \end{bmatrix}$	$\begin{bmatrix} 2 \\ 4 \end{bmatrix}$	$[0, 0, 2, 4]$	4	
A	$x_2,$						
B	$, x_2$	$[A_3, A_2] = \begin{bmatrix} 1 & 1 \\ 0 & 1 \end{bmatrix}$		$\begin{bmatrix} -2 \\ 4 \end{bmatrix}$	$[0, 4, -2, 0]$	4	
C	x_1, x_4						
C							YES
C	x_1, x_2	$[A_1, A_2] = \begin{bmatrix} 1 & 1 \\ 2 & 1 \end{bmatrix}$	$\begin{bmatrix} -1 & 1 \\ 2 & -1 \end{bmatrix}$	$\begin{bmatrix} 2 \\ 0 \end{bmatrix}$	$[2, 0, 0, 0]$	0	YES

Table 7.5.6

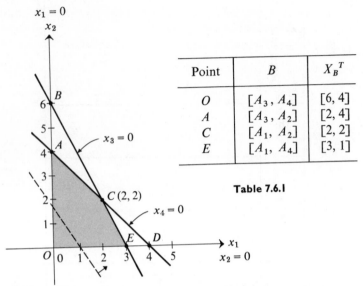

Figure 7.6.1

So, as far as corner points are concerned, f takes on its maximum value at C, as we saw previously, and the maximum value of f is 16.

As we noted in Section 7.2, the geometry of the situation makes it clear that the optimal feasible solution occurs at the extreme point C. It may help, in considering larger LP problems, to consider the many "points" and faces of a many-faceted diamond. It is just such an enclosed solid (known as a polyhedron) which is created as a feasible region in a problem with planes rather than straight lines as boundaries.

We can state now, and we shall later attempt to make it seem more plausible, that for an LP problem which has an optimal feasible solution, *at least one optimal feasible solution will always occur at one of the corner points of the feasible region.* Thus, if we were to find all of the corner points, and then evaluate the objective function at each one, we could find the optimal feasible solution by exhaustively comparing these functional values.

Such a method is not computationally practical for problems of even moderate size. We have seen that (excluding the degenerate case) we get a different basis and thus a different extreme point for each possible *BFS*. We can choose the m basic variables from the n variables in $\binom{n}{m}$ ways.* To determine which do correspond to corner points

* The binomial coefficient $\binom{n}{m}$ is the standard notation for the number of different combinations of n objects taken m at a time. $\binom{n}{m} = \dfrac{n!}{(n-m)!\,m!}$.

(rather than points such as B and D) the basic solutions must be computed and examined for feasibility. The objective function f must then be evaluated for each remaining BFS. In even a comparatively small practical LP problem with $n = 20$ and $m = 10$, there are $\binom{20}{10} = 184{,}756$ basic solutions to compute, examine, evaluate, and compare.

The simplex technique, to which we now turn, is an ingenious method that examines only a subset of the entire set of basic feasible solutions (or associated extreme points), and usually only a small subset of them, until an optimum one is reached, at which time the algorithm terminates. The number of BFS examined is usually amazingly small, when compared with the total number which exist.

Exercises 7.6

1. Consider the LP problem with $C = [1, 2, -1, 3]$. If $B = [A_1, A_3]$ then $C_B = [\ , \ ]$. If $X_B = \begin{bmatrix} 1 \\ 2 \end{bmatrix}$ then $X^T = [\ , \ , \ ]$ and $f(X) = C_B X_B =$ _____.

2. Let $C = [3, -1, 4, 2]$ and $B = [A_3, A_4]$. Then, if _____ $= \begin{bmatrix} 5 \\ 6 \end{bmatrix}$, $f(X) = C_B X_B = [\ , \ ]\begin{bmatrix} \ \\ \ \end{bmatrix} = 32$.

3. Let $A = \begin{bmatrix} 1 & 3 & 1 & 0 \\ 3 & 1 & 0 & 1 \end{bmatrix}$, $C = [1, 2, 0, 0]$, and $R = \begin{bmatrix} 4 \\ 4 \end{bmatrix}$.

    a. Find all possible BFS by choosing 2 columns of A as basic columns to form $B = [A_i, A_j]$ and then finding $X_B = B^{-1}R$. If $x_{Bi} < 0$ for some i, discard X_B.
    b. For each of the 4 BFS in a., find C_B and $f(X) = C_B X_B$.
    c. Assuming that we wish to maximize f and that a corner point is optimal, find the optimal BFS.
    d. Find $C_B X_B$ for each BFS if $C = [1, 0, 0, 0]$. What is the optimal BFS now?
    e. Draw a sketch and verify your results graphically.

4. In an LP problem with m constraints and n variables C_B will have _____ components as will _____. To find X from X_B we first must know the columns of the _____ _____ B. If A_3 is in column 1 of B then $x_{B1} = x_3$ and $c_{B1} =$ _____. We fill in the value of $x_{B1} = x_3$ in X and continue to do so for each of the m numbers x_{Bi}. We then merely fill in the remaining $n - m$ numbers x_i with _____.

5. Suppose that $C = [-3, -1, 0, 0]$ in Exercise 5 of Section 7.5, and suppose that you wish to minimize f.
    a. Find $C_B X_B = f(X_B)$ for each feasible basis B in Table 7.5.5.
    b. At what point X does the optimum BFS occur?
    c. What is it?

6. Let $C = [1, -1, 0, 0]$ in Exercise 5 and suppose that you wish to maximize f. Find $C_B X_B = f(X_B)$ for each feasible basis B and find the optimum BFS.

7. Consider the maximization problem of Example 7.5.1 with $A = \begin{bmatrix} 2 & 1 & 1 & 0 \\ 1 & 1 & 0 & 1 \end{bmatrix}$, $R = \begin{bmatrix} 8 \\ 6 \end{bmatrix}$, and $C = [3, 2, 0, 0]$.
    a. Using X_B as shown in Table 7.5.4 compute $f(X_B)$ for each feasible basis.
    b. The optimal X_B is _____, where $f(X_B) =$ _____.
    c. The solution X associated with the optimum X_B is [_____, _____, _____, _____]^T.

8. Use the method of this section and the information in Table 7.5.6 to find three optimal basic feasible solutions if $C = [3, 1, 0, 0]$.

7.7   The simplex algorithm in equation form

We shall continue to assume that if an optimal feasible solution to an LP problem exists at all, then at least one optimal feasible solution will occur at an extreme or corner point of the feasible region. In this section we will show how it is possible to start at a given corner point and establish whether or not it would be beneficial, in terms of improvement of the value of the objective function, to move to an adjacent corner point. If there is an adjacent corner point (one connected to the original by an edge of the feasible region) to which we could move and improve the value of z, we will do so. If there is more than one such point, we will choose the one to move to by first establishing the rate of change of z in each possible direction. We shall then move along the boundary of the feasible region to that adjacent corner point which offers the best rate of change of z. On reaching the new corner point we repeat the process, and keep moving from corner point to adjacent corner point until we reach an optimal corner point. The fact that we can tell when we have reached an optimal corner point is a happy phenomenon associated with the fact that we are dealing with a *linear* programming problem. If we ever reach a corner point from which it would not be profitable to move to any adjacent corner point, we can stop and know that no other point in the feasible region—corner point, boundary point, or interior point—has a better value of z than the present one. This is proved in many of the references mentioned in this chapter. We shall attempt to make it seem plausible in Section 7.11.

Let us use problem P to describe the procedure that we have in mind. The objective function is $f(x_1, x_2, x_3, x_4) = 5x_1 + 3x_2$ and our equality constraints are

$$2x_1 + x_2 + x_3 \quad\;\; = 6$$
$$x_1 + x_2 \quad\;\; + x_4 = 4.$$

The other information which we need is contained in Figure 7.7.1 and Table 7.7.1.

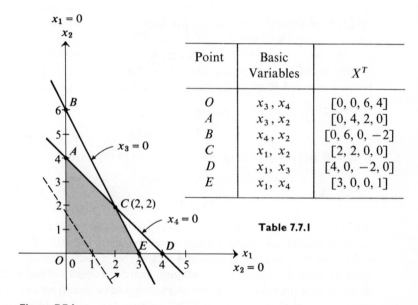

Point	Basic Variables	X^T
O	x_3, x_4	$[0, 0, 6, 4]$
A	x_3, x_2	$[0, 4, 2, 0]$
B	x_4, x_2	$[0, 6, 0, -2]$
C	x_1, x_2	$[2, 2, 0, 0]$
D	x_1, x_3	$[4, 0, -2, 0]$
E	x_1, x_4	$[3, 0, 0, 1]$

Table 7.7.1

Figure 7.7.1

Because of the ease in so doing, we shall start at O. At this point the basic variables are x_3 and x_4. Let us solve the constraint equations for these variables. We obtain

$$x_3 = 6 - 2x_1 - x_2$$
$$x_4 = 4 - \;\; x_1 - x_2.$$

Since, in reality, $x_1 = x_2 = 0$ at this point, it is clear that $x_3 = 6$ and $x_4 = 4$. We can proceed toward and eventually arrive at an adjacent extreme point by increasing *one* of the non-basic variables from 0 to an appropriate value and leaving the other non-basic variable at 0.

Which non-basic variable should we choose to increase from 0? If we decide to increase x_1 and leave $x_2 = 0$ we will proceed from O in the direction toward extreme points E and D along the line $x_2 = 0$. If we increase x_2 and leave $x_1 = 0$ we will move toward A and B. We use the objective function to help us decide whether or not we are at an optimal corner point, and, if not, to choose which direction to go.

Now, $z = 5x_1 + 3x_2 + 0x_3 + 0x_4 = f(x_1, x_2, x_3, x_4)$. At $O, f(0, 0, 6, 4) = 0$. What will happen to z if we increase x_1 and hold $x_2 = 0$? For each unit which we increase x_1, z will increase by 5 units. Similarly, if we hold $x_1 = 0$ and increase x_2, z will increase 3 units for each unit increase in x_2. Without looking at the graph or table, or making further computations, we do not know how much we will be able to increase either x_1 or x_2 *and still remain feasible*. We do know that z will increase regardless of which of x_1 or x_2 we choose. Since the per unit rate of change (increase) of z is higher for x_1, let us increase x_1 and move out along the x_1 axis.

We know from the geometry that we should stop at E in order to remain in the feasible region. How does algebra solve this geometrical problem for us? Reconsider the basic equations at O, namely

$$x_3 = 6 - 2x_1 - x_2$$
$$x_4 = 4 - x_1 - x_2.$$

If $x_2 = 0$ and is to remain at the value 0, we really have

$$x_3 = 6 - 2x_1$$
$$x_4 = 4 - x_1.$$

What happens to the values of the previously basic variables x_3, x_4 as x_1 is increased *and these equations are required to hold*? The (-2) coefficient of x_1 in the first equation tells us that x_3 will *decrease* 2 units from its present value of 6 for each unit that x_1 increases. That x_3 does decrease as x_1 increases from O toward E should be clear from the graph, since $x_3 = 6$ at O and $x_3 = 0$ at E. When x_1 is 3, x_3 will be down to 0 on the 2 for 1 basis indicated by the equation. We thus have one limitation on the increase of x_1. If there were no limitation on increasing x_1, of course, we would let x_1 increase without bound, which would allow z to increase without bound also. Very few practical problems fall into this category, unfortunately, as we would then be able to obtain an infinite profit.

Consider the second equation,

$$x_4 = 4 - x_1.$$

As x_1 increases, x_4 *decreases* on a 1 for 1 basis from its present value of 4. Thus x_4 will be down to 0 when $x_1 = 4$. We have obtained a second limitation on the new value of x_1, that $x_1 \leqslant 4$. The prior limitation thus requires us to stop when $x_1 = 3$, at E. If we continued to let x_1 increase until $x_4 = 0$, we would have arrived at D in the infeasible region. The algebra of the situation has indeed enabled us to stop at a corner of the boundary of the feasible region, thus fulfilling the non-negativity restrictions.

We now know that if we increase x_1, then x_3 and x_4 will both decrease, but that x_3 will reach 0 first, and thus become non-basic. We should note that the negative coefficients of x_1, along with the present values 6, 4 of the basic variables, as indicated in the original equations,

$$x_3 = 6 - 2x_1 - x_2$$
$$x_4 = 4 - x_1 - x_2$$

were the clue to this fact. A coefficient of $(+2)$ instead of (-2) would have indicated that x_3 would have increased on a 2 for 1 basis as x_1 increased. We would then have had no x_3 restriction on the increase of x_1.

Let us now re-solve the basic equations at O to find the new basic equations that apply at point E. The new basic variable is x_1 and it replaces x_3. We therefore use the first equation to solve for x_1. Thus

$$2x_1 = 6 - x_2 - x_3$$

so that

$$x_1 = 3 - (1/2)x_2 - (1/2)x_3 .$$

We use this value of x_1 to eliminate x_1 from the second equation. Thus

$$x_4 = 4 - x_1 - x_2 = 4 - [3 - (1/2)x_2 - (1/2)x_3] - x_2$$
$$x_4 = 1 - (1/2)x_2 + (1/2)x_3 .$$

Our new basic equations at E are thus

$$x_1 = 3 - (1/2)x_2 - (1/2)x_3$$
$$x_4 = 1 - (1/2)x_2 + (1/2)x_3 .$$

Since $x_2 = x_3 = 0$ we see that $x_1 = 3$ and $x_4 = 1$ at E, values which we have determined earlier by other methods.

What is the value of z at E? We had hoped to increase z by 5 units for each unit increase in x_1. Since $x_1 = 3$ at E, z should be 15. Since $f(3, 0, 0, 1) = 5(3) + 3(0) + 0(0) + 0(1) = 15$, we have reached our goal. We could have discovered this in another way, by expressing z in terms of the present non-basic variables as follows:

$$z = 5x_1 + 3x_2$$

in terms of the non-basic variables at O. Since

$$x_1 = 3 - (1/2)x_2 - (1/2)x_3,$$

then

$$z = 5 \cdot [3 - (1/2)x_2 - (1/2)x_3] + 3x_2$$
$$= 15 + (1/2)x_2 - (5/2)x_3$$

at E. Since $x_2 = x_3 = 0$, we have $z = 15$.

The plus and minus signs for the non-basic variables x_2 and x_3, now 0, are significant. We see that an increase in x_2 with $x_3 = 0$ will lead to an increase in z of 1/2 unit for each units increase in x_2. On the other hand, an increase in x_3 will lead to a decrease in z. We might have expected the latter, since we just decreased x_3 to increase z in going from O to E.

Our algebraic representation of z at E is thus sufficient to notify us that an increase in x_2 is appropriate. A look at the geometrical diagram would, of course, have told us the same thing. We still need to know where to stop, however, in order that we do not skip point C and go all the way to the infeasible point B, along the line $x_3 = 0$. The constraint equations again tell us which of the basic variables to remove in order to remain feasible. Consider

$$x_1 = 3 - (1/2)x_2 - (1/2)x_3$$
$$x_4 = 1 - (1/2)x_2 + (1/2)x_3,$$

where we have decided to increase x_2 and hold $x_3 = 0$. In this case both x_1 and x_4 decrease as x_2 increases, and they decrease at the same rate, namely 1/2 unit for each unit increase in x_2. Since x_4 started out at the lesser value 1, it will arrive at 0 faster, that is, when x_2 has increased by 2 units, from 0 to 2. At that point, the new value of x_1, on the same basis, should be 2 and the new value of z should be $15 + (1/2)(2) = 16$. (Why?)

We re-solve the old basic equations, replacing x_4 by x_2 in the basic set. We first solve for x_2 in terms of the new non-basic variables, x_4 and x_3, to obtain

$$(1/2)x_2 = 1 + (1/2)x_3 - x_4$$

or

$$x_2 = 2 + x_3 - 2x_4.$$

Using the latter equation to eliminate x_2 from the x_1-equation so as to express x_1 in terms of the non-basic variables alone, we have

$$x_1 = 3 - (1/2)[2 + x_3 - 2x_4] - (1/2)x_3$$

or

$$x_1 = 2 - x_3 + x_4$$

so that our new equations are

$$x_1 = 2 - x_3 + x_4$$
$$x_2 = 2 + x_3 - 2x_4 .$$

Thus at C, $X = [2, 2, 0, 0]^T$, as we have seen before. Expressing z in terms of the present non-basic variables, x_3 and x_4, we have

$$z = 15 + (1/2)x_2 - (5/2)x_3 \quad \text{(at } E)$$
$$= 15 + (1/2)(2 + x_3 - 2x_4) - (5/2)x_3$$
$$= 16 - 2x_3 - x_4 \quad \text{(at } C).$$

The coefficients of each of the non-basic variables are now negative, indicating that an increase in either would lead to a decrease in z. Since $x_3 = x_4 = 0$, they cannot be decreased. Thus, it would do no good to move to either of the two adjacent extreme points that can be reached from C; so we stop. The optimal feasible solution is $X = [2, 2, 0, 0]^T$ and the maximum value of z is 16.

You should recall that we started this exercise by increasing x_1 because it provided a greater *rate of increase* of z, while we realized that we could just as well have increased x_2 and proceeded toward A with $x_1 = 0$. You should now go through the manipulations required to proceed to point C through point A. You will note that exactly the same number of iterations (steps in our process) are required, namely 2.

Exercises 7.7

1. Consider the LP problem of Example 7.4.2 with $A = \begin{bmatrix} 2 & 3 & 1 & 0 \\ 3 & 2 & 0 & 1 \end{bmatrix}$, $R = \begin{bmatrix} 6 \\ 6 \end{bmatrix}$, and $C = [4, 3, 0, 0]$ where we wish to maximize $f(X) = CX$. Complete the blanks in the following solution. Draw a sketch of the feasible region.

    a.   The original constraint equations are

$$2x_1 + 3x_2 + x_3 \qquad = 6$$
$$3x_1 + 2x_2 \qquad + x_4 = 6.$$

The basic variables at the origin are x_3 and x_4. We solve the original equations and obtain

$$x_3 = \underline{\hspace{3cm}}$$
$$x_4 = \underline{\hspace{3cm}},$$

and $f(X) = 4x_1 + 3x_2 = 0$, in terms of the present basic variables. We see that f will increase if either x_1 or x_2 is increased.

b. Since the rate of change of f is 4 for x_1 and only 3 for x_2, we choose to let x_1 increase. Both _____ and _____ will decrease as x_1 increases, and _____ at a faster rate. We decide to make _____ non-basic since it reaches 0 first. We thus solve for x_1 in terms of x_2, x_4 to obtain and eliminate x_1 from the x_3 equation to obtain

$$x_3 = 2 - (5/3)x_2 + (2/3)x_4$$
$$x_1 = 2 - (2/3)x_2 - (1/3)x_4.$$

We now can express f in terms of the new non-basic variables _____, _____ and obtain

$$f(X) = 4x_1 + 3x_2$$
$$= 4(2 - (2/3)x_2 - (1/3)x_4) + 3x_2$$
$$= 8 + (1/3)x_2 - (4/3)x_4.$$

c. f will increase if _____ is increased. Both _____ and _____ will _____ as x_2 increases, but _____ will reach 0 first, so we make _____ non-basic. We re-solve our equations for the new basic set {_____, _____} and obtain

$$x_2 = \underline{\hspace{3cm}}$$
$$x_1 = \underline{\hspace{3cm}}$$

and

$$f(X) = 8 + (1/3)(6/5 - (3/5)x_3 + (2/5)x_4) - (4/3)x_4$$
$$= 42/5 - (1/5)x_3 - (6/5)x_4.$$

d. Since $f(X)$ will decrease if either x_3 or x_4 is increased, we stop with optimal BFS $X^T = [6/5, 6/5, 0, 0]$ and $f(X) = 42/5$.

2. Suppose we have solved for the basic variables x_3, x_4 in terms of the non-basic variables x_1, x_2 and have obtained

$$x_3 = 4 - 3x_1 + 2x_2$$
$$x_4 = 2 - 1x_1 - 5x_2$$

and $f(X) = 0 + 4x_1 + 3x_2$.

a. If we increase x_1 we will increase f by _____ units for each unit x_1 increases, assuming that we hold x_2 at _____, and let x_3 and x_4 change as they must in order to keep the equations satisfied.

b. For each unit of increase of x_1, x_3 will _____ by _____ units and x_4 will _____ by _____ units. Since $4/3 < 2/1$ we must let x_3 become non-basic as _____ will have reached 0 when x_1 reaches $4/3$. Since x_1 can only increase to $4/3$ the new value of f will be equal to the old value, 0, plus $4(4/3) = 16/3$.

c. The new set of basic equations is

$$x_1 = \underline{\hspace{4cm}}$$
$$x_4 = (2/3) - (17/3)x_2 + (1/3)x_3$$

and $f(X) = 16/3 + (17/3)x_2 - (4/3)x_3$. We note that the new value of x_1 is $4/3$ as expected and that f has increased by $16/3$ as predicted.

d. We now wish to increase _____.

e. If, instead of increasing x_1 at the beginning, we had chosen to increase x_2, we would have made _____ non-basic and achieved a change in f of _____.

3. Use the method of this section to solve the maximization LP problem of Exercise 3, Section 7.6, with $A = \begin{bmatrix} 1 & 3 & 1 & 0 \\ 3 & 1 & 0 & 1 \end{bmatrix}$, $R = \begin{bmatrix} 4 \\ 4 \end{bmatrix}$, and $C = [1, 2, 0, 0]$.

4. Use the method of this section to solve the minimization LP problem of Exercise 5, Section 7.6, with $A = \begin{bmatrix} 1 & 2 & 1 & 0 \\ 2 & 1 & 0 & 1 \end{bmatrix}$, $R = \begin{bmatrix} 3 \\ 3 \end{bmatrix}$, and $C = [-3, -1, 0, 0]$.

5. In the following basic equations for a maximization problem

$$x_3 = 5 + ax_1 + bx_2$$
$$x_4 = 6 + cx_1 + dx_2$$

and $f(X) = 0 + ex_1 + gx_2$:

a. We wish to increase x_1 if e is _____.

b. If x_1 is increased, x_3 will decrease if _____ is _____.

c. If x_4 is to be made non-basic when x_1 increases, the new value of x_1 will be _____, while the new value of f will be _____. The new value of x_3, which remains basic, will be _____.

d. If we should remove x_4 in order to maintain a feasible solution, and mistakenly remove x_3, how will the mistake show itself in the next set of equations?

e.   Verify your conjecture in d. by letting $a = b = -1$, $c = -2$, $d = e = g = 3$ above and letting x_1 replace x_3 in the basic set.

Suggested reading

G. B. Dantzig, *Linear Programming and Extensions*, Princeton University Press, Princeton, N.J. (1963).

7.8   The simplex algorithm in tableau form

The simplex algorithm of Dantzig is usually presented in a so-called tableau format that we shall introduce in this section. The tableaus developed in this version of the algorithm are very closely related to the sequence of sets of equations developed in the last section. For this reason, let us consider the graph for problem P in Figure 7.8.1 and the

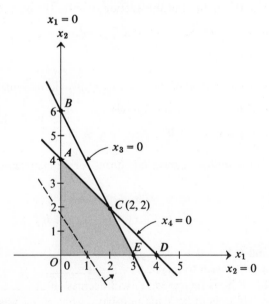

Figure 7.8.1

equations associated with the solution. To emphasize the similarity between the ideas of the two sections, we shall rewrite the previous equations, putting all of the variables on the same side of the equation.

Point	Equations	Basic Variables
O	$6 = 2x_1 + \quad x_2 + \quad x_3$ $4 = \quad x_1 + \quad x_2 \quad\quad + x_4$ $z - 0 = 5x_1 + \quad 3x_2$	x_3 x_4
E	$3 = \quad x_1 + (1/2)x_2 + (1/2)x_3$ $1 = \quad\quad\quad (1/2)x_2 - (1/2)x_3 + x_4$ $z - 15 = \quad\quad (1/2)x_2 - (5/2)x_3$	x_1 x_4
C	$2 = x_1 \quad\quad + \quad x_3 - x_4$ $2 = \quad\quad\quad x_2 - \quad x_3 + 2x_4$ $z - 16 = \quad\quad - \quad 2x_3 - x_4$	x_1 x_2

We note that the z value for the appropriate point is obtained by setting the non-basic variables equal to 0. At point C, for example, $x_3 = x_4 = 0$, so that $z = 16$.

We now begin to develop the simplex tableau by writing down the augmented matrix for the equations at point O in Tableau 7.8.1.

R	A_1	A_2	A_3	A_4
6	2	1	1	0
4	1	1	0	1

Tableau 7.8.1

Conventionally in LP, the R matrix is written on the left. We now add a column B denoting the basis vectors at point O and another column $C_B{}^T$ containing the cost coefficients of the variables associated with the basis vectors. Since $B = [A_3, A_4]$ at O, $C_B{}^T = \begin{bmatrix} c_3 \\ c_4 \end{bmatrix} = \begin{bmatrix} 0 \\ 0 \end{bmatrix}$. In order to keep track of the cost coefficients of all of the variables, we write C, the row matrix of such coefficients, along the top of the tableau. We then have Tableau 7.8.2.

B	$C_B{}^T$	C R	5 A_1	3 A_2	0 A_3	0 A_4
A_3	0	6	2	1	1	0
A_4	0	4	1	1	0	1

Tableau 7.8.2

The tableau thus contains all of the information required to describe the *BFS* corresponding to extreme point O, namely $X^T = [0, 0, 6, 4]$. In skeleton form, we have, in the tableau body, the quantities indicated in Tableau 7.8.3.

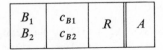

Tableau 7.8.3

As in the method described in the last section we wish to determine whether or not the present *BFS* at extreme point O is optimal. We create the last row of our tableau to provide us with this information. For reasons which we will make clear, we use the symbol z_j and call this new row the $(c_j - z_j)$ row as shown in Tableau 7.8.4.

$c_j - z_j$	z	$(c_1 - z_1)$ $(c_2 - z_2)$ $(c_3 - z_3)$ $(c_4 - z_4)$

Tableau 7.8.4

The second place in this new row is filled in with the value of z at O, namely $C_B R = [0, 0] \begin{bmatrix} 6 \\ 4 \end{bmatrix} = 0$, which, as shown, can easily be computed from the second and third columns of Tableau 7.8.2. We thus have Tableau 7.8.5.

$c_j - z_j$	0	

Tableau 7.8.5

The elements in the remainder of the row are computed in the same manner as z. Under A_1 we wish to compute

$$c_1 - z_1 = c_1 - C_B A_1 = 5 - [0, 0] \begin{bmatrix} 2 \\ 1 \end{bmatrix} = 5;$$

again, this is a computation that is easily done with the matrices C_B^T and A_1, conveniently placed as they are in Tableau 7.8.2. We now compute

$$c_2 - z_2 = c_2 - C_B A_2 = 3 - [0, 0] \begin{bmatrix} 1 \\ 1 \end{bmatrix} = 3,$$

$$c_3 - z_3 = c_3 - C_B A_3 = 0 - [0, 0]\begin{bmatrix} 1 \\ 0 \end{bmatrix} = 0,$$

and

$$c_4 - z_4 = c_4 - C_B A_4 = 0 - [0, 0]\begin{bmatrix} 0 \\ 1 \end{bmatrix} = 0.$$

The entire last row is shown in Tableau 7.8.6.

$c_j - z_j$	0	5	3	0	0

Tableau 7.8.6

Tableau 7.8.7 is the completed starting tableau.

		C	5	3	0	0
B	$C_B{}^T$	R	A_1	A_2	A_3	A_4
A_3	0	6	2	1	1	0
A_4	0	4	1	1	0	1
$c_j - z_j$		0	5	3	0	0

Tableau 7.8.7

We recall that at O,

$$z - 0 = 5x_1 + 3x_2 + 0x_3 + 0x_4.$$

The newly-created row contains constants which are identical to these. We used these constants before to tell us whether or not the present extreme point or basic feasible solution was optimal. The (5) corresponding to A_1 and the (3) corresponding to A_2 tell us that we are not optimal at O; that is, that z may be increased by moving to either adjacent extreme point that may be reached from O. Again, z will be increased by 5 units for each unit that x_1 increases as we move to the appropriate adjacent extreme point, namely E. Similarly, z will be increased by 3 units for each unit that x_2 increases as we move to A, if we so choose.

So as to conform to the procedure in the previous section, let us move to point E by making x_1 basic or putting A_1 into the basis matrix

B. We emphasize that this is a purely arbitrary decision and that we could just as well have chosen to increase x_2 and go to *A*. Most computer algorithms use this same criterion—the maximum rate of change of z—for choice of a variable to be made basic, or equivalently, a choice of vector to be brought into the basis matrix *B*. From computational experience it appears to be, *on the average*, the criterion which leads to an optimal *BFS* in the least number of steps.

From the old tableau, we construct a new tableau as follows:

1. Determine which vector (variable) should leave the basis (become non-basic) in order to maintain a basic *feasible* solution.

2. Perform Gauss-Jordan reduction on the augmented matrix portion of the tableau to obtain a new tableau with a new augmented matrix whose equations are those for point *E*.

Let us first determine which vector should leave the basis if A_1 enters. We use the elements of column A_1 to help us decide. We note from the ideas of the previous section* that the $(+2)$ in the a_{11} spot means that x_3 will decrease 2 units for each unit that x_1 increases. Since x_3 is presently 6, x_1 could increase $6/2 = 3$ units before x_3 reaches 0. Similarly, the $(+1)$ in the a_{21} position indicates that x_4 will *decrease* 1 unit for each unit that x_1 increases. Thus x_1 could increase $4/1 = 4$ units before x_4 reaches 0. Since the minimum of $\{3, 4\} = \min\{6/2, 4/1\} = 3$, we must replace A_3 with A_1 in order to remain feasible and prevent our going to point *D* rather than *E*. Our general criterion will be derived later.

Having decided to let A_1 replace A_3 in the basis we merely use the Gauss-Jordan operations to (1) replace x_3 by x_1 as the basic variable in row 1 and (2) to eliminate x_1 from the set of non-basic variables in row 2, replacing it with the new non-basic x_3. We perform the first operation by designating the element in the A_1 column and the A_3 row as the **pivot element** and so indicate by circling it as shown in Tableau 7.8.8.

B	$C_B{}^T$	R	A_1	A_2	A_3	A_4
	C		5	3	0	0
A_3	0	6	②	1	1	0
A_4	0	4	1	1	0	1
$c_j - z_j$		0	5	3	0	0

Tableau 7.8.8

* It may be helpful to write down the entire equation with all of the non-basic variables transposed to the opposite side of the equation.

We now obtain the first row of the new tableau by dividing each element of the old first row by the pivot element, 2, and obtain Tableau 7.8.9.

		3	1	1/2	1/2	0

Tableau 7.8.9

We then eliminate x_1 from row 2 by letting $R_2 \Leftarrow -R_1 + R_2$ to obtain Tableau 7.8.10.

		C	5	3	0	0
		3	1	1/2	1/2	0
		1	0	1/2	−1/2	1

Tableau 7.8.10

We now label Tableau 7.8.10 with the appropriate notation for the new extreme point. The new basis $B = [A_1, A_4]$. Thus C_B, the matrix of cost coefficients, is $[5, 0] = [c_1, c_4]$. In the old R column we have X_B, the matrix of coordinates of R in terms of the new basis $B = [A_1, A_4]$. We verify that

$$R = \begin{bmatrix} 6 \\ 4 \end{bmatrix} = 3\begin{bmatrix} 2 \\ 1 \end{bmatrix} + 1\begin{bmatrix} 0 \\ 1 \end{bmatrix} = 3A_1 + 1A_4 = \begin{bmatrix} 2 & 0 \\ 1 & 1 \end{bmatrix}\begin{bmatrix} 3 \\ 1 \end{bmatrix} = BX_B.$$

How should we label the columns which replaced the columns of A? Certainly the A_i are no longer there. Suppose we let the matrix

$$\begin{bmatrix} 1 & 1/2 & 1/2 & 0 \\ 0 & 1/2 & -1/2 & 1 \end{bmatrix} = Y = [Y_1, Y_2, Y_3, Y_4],$$

and label the columns accordingly. Then, since

$$BY_1 = \begin{bmatrix} 2 & 0 \\ 1 & 1 \end{bmatrix}\begin{bmatrix} 1 \\ 0 \end{bmatrix} = \begin{bmatrix} 2 \\ 1 \end{bmatrix} = A_1,$$

$$BY_2 = \begin{bmatrix} 2 & 0 \\ 1 & 1 \end{bmatrix}\begin{bmatrix} 1/2 \\ 1/2 \end{bmatrix} = \begin{bmatrix} 1 \\ 1 \end{bmatrix} = A_2,$$

$$BY_3 = \begin{bmatrix} 2 & 0 \\ 1 & 1 \end{bmatrix}\begin{bmatrix} 1/2 \\ -1/2 \end{bmatrix} = \begin{bmatrix} 1 \\ 0 \end{bmatrix} = A_3,$$

and

$$BY_4 = \begin{bmatrix} 2 & 0 \\ 1 & 1 \end{bmatrix}\begin{bmatrix} 0 \\ 1 \end{bmatrix} = \begin{bmatrix} 0 \\ 1 \end{bmatrix} = A_4$$

we see that

$$BY = B[Y_1, Y_2, Y_3, Y_4] = [BY_1, BY_2, BY_3, BY_4]$$
$$= [A_1, A_2, A_3, A_4] = A.$$

We then have the partial Tableau 7.8.11

		C	5	3	0	0
B	$C_B{}^T$	X_B	Y_1	Y_2	Y_3	Y_4
A_1	5	3	1	1/2	1/2	0
A_4	0	1	0	1/2	$-1/2$	1

Tableau 7.8.11

which we see is related to the original tableau by the relation

$$B[X_B \mid Y] = [BX_B \mid BY] = [R \mid A].$$

We fill in the last row to find the present z value at point E and to see if we are optimal by the same method as before, except that we replace A_j by Y_j in our computation of z_j. Now,

$$z = C_B X_B = [5, 0]\begin{bmatrix} 3 \\ 1 \end{bmatrix} = 15,$$

$$c_1 - z_1 = c_1 - C_B Y_1 = 5 - [5, 0]\begin{bmatrix} 1 \\ 0 \end{bmatrix} = 0,$$

$$c_2 - z_2 = c_2 - C_B Y_2 = 3 - [5, 0]\begin{bmatrix} 1/2 \\ 1/2 \end{bmatrix} = 1/2,$$

$$c_3 - z_3 = c_3 - C_B Y_3 = 0 - [5, 0] \begin{bmatrix} 1/2 \\ -1/2 \end{bmatrix} = -5/2,$$

and

$$c_4 - z_4 = c_4 - C_B Y_4 = 0 - [5, 0] \begin{bmatrix} 0 \\ 1 \end{bmatrix} = 0.$$

We thus have the completed Tableau 7.8.12.

		C	5	3	0	0
B	$C_B{}^T$	X_B	Y_1	Y_2	Y_3	Y_4
A_1	5	3	1	1/2	1/2	0
A_4	0	1	0	1/2	$-1/2$	1
$c_j - z_j$		15	0	1/2	$-5/2$	0

Tableau 7.8.12

You should now compare the equations represented by the body of the tableau, that is, by $[X_B \mid Y]$, and those equations which we found to represent point E. They are exactly the same. We have merely used the Gauss-Jordan reduction process to move us from O to E.

We now examine the last row to see if the present BFS is optimal. Since there is a positive element, namely $(1/2)$ in the $c_2 - z_2$ position we know that we can increase z by increasing x_2 or by bringing A_2 into the basis. Thus Y_2 is the new pivot column. The signs of both $y_{21} = 1/2$ and $y_{22} = 1/2$ are positive, indicating that x_1 and x_4 will decrease as x_2 increases and both at the same rate.

$$\frac{x_{B1}}{y_{12}} = \frac{x_1}{y_{12}} = \frac{3}{1/2} = 6$$

represents the maximum allowable increase in x_2 that can occur if x_1 is to remain feasible. On the other hand

$$\frac{x_{B2}}{y_{22}} = \frac{x_4}{y_{22}} = \frac{1}{1/2} = 2$$

represents the maximum allowable increase in x_2 that can occur if x_4 is to remain feasible. Since the minimum of

$$\left\{ \frac{3}{1/2}, \frac{1}{1/2} \right\} = \min\left\{ \frac{x_{B1}}{y_{12}}, \frac{x_{B2}}{y_{22}} \right\} = \min\{6, 2\} = 2,$$

we see that x_4 will reach 0 first when x_2 reaches 2. Thus A_4 must be removed from the basis to preserve feasibility and keep us from moving to point B, rather than C. The pivot element is thus $y_{22} = 1/2$ which we circle in Tableau 7.8.13.

B	$C_B{}^T$	C	5	3	0	0
		X_B	Y_1	Y_2	Y_3	Y_4
A_1	5	3	1	1/2	1/2	0
A_4	0	1	0	(1/2)	$-1/2$	1
$c_j - z_j$		15	0	1/2	$-5/2$	0

Tableau 7.8.13

The new basis will be $B = [A_1, A_2]$. In order to allay some confusion we will not label the various bases as $B^{(1)}$, $B^{(2)}$, and so forth. Similarly, we will not relabel the X_B or Y columns after the first iteration.

We now use the pivot element to make x_2 a basic variable in row 2 to create a 1 in the pivot position by multiplying the entire row by 2. We then use this element to eliminate x_2 in the first row and have the partial Tableau 7.8.14.

B	$C_B{}^T$	C	5	3	0	0
		X_B	Y_1	Y_2	Y_3	Y_4
A_1	5	2	1	0	1	-1
A_2	3	2	0	1	-1	2
$c_j - z_j$						

Tableau 7.8.14

We now proceed as before to fill in the $c_j - z_j$ row, observing that

$$z = C_B X_B = 10 + 6 = 16,$$

$$c_1 - z_1 = c_1 - C_B Y_1 = 5 - [5, 3]\begin{bmatrix} 1 \\ 0 \end{bmatrix} = 0,$$

$$c_2 - z_2 = c_2 - C_B Y_2 = 3 - [5, 3]\begin{bmatrix} 0 \\ 1 \end{bmatrix} = 0,$$

$$c_3 - z_3 = c_3 - C_B Y_3 = 0 - [5, 3]\begin{bmatrix} 1 \\ -1 \end{bmatrix} = -2,$$

and

$$c_4 - z_4 = c_4 - C_B Y_4 = 0 - [5, 3]\begin{bmatrix} -1 \\ 2 \end{bmatrix} = -1.$$

The completed tableau representing the situation at point C is shown in Tableau 7.8.15.

	C	5	3	0	0
B	$C_B^{\ T}$	X_B	Y_1	Y_2	Y_3	Y_4
A_1	5	2	1	0	1	-1
A_2	3	2	0	1	-1	2
$c_j - z_j$		16	0	0	-2	-1

Tableau 7.8.15

The last row indicates that

$$z = 16 + 0x_1 + 0x_2 - 2x_3 - 1x_4.$$

An increase of either of the non-basic variables would lead to a decrease in z. Thus we know that we can stop the algorithm and that we have the optimal BFS. At this point $X_B = \begin{bmatrix} 2 \\ 2 \end{bmatrix} = \begin{bmatrix} x_1 \\ x_2 \end{bmatrix}$, so the optimal BFS consists of

$$X = \begin{bmatrix} 2 \\ 2 \\ 0 \\ 0 \end{bmatrix},$$

with the optimum value of z being 16. You should now compare equations in the last tableau, obtained by the Gauss-Jordan procedure, with the appropriate set of equations derived for point C in the previous section.

The next section contains a recapitulation of the simplex algorithm as developed so far, and another example. Before proceeding, however, it would be instructive to recall from Chapter 3 that if a matrix $[B \mid I_m]$ is row-reduced to $[I_m \mid E]$, say, then $E = B^{-1}$. We note that we have used Gauss-Jordan reduction to replace, at each stage, the columns A_i of B by identity columns. Thus, the columns that were the original identity columns should now contain B^{-1}. In Tableau 7.8.7, $B = [A_3, A_4]$ $= I_2$, and $B^{-1} = I_2$ is contained in columns A_3, A_4. In Tableau 7.8.12, $B = [A_1, A_4] = \begin{bmatrix} 2 & 0 \\ 1 & 1 \end{bmatrix}$, and $B^{-1} = \begin{bmatrix} 1/2 & 0 \\ -1/2 & 1 \end{bmatrix}$ appears in columns Y_3, Y_4, the original identity columns. In Tableau 7.8.15, $B = [A_1, A_2]$ $= \begin{bmatrix} 2 & 1 \\ 1 & 1 \end{bmatrix}$, and $B^{-1} = \begin{bmatrix} 1 & -1 \\ -1 & 2 \end{bmatrix}$ again appears in columns Y_3, Y_4. In general, B^{-1} will appear in the columns that contain the original identity matrix.

Exercises 7.8

1. Consider the LP maximization problem of Example 7.4.2 with $A = \begin{bmatrix} 2 & 3 & 1 & 0 \\ 3 & 2 & 0 & 1 \end{bmatrix}$, $R = \begin{bmatrix} 6 \\ 6 \end{bmatrix}$, and $C = [4, 3, 0, 0]$.

   a. Fill in the blanks in the first tableau.

		C				
B	$C_B{}^T$	R	A_1	A_2	A_3	A_4
A_3 A_4						
$c_j - z_j$		4				

   b. Is the present basis optimal? _____, $c_1 - z_1 = 4$ and $c_2 - z_2 =$ _____ are each _____.

   c. Which vector should enter B in accordance with our arbitrary criterion? _____.

   d. Let A_1 enter the basis. In order to preserve _____, _____ must leave the basis since $\min\{6/2, 6/3\} = 2$. Thus _____ is the pivot element.

   e. Construct the new tableau.

		C	4	3	0	0
B	$C_B{}^T$	X_B	Y_1	Y_2	Y_3	Y_4
A_3						
$c_j - z_j$						

Compare the constants obtained with those in Exercise 1 b. of Section 7.7. In this tableau, $x_{B1} = $ ——— , $y_{12} = $ ——— , and $y_{24} = $ ——— .

f. Since $c_2 - z_2 = $ ——— > 0 we may improve on the present value of f by bringing ——— into the basis. Since min{———, ———} $= 6/5$, A_3 must leave the basis in order to preserve feasibility. If we were to remove A_1 instead, the new value of ——— would be negative. If A_2 replaces A_3 the pivot element is ——— .

g. Construct the new tableau.

	C	4	3	0	0
B	$C_B{}^T$				
A_1					
$c_j - z_j$					

Compare the constants obtained with those in Exercise 1 c. of Section 7.7. In this tableau $c_{B2} = $ ——— , $y_{11} = $ ——— , and $y_{23} = $ ——— .

h. Since $c_j - z_j \leqslant 0$ for all j, the optimal solution is $X^T = [6/5, 6/5, 0, 0]$ with $f = 42/5$.

2. Consider the last two columns of the tableaus obtained in Exercise 1.

a. In Tableau 1, $B = I_2$ and B^{-1} is contained in the last two columns.

b. In Tableau 2, $B = [A_3, A_1] = \begin{bmatrix} 1 & 2 \\ 0 & 3 \end{bmatrix}$. Verify that B^{-1} is contained in columns $[Y_3, Y_4]$.

c. In Tableau 3, $B = [\underline{\quad}, \underline{\quad}] = \begin{bmatrix} \underline{\quad} & \underline{\quad} \\ \underline{\quad} & \underline{\quad} \end{bmatrix}$. $B^{-1} = \begin{bmatrix} \underline{\quad} & \underline{\quad} \\ \underline{\quad} & \underline{\quad} \end{bmatrix}$ is contained in $[Y_3, Y_4]$.

d. For any basis matrix B, $BY_j = A_j$. Suppose that you only had the information in Tableau 3 and no longer knew the original tableau. How could you find the matrix A?

3. Solve the LP maximization problem of Section 7.5, Exercise 5 with $A = \begin{bmatrix} 1 & 2 & 1 & 0 \\ 2 & 1 & 0 & 1 \end{bmatrix}$, $R = \begin{bmatrix} 3 \\ 3 \end{bmatrix}$, and $C = [3, 1, 0, 0]$. (Also, see Section 7.6, Exercise 5 and Section 7.7, Exercise 4.)

Suggested reading

S. I. Gass, *Linear Programming*, McGraw-Hill, New York (1964).
G. Hadley, *Linear Programming*, Addison-Wesley, Reading, Mass. (1962).

New terms

pivot element, 284

7.9   The simplex algorithm and an example

We have completely developed the computational aspects of the tableau form of the simplex algorithm in the case where each of the equations contains a slack variable. The remaining cases will be discussed in the following section. We recall that we start with a tableau in which we have an augmented matrix $[R \mid A] = [R, A_1, A_2, \ldots, A_n]$ and then proceed through a sequence of tableaus each of which has an augmented matrix of the form $[X_B \mid Y] = [X_B, Y_1, Y_2, \ldots, Y_n]$, with associated basis matrix B, where, since $BY_j = A_j$, we have $Y_j = B^{-1}A_j$ for each j. In general, $BY = B[Y_1, Y_2, \ldots, Y_n] = [BY_1, \ldots, BY_n] = [A_1, \ldots, A_n] = A$, and $BX_B = R$. If we start at the origin with $B = I_m$, then

$$I_m Y = Y = A \quad \text{and} \quad I_m X_B = X_B = R,$$

so that in the first tableau, even, it is valid to refer to a_{12} as y_{12} and r_1 as x_{B1}.

The quantity z_j which contributes to the $c_j - z_j$ row is defined in general by the equation

$$z_j = C_B Y_j = C_B B^{-1}A_j.$$

Thus we could form a matrix

$$Z = [z_1, z_2, \ldots, z_n]$$

such that the last row of the tableau is merely $C - Z = C - C_B Y$. For obvious reasons, this matrix is sometimes called the **revised-cost matrix**.

The Simplex Algorithm

Step 1. Find a *BFS.* We let the slack variables be basic and start at the origin with $B = I_m$.

Step 2. Is the *BFS* optimal? We create the $C - Z$ row and examine it. For a max problem, a *BFS* will be optimal if $c_j - z_j \leqslant 0$ for all j. In the case of a min problem, a given *BFS* will be optimal if $c_j - z_j \geqslant 0$ for all j. If the *BFS* is optimal we stop. If the *BFS* is not optimal, then we proceed to step 3.

Step 3. Toward which adjacent extreme point should we proceed to obtain the greatest rate of increase in z? We choose a vector A_k to enter the basis B by examining those elements of the $c_j - z_j$ row which have the correct sign for the type of problem (max or min). For a max problem we choose A_k such that $c_k - z_k = \text{Max}_j\{c_j - z_j \mid c_j - z_j > 0\}$. For a min problem we choose A_k such that $c_k - z_k = \text{Min}_j\{c_j - z_j \mid c_j - z_j < 0\}$. In this case $c_j - z_j$ will be a set of negative numbers, and we pick the most negative. In the event of a tie, we arbitrarily pick the column Y_k with lowest subscript, and let A_k enter the basis.

Step 4. Where should we stop in order to remain feasible? We choose a vector B_s to leave the basis in such a way as to obtain a new *BFS.* By dividing the present values of the old basic variables by their rates of change, y_{ik}, that will occur if A_k enters, we could obtain a set

$$S_1 = \left\{ \frac{x_{B1}}{y_{1k}}, \frac{x_{B2}}{y_{2k}}, \ldots, \frac{x_{Bm}}{y_{mk}} \right\}.$$

Since only those basic variables x_{Bi} for which y_{ik} is positive will decrease in value if A_k enters, we consider only

$$S = \left\{ \frac{x_{Bi}}{y_{ik}} \mid y_{ik} > 0, i = 1, 2, \ldots, m \right\}.$$

We choose s such that x_{Bs}/y_{sk} is the smallest non-negative number in S and let B_s leave the basis, whichever one of the columns of A it was. In case of a tie, we arbitrarily choose the lower-numbered basic column to leave. If it should happen that any other column were chosen to leave, then the next tableau would represent a basic, *infeasible* solution. (Which variables would have negative values?)

Step 5. Let the element in row s and column k of Y, namely y_{sk}, be the pivot element. Divide each element of row s by y_{sk} to make x_k basic. Use Gauss-Jordan elimination to eliminate x_k from all rows except row s. Label the new tableau, replacing B_s, whatever A column it was, by A_k. Replace the old value of c_{Bs} with c_k. Return to Step 2.

Let us now use the algorithm to solve the problem of Example 7.5.1 which we repeat here for convenience.

Example 7.9.1

Find X such that for $A = \begin{bmatrix} 2 & 1 & 1 & 0 \\ 1 & 1 & 0 & 1 \end{bmatrix}$, $R = \begin{bmatrix} 8 \\ 6 \end{bmatrix}$, $C = [3, 2, 0, 0]$,

1. $X \geqslant 0$
2. $AX = R$
3. $z = CX$ is maximized.

The extreme points are shown in Figure 7.9.1.

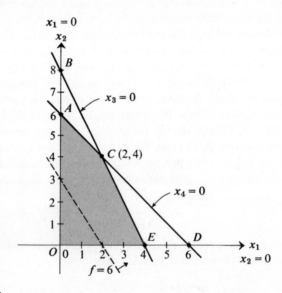

Figure 7.9.1

Step 1. The partial first tableau is shown in Tableau 7.9.1. We have completed Step 1. The *BFS* is $X^T = [0, 0, 8, 6]$.

		C	3	2	0	0
B	$C_B{}^T$	R	A_1	A_2	A_3	A_4
A_3	0	8	2	1	1	0
A_4	0	6	1	1	0	1
$C - Z$						

Tableau 7.9.1

Step 2. Are we optimal? We create the $C - Z$ row by finding

$$z = C_B X_B = C_B R = 0(8) + 0(6) = 0,$$
$$c_1 - z_1 = c_1 - C_B Y_1 = c_1 - C_B A_1 = 3 - 0 = 3,$$
$$c_2 - z_2 = c_2 - C_B Y_2 = c_2 - C_B A_2 = 2 - 0 = 2,$$
$$c_3 - z_3 = c_3 - C_B Y_3 = c_3 - C_B A_3 = 0 - 0 = 0,$$

and

$$c_4 - z_4 = c_4 - C_B Y_4 = c_4 - C_B A_4 = 0 - 0 = 0.$$

The columns of the tableau have been arranged to make these calculations as simple as possible. Since $c_1 - z_1 = 3$ and $c_2 - z_2 = 2$ are each greater than 0, we are not optimal. The completed first tableau, Tableau 7.9.2, is shown below. (Disregard the arrow and the circle for the moment.)

B	$C_B{}^T$	C R	3 A_1	2 A_2	0 A_3	0 A_4
A_3	0	8	②	1	1	0
A_4	0	6	1	1	0	1
$C - Z$		0	3	2	0	0

↑

Tableau 7.9.2

Step 3. Which vector should enter? We consider $\{c_1 - z_1, c_2 - z_2\}$ $= \{3, 2\}$. Since $\max\{3, 2\} = 3$, we let A_1 enter B, and so indicate by putting an arrow under the column in Tableau 7.9.2 above.

Step 4. Which vector must leave? We consider $\min\{8/2, 6/1\} =$ $\min\left\{\dfrac{x_{B1}}{y_{11}}, \dfrac{x_{B2}}{y_{21}}\right\} = 4$. Thus $s = 1$ and $B_1 = A_3$ must leave the basis.

Step 5. $y_{11} = 2$ is the pivot element which we circle in Tableau 7.9.2. We create a partial tableau as shown in Tableau 7.9.3.

B	$C_B{}^T$	C X_B	3 Y_1	2 Y_2	0 Y_3	0 Y_4
A_1	3	4	1	1/2	1/2	0
A_4	0	2	0	1/2	$-1/2$	1
$C - Z$						

Tableau 7.9.3

Step 2. Are we optimal?

$$z = C_B X_B = 12,$$

$$c_1 - z_1 = c_1 - C_B Y_1 = 3 - 3 = 0,$$

$$c_2 - z_2 = c_2 - C_B Y_2 = 2 - 3/2 = 1/2,$$

$$c_3 - z_3 = c_3 - C_B Y_3 = 0 - 3/2 = -3/2,$$

and

$$c_4 - z_4 = c_4 - C_B Y_4 = 0 - 0 = 0.$$

Since $c_2 - z_2 = 1/2 > 0$, we are not optimal. The completed tableau is Tableau 7.9.4.

		C	3	2	0	0
B	$C_B{}^T$	X_B	Y_1	Y_2	Y_3	Y_4
A_1	3	4	1	1/2	1/2	0
A_4	0	2	0	(1/2)	−1/2	1
$C - Z$		12	0	1/2	−3/2	0

↑

Tableau 7.9.4

Step 3. Which vector should enter? Since $c_2 - z_2$ is the only positive element in the $C - Z$ row, A_2 must enter.

Step 4. Which vector must leave? We consider

$$\min\left\{\frac{x_{B1}}{y_{12}}, \frac{x_{B2}}{y_{22}}\right\} = \min\left\{\frac{4}{1/2}, \frac{2}{1/2}\right\} = \min\{8, 4\} = 4.$$

Thus $B_2 = A_4$ must leave.

Step 5 and *Step 2.* $y_{22} = 1/2$ is the new pivot element. The complete new tableau is shown as Table 7.9.5.

		C	3	2	0	0
B	$C_B{}^T$	X_B	Y_1	Y_2	Y_3	Y_4
A_1	3	2	1	0	1	−1
A_2	2	4	0	1	−1	2
$C - Z$		14	0	0	−1	−1

Tableau 7.9.5

Since $c_j - z_j \leqslant 0$ for each j, the tableau is optimal. $X^T = [2, 4, 0, 0]$, with $z = 14$, is the optimal BFS shown at point C in the graph in Figure 7.9.1.

Exercises 7.9

1. We begin the simplex algorithm in Tableau 1 with $[R\,|\,A]$ and proceed through a sequence of tableaus of the form $[\underline{\quad\quad}\,|\,\underline{\quad\quad}]$ where $BX_B = \underline{\quad\quad}$ and $BY_j = \underline{\quad\quad}$. Since $Y_j = B^{-1}A_j$ and $z_j = C_B\,Y_j$, we see that $(c_j - z_j)$ could be computed as $c_j - C_B\,Y_j = c_j - C_B\,B^{-1}A_j$. Verify this formula by using it to compute $c_3 - z_3$ in Tableau 7.9.4.

2. Verify that the information in the $C - Z$ row of Tableau 7.9.5 (with the exception of z) could have been obtained by performing Gauss-Jordan reduction on the $C - Z$ row of Tableau 7.9.4 just as you did on row 1; that is, you wish to create a 0 in the $c_2 - z_2$ position.

3. a. Solve the LP maximization problem with $A = \begin{bmatrix} 1 & 3 & 1 & 0 \\ 3 & 1 & 0 & 1 \end{bmatrix}$, $R = \begin{bmatrix} 4 \\ 4 \end{bmatrix}$, and $C = [1, 2, 0, 0]$. See Section 7.7, Exercise 3.

   b. Verify in the final tableau that $A_3 = y_{13}B_1 + y_{23}B_2 = (3/8)A_2 - (1/8)A_1$.

4. Consider Tableaus 7.9.2 and 7.9.4 in this section.

   a. In Tableau 7.9.2 we see that $A_1 = \begin{bmatrix} 2 \\ 1 \end{bmatrix}$, $A_2 = \begin{bmatrix} 1 \\ 1 \end{bmatrix}$, and that $B = I_2$ is the basis matrix. In Tableau 7.9.4 the new basis matrix $B = [A_1, A_4] = \begin{bmatrix} 2 & 0 \\ 1 & 1 \end{bmatrix}$. Verify that the Y matrix $\begin{bmatrix} 1 & 1/2 & 1/2 & 0 \\ 0 & 1/2 & -1/2 & 1 \end{bmatrix}$ is nothing more than the matrix of coordinates of the original vectors A_j with respect to the new basis. For example, $Y_2 = \begin{bmatrix} 1/2 \\ 1/2 \end{bmatrix}$ is the coordinate matrix of A_2 since

$$A_2 = \begin{bmatrix} 1 \\ 1 \end{bmatrix} = 1/2 \begin{bmatrix} 2 \\ 1 \end{bmatrix} + 1/2 \begin{bmatrix} 0 \\ 1 \end{bmatrix} = 1/2A_1 + 1/2A_4$$

$$= [A_1, A_4] \begin{bmatrix} 1/2 \\ 1/2 \end{bmatrix} = BY_2.$$

b. Verify that $Y_j = B^{-1}A_j$ for each j in Tableau 7.9.4.
c. Verify that $C - Z = C - C_B Y = C - C_B B^{-1}A$ in Tableau 7.9.4.
d. Show that $c_j - z_j = 0$ if A_j is in B.

5. a. How would the criterion for the choice of the vector to enter the basis change in a minimization problem?
    b. How would the criterion for the choice of the vector to leave the basis change in a minimization problem?

6. In general, $C - Z = C - C_B$————.

7. a. Solve the LP maximization production problem of Section 7.2, Exercise 9, with $A = \begin{bmatrix} 1 & 2 & 1 & 0 \\ 3 & 1 & 0 & 1 \end{bmatrix}$, $R = \begin{bmatrix} 480 \\ 480 \end{bmatrix}$, and $C = [5, 4, 0, 0]$.
    b. Verify that the inverse of the final basis is contained in the last two columns of the final tableau. Note that $B = [A_2, A_1]$.

8. Show graphically for one of your solved problems that $\max f = -(\min(-f))$. Since this is valid in general, any minimization problem may be solved by converting it to a maximization problem by changing the signs of the criterion coefficients, solving the problem as a maximization problem, and changing the sign of the optimum criterion value. The values of X which solve the different problems are the same and need not be changed.

9. a. Use the simplex algorithm to solve the LP problem

Find X such that $X \geqslant 0$,

$$x_1 + x_2 \leqslant 4$$
$$-x_1 + x_2 \leqslant 1$$
$$x_1 + 2x_2 \leqslant 5,$$

and $z = 2x_1 + 3x_2$ is maximized.

---

b. Solve the problem graphically and note that fewer iterations would have been required if we had let A_1 enter the basis at step 1 rather than A_2.
c. The last basis matrix is $B = [B_1, B_2, B_3] = [$————, ————, ————$]$. Verify that $B^{-1} = [Y_3, Y_4, Y_5] = \begin{bmatrix} 3 & 1 & -2 \\ -1 & 0 & 1 \\ 2 & 0 & -1 \end{bmatrix}$ from the last three columns of the last tableau.

d.   Since $Y_3 = \begin{bmatrix} 3 \\ -1 \\ 2 \end{bmatrix}$ we know that

$$A_3 = \underline{\hspace{1cm}} A_4 + \underline{\hspace{1cm}} A_2 + \underline{\hspace{1cm}} A_1.$$

Suggested reading

S. I. Gass, *Linear Programming*, McGraw-Hill, New York (1964).
G. Hadley, *Linear Programming*, Addison-Wesley, Reading, Mass. (1962).

New terms

revised-cost matrix, 292   simplex algorithm, 293

7.10   Artificial variables and alternate optimum solutions

The ease of finding a starting *BFS* in the case where each constraint has a slack variable is evident from the previous section. We merely let the slack variables be the basic variables. Since there are m such variables and each one corresponds to a column of the identity matrix we have $B = I_m$ as the starting basis. The question arises as to what should be done in the case where some of the constraints are of the $\geqslant$ or $=$ variety. For example, suppose that we have the problem

---

Find x_1, x_2 such that

1. $x_i \geqslant 0$ $i = 1, 2$
2. $x_1 + 2x_2 \geqslant 3$
         $-x_1 + 3x_2 \geqslant 4$
3. $z = x_1 + 2x_2$ is minimized.

---

and that we subtract surplus variables x_3, x_4 to form the set of equations

$$x_1 + 2x_2 - x_3 \qquad = 3$$
$$-x_1 + 3x_2 \qquad - x_4 = 4.$$

There is clearly no identity matrix to be chosen as an initial basis. In addition, if x_3 were made basic in equation 1, then $x_3 = -3$ would be infeasible as would $x_4 = -4$. In order to handle this situation we add an **artificial variable** to each equation. Thus the set of equations

$$x_1 + 2x_2 - x_3 \qquad + x_5 \qquad = 3$$
$$-x_1 + 3x_2 \qquad - x_4 \qquad + x_6 = 4$$

provides a matrix

$$A = \begin{bmatrix} 1 & 2 & -1 & 0 & 1 & 0 \\ -1 & 3 & 0 & -1 & 0 & 1 \end{bmatrix}$$

with an I_2 sub-matrix, where $I_2 = [A_5, A_6]$, which may be used as an initial basis. If I_2 is chosen as the initial basis, then $x_5 = 3$ and $x_6 = 4$ are the initial basic variables. Then

$$x_1 + 2x_2 - x_3 \qquad = 0$$
$$-x_1 + 3x_2 \qquad - x_4 = 0$$

and the original equations are clearly *not* satisfied. Thus, although we have a *BFS* for the artificial problem we have created, we do not have a *BFS* for the original problem. To achieve a *BFS* for the latter, we merely need to insure that the artificial variables x_5 and x_6 eventually have the value 0; that is, that they either become non-basic variables or have the value 0 even though basic. We can insure, in a minimization problem, that the variables will eventually leave the basis (if there exists a *BFS* to the original problem) by attaching an extraordinarily high cost coefficient to these variables. They will then naturally be chosen to leave the basis as soon as possible. After A. Charnes et al. (see Suggested Reading), we will use $M > 0$ to represent an arbitrarily large number to be used in such cases. For a maximization problem we would want a negative number whose absolute value is very large. We thus use $(-M)$ in that case. If it is impossible ultimately to remove one of the artificial vectors from the basis, then, if the corresponding basic variable is positive, it can be shown that there is no feasible solution to the original problem.

We shall now use this new technique to solve the equivalent problem

---

Minimize $z = x_1 + 2x_2 + Mx_5 + Mx_6$
such that

$$x_1 + 2x_2 - x_3 \qquad + x_5 \qquad = 3$$
$$-x_1 + 3x_2 \qquad - x_4 \qquad + x_6 = 4$$

and

$$x_i \geqslant 0,$$

---

with the provision that x_5 and x_6 must be 0 at the conclusion of the algorithm. The graph of the feasible region for the original problem is shown in Figure 7.10.1.

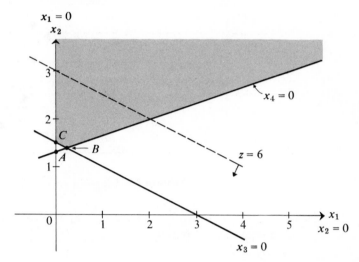

Figure 7.10.1

The completed first tableau is Tableau 7.10.1. For convenience, the $C - Z$ row has been split into two levels, the top row being the constants and the bottom row the M part of the objective function.

		C	1	2	0	0	M	M
B	C_B^T	R	A_1	A_2	A_3	A_4	A_5	A_6
A_5	M	3	1	2	-1	0	1	0
A_6	M	4	-1	③	0	-1	0	1
$C - Z$		0	1	2	0	0	0	0
		$7M$	0	$-5M$	M	M	0	0

↑

Tableau 7.10.1

First Iteration

Step 1. $B = I_2$.
2. $c_2 - z_2 = -5M + 2 < 0$; not optimal.
3. A_2 enters.
4. Min$\{3/2, 4/3\} = 4/3$. $B_2 = A_6$ leaves.

5. $y_{22} = 3$ is pivot. Use Gauss-Jordan reduction to obtain Tableau 7.10.2.

	C		1	2	0	0	M	M
B	$C_B{}^T$	X_B	Y_1	Y_2	Y_3	Y_4	Y_5	Y_6
A_5	M	$1/3$	$\textcircled{5/3}$	0	-1	$2/3$	1	$-2/3$
A_2	2	$4/3$	$-1/3$	1	0	$-1/3$	0	$1/3$
$C - Z$		$8/3$	$5/3$	0	0	$2/3$	0	$-2/3$
		$M/3$	$-5M/3$	0	M	$-2M/3$	0	$5M/3$

↑

Tableau 7.10.2

Step 2. $c_1 - z_1 = -5M/3 + 5/3$ and $c_4 - z_4 = -2M/3 + 2/3$ are each negative; not optimal.

3. A_1 enters.
4. $B_1 = A_5$ leaves.
5. $y_{11} = 5/3$ is pivot. Obtain Tableau 7.10.3.

	C		1	2	0	0	M	M
B	$C_B{}^T$	X_B	Y_1	Y_2	Y_3	Y_4	Y_5	Y_6
A_1	1	$1/5$	1	0	$-3/5$	$2/5$	$3/5$	$-2/5$
A_2	2	$7/5$	0	1	$-1/5$	$-1/5$	$1/5$	$1/5$
$C - Z$		3	0	0	1	0	-1	0
		0	0	0	0	0	M	M

Tableau 7.10.3

Step 2. $c_j - z_j \geqslant 0$ for all j. Optimal solution, since both x_5 and x_6 are 0.

For the original problem in equation form, the solution is $X = [1/5, 7/5, 0, 0]^T$ with $z = 3$. In the diagram (Figure 7.10.1) we have proceeded from point O to point A to point B. You may have noticed that $c_4 - z_4 = 0$ but that A_4 is not in the final basis. Thus the rate of change of z, if A_4 enters the basis, will be 0 and z will not change.

From Figure 7.10.1, we see that if we are at B and A_4 enters the basis, A_1 will leave the basis in order to remain feasible; we will move to point C along a boundary which has the same slope as the objective function. The BFS at point C has an equal value of z and is called an **alternate optimum** BFS. Such alternates will always be indicated by the presence of more than m zeros in the $C - Z$ row of an optimal tableau.

In Tableau 7.10.4 we show the tableau that results if A_4 replaces A_1 in B. The pivot element was $y_{14} = 2/5$.

		C	1	2	0	0	M	M
B	$C_B{}^T$	X_B	Y_1	Y_2	Y_3	Y_4	Y_5	Y_6
A_4	0	1/2	5/2	0	$-3/2$	1	3/2	-1
A_2	2	3/2	1/2	1	$-1/2$	0	1/2	0
$C - Z$		3	0	0	1	0	-1	0
		0	0	0	0	0	M	M

Tableau 7.10.4

We thus have an alternate optimum solution $X = [0, 3/2, 0, 1/2]^T$ with $z = 3$. We repeat that in this exceptional case one of the constraint-defining equations represents a straight line with the same slope as that of the objective function. It is that phenomenon which enabled the alternate optimum solution to exist. Any point between B and C would also be an alternate optimum feasible solution, but it would not be a basic feasible solution since more than two variables would be positive.

Exercises 7.10

1. Use slack, surplus, and artificial variables where necessary to put the following constraints in proper form for the simplex algorithm. Number artificial variables last.

$$x_1 + x_2 \leqslant 3$$
$$-x_1 + 2x_2 \geqslant 4.$$

2. An _____ _____ is added to an equation arising from an _____ constraint or an inequality constraint of the _____ type in order to obtain an _____ _____ as a starting basis matrix.

3. Use the method of this section to solve the aircraft LP problem of Example 7.1.1. See Exercise 11 of Section 7.2 for a graphical solution. Number any artificial variables last. For simplicity, divide each constant in the first constraint by 50 and each cost coefficient by 1000.

4. Illustrate the procedure used to find alternate optima in the solution of the LP problem with $A = \begin{bmatrix} 2 & 1 & 1 & 0 \\ 1 & 2 & 0 & 1 \end{bmatrix}$, $R = \begin{bmatrix} 6 \\ 6 \end{bmatrix}$, and $C = [2, 1, 0, 0]$. Draw a sketch to illustrate what occurs algebraically.

5. Use the method of this section to solve the LP problem you solved graphically in Section 7.2 as Exercise 5. Use your previously-prepared sketch to follow the algorithm's progress toward the optimal *BFS*. For uniformity, number all slack/surplus variables before you number any artificial variables. Let x_5 denote the slack variable and let A_2 enter the basis at the first step.

6. Solve the LP diet problem of Example 7.1.4. (See Section 7.2, Exercise 10 for a graphical solution).

Suggested reading

A. Charnes, W. Cooper, and A. Henderson, *An Introduction to Linear Programming*, John Wiley & Sons, New York (1953).

S. I. Gass, *Linear Programming*, McGraw-Hill, New York (1964).

G. Hadley, *Linear Programming*, Addison-Wesley, Reading, Mass. (1962).

New terms

artificial variable, 300   alternate optimum BFS, 303

7.11   Why does the simplex algorithm work?

In this section we shall attempt to make plausible some of the underlying theory of the simplex algorithm. In equation form we shall discuss the problem:

Find X such that

1. $X \geqslant 0$
2. $AX = R$ and
3. $f(X) = CX$ is maximized.

We assume that an optimal feasible solution exists and degeneracy does not occur. We stated in Section 7.2 that z is a linear function and that each of the constraints is linear. We also showed an example of a programming problem (with linear constraints but a non-linear objective function) with the property that the unique optimum solution occurs at an interior point of the feasible region. Thus an algorithm which searched only extreme points of the feasible region would be doomed to failure. Such is not the case for an LP problem.

We shall first show that the feasible region S of an LP problem is a so-called convex set. We then illustrate by an example a method whereby any point X of S may be expressed as a special linear combination of the finite number of extreme points of S. Using this, we prove that f must achieve its optimum value at one of the extreme points of S. Thus a method which examines only extreme points must succeed. The simplex algorithm provides a method of examining a subset of these extreme points, with each succeeding point having an improved value of z (barring degeneracy). Since there are only a finite number of such points the algorithm must terminate. We conclude by showing that if a *BFS* is obtained with the property that for all j, $c_j - z_j \leqslant 0$, then the *BFS* and its associated extreme point are optimum.

A subset T of n-space is said to be a **convex subset of n-space** provided that if X_1 and X_2 are in T and c_1 and c_2 are non-negative numbers such that $c_1 + c_2 = 1$ then the point $X = c_1 X_1 + c_2 X_2$ is also in T. X is said to be a **convex combination** of X_1 and X_2. The set formed by taking all possible values for c_1 and c_2 is merely the straight line segment connecting X_1 and X_2. A particular example in 2-space for the case where $c_1 = c_2 = 1/2$ is shown in Figure 7.11.1.

The term **extreme point of a convex set** S which we have been using intuitively can be precisely defined to be a point X in S that is not a

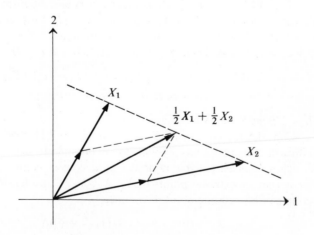

Figure 7.11.1

convex combination of any *two* other points of S. Thus X is not an interior point of any line segment in S. Examples of convex and non-convex subsets of 2-space are shown in Figure 7.11.2.

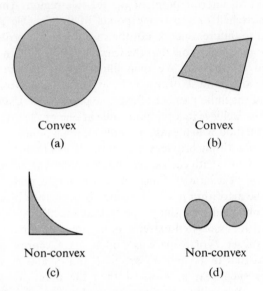

Convex
(a)

Convex
(b)

Non-convex
(c)

Non-convex
(d)

Figure 7.11.2

THEOREM 7.11.1

The feasible region S of an LP problem is a convex subset of n-space.

Proof:

$S = \{X \mid X \geqslant 0, \ AX = R\}$ is clearly a subset of n-space. Suppose X_1 and X_2 are in S. Then $X_1 \geqslant 0$ and $AX_1 = R$. Further, $X_2 \geqslant 0$ and $AX_2 = R$. Consider the convex combination $Y = c_1 X_1 + c_2 X_2$, $c_1 + c_2 = 1$, $c_i \geqslant 0$. Then $Y \geqslant 0$ since $X_i \geqslant 0$ and $c_i \geqslant 0$. In addition,

$$AY = A(c_1 X_1 + c_2 X_2) = c_1(AX_1) + c_2(AX_2)$$
$$= c_1 R + c_2 R = (c_1 + c_2)R = R.$$

Thus Y is in S and S is convex. $\square$

Consider the convex set S shown in Figure 7.11.3. We would like to illustrate the procedure by which it is possible to express any point of such a *bounded* feasible region S as a convex combination of the four corner or extreme points 0, X_1, X_2, X_3. Consider first X_2, as an example of an extreme point of S. Since

$$X_2 = (0)0 + (0)X_1 + (1)X_2 + (0)X_3,$$

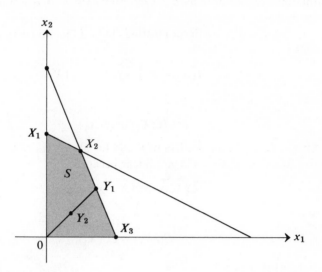

Figure 7.11.3

X_2 is trivially a convex combination of the entire set of extreme points of S. Suppose that Y_1 is a non-extreme boundary point of S. We wish to show how Y_1 may also be expressed as a convex combination of the extreme points of S. Y_1 lies on the line between X_2 and X_3. Thus $Y_1 = c_1 X_2 + c_2 X_3$ for some choice of c_1, c_2 such that $c_1 + c_2 = 1$ and $c_i \geqslant 0$. Finally, we wish to express the interior point Y_2, on the line between 0 and Y_1, as the convex combination of the four extreme points. As shown in Figure 7.11.3, for some choice of d_1, d_2,

$$Y_2 = d_1 0 + d_2 Y_1, \quad d_1 + d_2 = 1, \quad d_i \geqslant 0.$$

Thus

$$Y_2 = d_1 0 + d_2 (c_1 X_2 + c_2 X_3), \quad c_1 + c_2 = 1, \quad c_i \geqslant 0,$$

so that

$$Y_2 = d_1 0 + (d_2 c_1) X_2 + (d_2 c_2) X_3.$$

Since $d_1, d_2 c_1$, and $d_2 c_2$ are each non-negative, and $d_1 + d_2 c_1 + d_2 c_2 = d_1 + d_2(c_1 + c_2) = d_1 + d_2 = 1$, then Y_2 is a convex combination of the extreme points of S.

We present the above only as an example of a method whereby we may express any point X of S as a convex combination of the extreme points of S. If there are t such points for our general problem, then for any X in S,

$$X = c_1 X_1 + c_2 X_2 + \cdots + c_t X_t$$

for some choice of scalars c_i such that $c_1 + \cdots + c_t = 1$ and $c_i \geq 0$ for $i = 1, 2, \ldots, t$.

We now define a **linear function** f to be a function with the properties that

$$f(X_1 + X_2) = f(X_1) + f(X_2)$$

and

$$f(cX_1) = cf(X_1)$$

for all X_1, X_2 in the domain of f, and for all scalars c. All of our objective functions $f(X) = CX$ are linear because

$$C(X_1 + X_2) = CX_1 + CX_2$$

and

$$C(cX_1) = cC(X_1).$$

THEOREM 7.11.2

If the linear function $f(X) = CX$ defined over the convex set S with extreme points $X_1, X_2, \ldots, X_t$ has an optimal feasible solution X_0, then at least one of the extreme points is optimal.

Proof*:

Assume that the t extreme points have been numbered in an increasing order in terms of their respective functional values; that is, that

$$f(X_1) \leqslant f(X_2) \leqslant \cdots \leqslant f(X_t).$$

X_0, as a point in S, may be expressed as a convex combination of the t extreme points. Thus

$$X_0 = c_1 X_1 + c_2 X_2 + \cdots + c_t X_t,$$

where $c_1 + c_2 + \cdots + c_t = 1$ and $c_i \geqslant 0$. Since f is a linear function,

$$f(X_0) = f(c_1 X_1 + c_2 X_2 + \cdots + c_t X_t)$$
$$= c_1 f(X_1) + c_2 f(X_2) + \cdots + c_t f(X_t).$$

Replacing $f(X_1), f(X_2), \ldots, f(X_{t-1})$ by $f(X_t)$, which in each case can be no smaller, we have, since S is convex,

$$f(X_0) \leqslant c_1 f(X_t) + c_2 f(X_t) + \cdots + c_t f(X_t)$$
$$= (c_1 + c_2 + \cdots + c_t)f(X_t) = f(X_t).$$

---

* The essential steps of this proof are due to S. I. Gass (see Suggested Reading).

Since $f(X_0) \leqslant f(X_t)$ and X_0 is given to be optimal, we must have $f(X_0) = f(X_t)$. Thus X_t is an extreme point which is optimal. $\square$

We shall recall some notation before stating the final theorem. We have started with an augmented matrix $[R \mid A]$ and developed an augmented matrix $[X_B \mid Y]$ in which $BY = A$ and $BX_B = R$. Since B is nonsingular, $Y = B^{-1}A$ and $X_B = B^{-1}R$. We have defined the matrix $Z = [z_1, z_2, \ldots, z_n]$ so that $C - Z = [c_1 - z_1, c_2 - z_2, \ldots, c_n - z_n]$. Since $z_j = C_B Y_j$ for each j, we have $Z = C_B Y$.

THEOREM 7.11.3

Suppose that X is a *BFS* such that for all j, we have $c_j - z_j \leqslant 0$. Then, for any feasible X_0, we have $f(X) \geqslant f(X_0)$.

Proof:

In matrix notation $C - Z \leqslant 0$, or $C \leqslant Z$. Let B be the basis matrix associated with X. Thus, since $X_0 \geqslant 0$,

$$f(X_0) = CX_0 \leqslant ZX_0 = C_B YX_0 = C_B(B^{-1}A)X_0$$
$$= C_B B^{-1}(AX_0) = C_B B^{-1}R = C_B X_B = f(X),$$

so we see that $f(X) \geqslant f(X_0)$.* $\square$

Because of this fact, we know that we have reached an optimum *BFS* when we reach a *BFS* with $C - Z \leqslant 0$ for a maximization problem.

Exercises 7.11

1. Find four different convex combinations of the vectors $\begin{bmatrix} 1 \\ 2 \end{bmatrix}$ and $\begin{bmatrix} 2 \\ 1 \end{bmatrix}$. Sketch your vectors in the plane and show that they lie on the line segment connecting the tip of $\begin{bmatrix} 1 \\ 2 \end{bmatrix}$ and $\begin{bmatrix} 2 \\ 1 \end{bmatrix}$.

2. a. Let $C = [1, 2, 3, 4]$, $Z = [2, 3, 4, 5]$ and suppose that $X_0 = [1, 1, 2, 3]^T$. Show that $CX_0 \leqslant ZX_0$.
    b. Let
    $C = [-4, 3, 0, 0], Z = [-3, 4, 0, 0]$ and $X_0 = [-1, -2, 3, 0]^T$. Show that although $C \leqslant Z$, $CX_0 > ZX_0$. What hypothesis of Theorem 7.11.3 is not satisfied?

3. Let $C = [c_1, c_2]$, $Z = [z_1, z_2]$ and $X = \begin{bmatrix} x_1 \\ x_2 \end{bmatrix}$. Prove that if $C \leqslant Z$ and $X \geqslant 0$ then $CX \leqslant ZX$.

* The proof of this theorem is essentially a matrix version of the scalar proof given by G. Hadley (see Suggested Reading).

4. Why did we assume that our problem to be examined in this section was non-degenerate?

5. Show that if f is a linear function then

$$f(c_1 x_1 + c_2 x_2 + \cdots + c_n x_n) = c_1 f(x_1) + c_2 f(x_2) + \cdots + c_n f(x_n).$$

6. Convince yourself that $z_j = C_B Y_j$ represents that portion of the per unit rate of change of z that will occur because of the changes in the values of the present basic variables that must occur if A_j enters the basis.

Suggested reading

C. R. Carr, and C. W. Howe, *Quantitative Decision Procedures in Management and Economics*, McGraw-Hill, New York (1964).

G. B. Dantzig, *Linear Programming and Extensions*, Princeton University Press, Princeton, N.J. (1963).

S. I. Gass, *Linear Programming*, McGraw-Hill, New York (1964).

G. Hadley, *Linear Programming*, Addison-Wesley, Reading, Mass. (1962).

New terms

convex subset of n-space, 305
convex combination, 305

extreme point of a convex set, 305
linear function, 308

[8] Stochastic matrices and Markov chains

8.1 Stochastic matrices

Certain types of matrices are very useful in the study of random or stochastic phenomena such as experiments, the outcome of which is not known in advance. The experiment may be very complex such as in a national election, or it may consist of the very simple act of turning on your light switch to see what will happen. Although, as in the toss of a fair coin, we can compute the probabilities of the possible outcomes, we cannot predict which one of them will occur with certainty. In this chapter we shall develop some of the standard terminology used to discuss such problems and show how matrices are used to express and solve them. We shall deal with only the most elementary aspects of probability and, even then, in a purely intuitive fashion.* Although we shall confine our examples to those which require matrices of small size, it is possible to extend all of our definitions to cover the general situation.

We first introduce the term stochastic vector. The 1×2 matrix $[p_1, p_2]$ will be called a **stochastic vector** provided that $p_1 + p_2 = 1$ and $p_i \geqslant 0$. We have used the letter p to point out that the elements of the matrix can, in fact, be interpreted as probabilities of possible

---

* For a more complete discussion see J. G. Kemeny *et al.*, *Introduction to Finite Mathematics*.

outcomes of a trial of an experiment with only 2 possible outcomes. It is because of this desired interpretation that the conditions $p_1 + p_2 = 1$ and $p_i \geqslant 0$ were inserted in the definition. The former expresses our hope that one or the other of the outcomes will occur and the latter points out that negative numbers cannot be probabilities of random events.

Example 8.1.1

If we let p_1 denote the probability of flipping a "head" with a fair coin, and p_2 denote the probability of a "tail," then $P = [p_1, p_2] = [1/2, 1/2]$ is a stochastic matrix containing these probabilities.

Example 8.1.2

The vectors $[1/3, 2/3]$, $[0, 1]$, $[1, 0]$, and $[5/6, 1/6]$ are each stochastic vectors. However, none of the vectors $[-1, 0]$, $[2, 1]$, or $[-1/3, 4/3]$ is a stochastic vector. (Why?)

The 2×2 matrix M is called a **stochastic matrix** provided that its rows are stochastic vectors. These are also sometimes called **probability matrices** or **Markov matrices**. It is clear that the elements of a stochastic matrix are non-negative.

Example 8.1.3

The matrices

$$\begin{bmatrix} 1/2 & 1/2 \\ 1/2 & 1/2 \end{bmatrix}, \qquad \begin{bmatrix} 1 & 0 \\ 0 & 1 \end{bmatrix}, \qquad \text{and} \qquad \begin{bmatrix} 1/3 & 2/3 \\ 1/4 & 3/4 \end{bmatrix}$$

are each stochastic. What about $\begin{bmatrix} 1/2 & 1/3 \\ 1/2 & 2/3 \end{bmatrix}$?

We can describe a general 2×2 stochastic matrix very easily. If M is such a non-negative matrix then

$$M = \begin{bmatrix} x & 1 - x \\ y & 1 - y \end{bmatrix} \qquad \text{for some} \quad [x, y] \geqslant 0.$$

We shall use this characterization to help us establish four of the elementary properties of stochastic matrices. These particular properties have been chosen to give the reader a feel for what happens when these matrices are manipulated.

Property 1 If M is a stochastic matrix then M^2 is a stochastic matrix.

Proof:

Let $M = \begin{bmatrix} x & 1-x \\ y & 1-y \end{bmatrix}$ with $\cdot[x, y] \geqslant 0$. Then

$$M^2 = \begin{bmatrix} x & 1-x \\ y & 1-y \end{bmatrix} \begin{bmatrix} x & 1-x \\ y & 1-y \end{bmatrix}$$

$$= \begin{bmatrix} x^2 + (1-x)y & x(1-x) + (1-x)(1-y) \\ yx + (1-y)y & y(1-x) + (1-y)(1-y) \end{bmatrix}.$$

From the latter display we see that each element of M^2 is a sum of products of non-negative numbers and is thus non-negative. Furthermore, the sum of the elements in row 1 is

$$x^2 + (1-x)y + x(1-x) + (1-x)(1-y)$$
$$= x^2 + (1-x)(y + x + 1 - y)$$
$$= x^2 + (1-x)(1+x)$$
$$= x^2 + 1 - x^2$$
$$= 1.$$

The reader should verify that the sum of the elements in row 2 is likewise 1, so that M^2 is a stochastic matrix.   □

Example 8.1.4

If $M = \begin{bmatrix} 1/2 & 1/2 \\ 1/4 & 3/4 \end{bmatrix}$, then

$$M^2 = \begin{bmatrix} 1/2 & 1/2 \\ 1/4 & 3/4 \end{bmatrix} \begin{bmatrix} 1/2 & 1/2 \\ 1/4 & 3/4 \end{bmatrix} = \begin{bmatrix} 3/8 & 5/8 \\ 5/16 & 11/16 \end{bmatrix},$$

which is stochastic.

A more general result is the following:

Property 2   If each of M_1 and M_2 is stochastic, then $M_1 M_2$ is stochastic.

We leave the proof of Property 2 to the reader as an exercise at the end of this section.

Example 8.1.5

Let $M_1 = \begin{bmatrix} 1/2 & 1/2 \\ 1/4 & 3/4 \end{bmatrix}$, $M_2 = \begin{bmatrix} 1/3 & 2/3 \\ 1/2 & 1/2 \end{bmatrix}$. Then

$$M_1 M_2 = \begin{bmatrix} 1/2 & 1/2 \\ 1/4 & 3/4 \end{bmatrix} \begin{bmatrix} 1/3 & 2/3 \\ 1/2 & 1/2 \end{bmatrix} = \begin{bmatrix} 5/12 & 7/12 \\ 11/24 & 13/24 \end{bmatrix}$$

is also stochastic.

Having Property 2 at our disposal enables us to extend the result of Property 1, where we showed that a sufficient reason for M^2 to be stochastic was that M was stochastic. Since each of M and M^2 is stochastic, we let $M_1 = M$ and $M_2 = M^2$ in Property 2, and see that $M^3 = M_1 M_2$ is also stochastic. Continuing in this fashion we could show that M^n is stochastic for any positive integer n. An important problem in the study of stochastic matrices is to examine the properties of M^n as n increases. It may be, for example, that M^n tends toward some limiting matrix M' as n increases.

Property 3   If M is a stochastic matrix and P is a stochastic vector, then PM is a stochastic vector.

Proof :

Let $P = [p_1, p_2]$ and $M = \begin{bmatrix} x & 1-x \\ y & 1-y \end{bmatrix}$, $[x, y] \geqslant 0$. Then

$$PM = [p_1, p_2] \begin{bmatrix} x & 1-x \\ y & 1-y \end{bmatrix} = [p_1 x + p_2 y, p_1(1-x) + p_2(1-y)].$$

The elements of PM are clearly non-negative and their sum is

$$p_1 x + p_2 y + p_1(1-x) + p_2(1-y) = p_1(x+1-x) + p_2(y+1-y)$$
$$= p_1 + p_2$$
$$= 1. \quad \square$$

Example 8.1.6

If $M = \begin{bmatrix} 1/2 & 1/2 \\ 3/4 & 1/4 \end{bmatrix}$ and $P = [1/3, 2/3]$ then

$$PM = [1/3, 2/3] \begin{bmatrix} 1/2 & 1/2 \\ 3/4 & 1/4 \end{bmatrix} = [2/3, 1/3].$$

The last property that we shall discuss is the following:

Property 4   If M is a stochastic matrix then M has the eigenvalue 1.

Proof :

Let $M = \begin{bmatrix} x & 1-x \\ y & 1-y \end{bmatrix}$ with $[x, y] \geqslant 0$. Then the characteristic equation for M is $\begin{vmatrix} x-c & (1-x) \\ y & (1-y)-c \end{vmatrix} = 0$ and we wish to show that $c = 1$ satisfies the equation. We let $c = 1$ in the determinant and obtain $\begin{vmatrix} x-1 & 1-x \\ y & -y \end{vmatrix}$ which is clearly 0 for any value of x, y (Why?). $\square$

Exercises 8.1

1. Consider the experiment of flipping a fair coin. Let $p(H)$ and $p(T)$ denote the probability of a head and tail, respectively, on the first toss.
   a. What is your estimate of $p(H)$ and $p(T)$?
   b. Two events A, B which are independent have the property that $p(AB) = p(A \text{ and } B) = p(A)p(B)$. Assuming that in two different flips of a coin that H_1 and H_2 (head on the first toss and head on the second toss) are independent events, find $p(H_1 H_2)$. Similarly, find $p(H_1 T_2)$, $p(T_1 H_2)$, $p(T_1 T_2)$.

2. Which of the following vectors are stochastic? For each vector which is not, explain why not.
   a. $[1, 2]$ b. $[1/2, 2/3]$ c. $[5/4, -1/4]$

   d. $[2/3, 1/3]$ e. $\left[\dfrac{\sqrt{2}-1}{\sqrt{2}}, \dfrac{1}{\sqrt{2}} \right]$

3. Which of the following matrices are stochastic?

   a. $\begin{bmatrix} 1/2 & 1/3 \\ 1/2 & 2/3 \end{bmatrix}$ b. $\begin{bmatrix} 0 & 1 \\ 1 & 0 \end{bmatrix}$ c. $\begin{bmatrix} 1/2 & -1/2 \\ -1/2 & 1/2 \end{bmatrix}$

   d. $\begin{bmatrix} 5/6 & 1/6 \\ 2/6 & 4/6 \end{bmatrix}$ e. $\begin{bmatrix} 4/5 & 1/5 \\ 1/5 & 4/5 \end{bmatrix}$ f. $\begin{bmatrix} -1 & 2 \\ 2 & -1 \end{bmatrix}$

   g. $\begin{bmatrix} 1/4 & 3/4 \\ 3/4 & 1/4 \end{bmatrix}$

4. A stochastic matrix with the property that its column elements sum to 1 and are non-negative is said to be **doubly-stochastic**. Which of the matrices in Exercise 3 are doubly stochastic?

5. Let M_1, M_2 be the matrices listed. Show that $M_1 M_2$ is stochastic when appropriate.

   a. $\begin{bmatrix} 1/3 & 2/3 \\ 1/2 & 1/2 \end{bmatrix}, \begin{bmatrix} 1/2 & 1/2 \\ 1/4 & 3/4 \end{bmatrix}$ b. $\begin{bmatrix} 1/5 & 4/5 \\ 0 & 1 \end{bmatrix}, \begin{bmatrix} 1 & 0 \\ 2/3 & 1/3 \end{bmatrix}$

   c. $\begin{bmatrix} -1/3 & 4/3 \\ 0 & 1 \end{bmatrix}, \begin{bmatrix} 1 & 0 \\ 0 & 1 \end{bmatrix}$.

6. If each of M_1 and M_2 is a stochastic matrix show that $M_1 M_2$ is stochastic.

7. Let $P = [4/5, 1/5]$ and $M = \begin{bmatrix} 2/3 & 1/3 \\ 1/5 & 4/5 \end{bmatrix}$. Show that PM is stochastic.

8. Let $M = \begin{bmatrix} 0 & 1 \\ 1 & 0 \end{bmatrix}$.

   a. Find the eigenvalues of M.

   b. A stochastic vector X such that $M^T X^T = X^T$ is called a **fixed point**. Find the fixed point of M.

9. Let $M = \begin{bmatrix} 1/3 & 2/3 \\ 2/3 & 1/3 \end{bmatrix}$.

   a. Find the eigenvalues of M

   b. Find the fixed point of M. (See Exercise 8.)

   c. Find the eigenvalues of M^2 and compare them with those of M. Can you form a conjecture about the relationship between the eigenvalues of M and those of M^2?

10. Find two matrices A and B neither of which is stochastic, but whose product $M = AB$ is stochastic.

Suggested reading

J. G. Kemeny, J. L. Snell, and G. L. Thompson, *Introduction to Finite Mathematics*, Prentice-Hall, Inc., Englewood Cliffs, N.J. (1957).

New terms

stochastic vector, 311	Markov matrix, 312
stochastic matrix, 312	doubly stochastic matrix, 315
probability matrix, 312	fixed point, 316

8.2   Markov chains—known initial state

We now consider a special type of random process. Suppose that we have a system which, upon the performance of an experiment, is found to be in one of two **states**, or situations, S_1 or S_2. The experiment could consist of flipping a light switch with possible states S_1 (denoting that the light is " on ") and S_2 (denoting the state that the light is " off "). We will suppose that the experiment can be performed repeatedly. Thus, we could progress from state to state as the experiments are performed.

    The system could consist of a rocket booster that is operated intermittently, in which case the states could be

    S_1: the rocket functions properly,
    S_2: the rocket malfunctions.

If we know two probabilities, namely

p_{11}: the probability that the rocket will function properly, given that it functioned properly last time; i.e., the probability of going from S_1 to S_1, and

p_{12}: the probability that the rocket will malfunction, given that it functioned properly last time; i.e., the probability of going from S_1 to S_2,

then we would expect that $p_{11} + p_{12} = 1$ and $p_{1j} \geqslant 0$ since the rocket must either function or malfunction regardless of what it did last time. We may similarly define p_{21} and p_{22}, supposing that we start in S_2 rather than S_1. If we are in S_2 then the probability of remaining there is p_{22}, while the probability of going to S_1 is p_{21}. These p_{ij} thus represent the probabilities of going from S_i to S_j in one particular firing attempt. Since their use is conditioned upon knowing which state we are in, they are called **conditional probabilities**. They also represent the probability of transition from S_i to S_j as shown in the Table 8.2.1. Thus they are called **transition probabilities** and the matrix $M = [p_{ij}]$ is called a **transition matrix**.

State	S_1	S_2
S_1	p_{11}	p_{12}
S_2	p_{21}	p_{22}

Table 8.2.1

A stochastic system such as we have described which moves from state to state in a fashion such that the probability of going from S_i to S_j depends only upon the state we are in, rather than on a more complete historical description, is called a 2-state **Markov chain**.

Example 8.2.1

Suppose that in our previous example the rocket has $p_{11} = .9$ and $p_{12} = .1$, while $p_{21} = .8$ and $p_{22} = .2$. The transition matrix $M = \begin{bmatrix} .9 & .1 \\ .8 & .2 \end{bmatrix}$. If the rocket functioned successfully on the previous trial, then we are in S_1 and the probability of a successful firing on the next trial is .9.

In many such random processes we are interested in knowing the probability of going from S_1 to S_1, say, in 2, or 3, or even n steps. For $n = 2$, in the rocket case, we would want to know the probability of the rocket firing on the second future attempt, given that it functioned properly on the last attempt. In this case we find that we can go from S_1

to S_1 in 2 steps in two different ways as illustrated in the **tree diagram** of Figure 8.2.1.

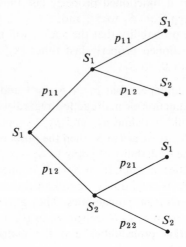

Figure 8.2.1

We use the symbol $p_{11}^{(2)}$ to denote the probability of going from S_1 to S_1 in two steps and note that it should be computed as the sum of the probabilities of going from S_1 to S_1 to S_1 and from S_1 to S_2 to S_1. Thus, using the tree as a guide, we obtain

$$p_{11}^{(2)} = p_{11}p_{11} + p_{12}p_{21}.$$

Similarly, we define $p_{12}^{(2)}$, $p_{21}^{(2)}$, and $p_{22}^{(2)}$ and obtain

$$p_{12}^{(2)} = p_{11}p_{12} + p_{12}p_{22}$$
$$p_{21}^{(2)} = p_{21}p_{11} + p_{22}p_{21}$$
$$p_{22}^{(2)} = p_{21}p_{12} + p_{22}p_{22}.$$

The entire matrix of 2-step transition probabilities, namely

$$M^{(2)} = [p_{ij}^{(2)}],$$

turns out fortunately to be nothing more than the stochastic matrix M^2 since

$$M^2 = \begin{bmatrix} p_{11} & p_{12} \\ p_{21} & p_{22} \end{bmatrix} \begin{bmatrix} p_{11} & p_{12} \\ p_{21} & p_{22} \end{bmatrix} = \begin{bmatrix} p_{11}p_{11} + p_{12}p_{21} & p_{11}p_{12} + p_{12}p_{22} \\ p_{21}p_{11} + p_{22}p_{21} & p_{21}p_{12} + p_{22}p_{22} \end{bmatrix}$$
$$= \begin{bmatrix} p_{11}^{(2)} & p_{12}^{(2)} \\ p_{21}^{(2)} & p_{22}^{(2)} \end{bmatrix}.$$

Example 8.2.2

With $M = \begin{bmatrix} .9 & .1 \\ .8 & .2 \end{bmatrix}$ as in Example 8.2.1, we obtain

$$M^{(2)} = M^2 = \begin{bmatrix} .9 & .1 \\ .8 & .2 \end{bmatrix} \begin{bmatrix} .9 & .1 \\ .8 & .2 \end{bmatrix} = \begin{bmatrix} .89 & .11 \\ .88 & .12 \end{bmatrix}$$

Thus, for example, $p_{12}{}^{(2)} = .11$.

It can be shown in general that the **n-step transition matrix** for going from S_i to S_j in n steps is such that $M^{(n)} = M^n$.*

Exercises 8.2

1. Suppose that you have a transition matrix $M = \begin{bmatrix} 0 & 1 \\ 1/3 & 2/3 \end{bmatrix}$ and you are in S_1.
   a. Find the probability of going to S_2.
   b. Find the probability of remaining in S_1.
   c. Find the probability of going from S_1 to S_2 to S_1.
   d. Use a tree diagram to find $p_{12}{}^{(2)}$.

2. Use M^2 to find $p_{11}{}^{(2)}$ and $p_{12}{}^{(2)}$ in Exercise 1 above.

3. a. With M as in Exercise 1 above, find $p_{11}{}^{(3)}$ and $p_{12}{}^{(3)}$ and verify that their sum is 1.
   b. Find $p_{21}{}^{(3)}$ and $p_{22}{}^{(3)}$ and verify that their sum is 1.

4. In general, the elements of the n-step transition matrix $M^{(n)}$ are given by the elements of _____.

5. Suppose that you have a sequence of two identical receiver-transmitter units which are supposed to receive a given message (either "yes" or "no") and transmit it exactly as received. If the probability of sending the message exactly as received is 2/3:
   a. Set up the transition matrix which reflects the situation above, assuming that the unit could have received either message.
   b. Find the 2-step transition matrix.

6. Suppose that a student either rides his bicycle or walks to class. If he rides his bicycle on a given day he is equally likely to walk as ride his bicycle on the next day. He never walks two days in a row. Set up a transition matrix reflecting this situation. Let the states be "W" and "R", for "walk" or "ride". If he walked Monday, what is the probability that he will walk on Wednesday? What if he rode his bicycle on Monday? Tuesday, of course, is a class day.

* J.G.Kemeny *et al.*, *Introduction to Finite Mathematics*, pp. 218 ff.

Suggested reading

J. G. Kemeny, J. L. Snell, and G. L. Thompson, *Introduction to Finite Mathematics*, Prentice-Hall, Inc., Englewood Cliffs, N.J. (1957).

New terms

state, 316
conditional probability, 317
transition probability, 317
transition matrix, 317

Markov chain, 317
tree diagram, 318
n-step transition matrix, 319

8.3 Markov chains—uncertain initial state

In the last section we discussed the procedure for describing a random process which moves from S_i to S_j with conditional probability p_{ij}. Under the assumption that we knew which state we started in, we obtained the probability of being in state S_1 or S_2 after $1, 2, \ldots, n$ steps by computing the proper power of $M = [p_{ij}]$.

Here we shall consider the case where we do not know which state we start in, but only have a stochastic vector $P^{(0)} = [a, b]$ expressing our probabilistic estimate of the state we start in. For example, if we are equally likely to be in either state, then $P^{(0)} = [a, b] = [1/2, 1/2]$.

We now compute the total probability $p_1^{(1)}$ of being in S_1 after 1 step as follows:

$$p_1^{(1)} = p_{11}a + p_{21}b,$$

where $p_{11}a$ represents the product of the conditional probability p_{11} of going from S_1 to S_1, and a, the probability of starting in S_1. The second summand, $p_{21}b$, has an analogous interpretation assuming a start in S_2. Similarly, $p_2^{(1)}$, the total probability of arriving in S_2 in 1 step is computed as

$$p_2^{(1)} = p_{12}a + p_{22}b.$$

We verify that

$$
\begin{aligned}
p_1^{(1)} + p_2^{(1)} &= (p_{11}a + p_{21}b) + (p_{12}a + p_{22}b) \\
&= a(p_{11} + p_{12}) + b(p_{21} + p_{22}) \\
&= a + b \\
&= 1.
\end{aligned}
$$

Example 8.3.1

Let $M = \begin{bmatrix} 1 & 0 \\ 1/2 & 1/2 \end{bmatrix} = \begin{bmatrix} p_{11} & p_{12} \\ p_{21} & p_{22} \end{bmatrix}$ and $P^{(0)} = [a, b] = [1/2, 1/2]$.
Then $p_1^{(1)} = 1(1/2) + 1/2(1/2) = 3/4$ and $p_2^{(1)} = 0(1/2) + 1/2(1/2) = 1/4$. Since $p_{11} = 1$ in M shows that we remain in S_1 if we are already there, then we would have expected the probabilities to change as they did. That is, we would think that our probability of being in S_1 would increase with the number of trials.

With M and $P^{(0)}$ defined as above, we see that the matrix

$$P^{(1)} = [p_1^{(1)}, p_2^{(1)}]$$

can also be computed as a matrix product where

$$P^{(1)} = P^{(0)}M = [a, b]\begin{bmatrix} p_{11} & p_{12} \\ p_{21} & p_{22} \end{bmatrix}$$

$$= [ap_{11} + bp_{21}, ap_{12} + bp_{22}].$$

Example 8.3.2

With M and $P^{(0)}$ as in Example 8.3.1, we have

$$P^{(1)} = P^{(0)}M = [1/2, 1/2]\begin{bmatrix} 1 & 0 \\ 1/2 & 1/2 \end{bmatrix} = [3/4, 1/4].$$

We now let $P^{(2)} = [p_1^{(2)}, p_2^{(2)}]$ where $p_i^{(2)}$ denotes the probability of being in S_i after 2 steps. Replacing our original estimate of state $P^{(0)}$ by $P^{(1)}$ we obtain

$$p_1^{(2)} = p_{11}p_1^{(1)} + p_{21}p_2^{(1)}$$

and

$$p_2^{(2)} = p_{12}p_1^{(1)} + p_{22}p_2^{(1)}.$$

In matrix format we have

$$P^{(2)} = [p_1^{(2)}, p_2^{(2)}] = [p_1^{(1)}, p_2^{(1)}]\begin{bmatrix} p_{11} & p_{12} \\ p_{21} & p_{22} \end{bmatrix}$$

$$= P^{(1)}M = (P^{(0)}M)M = P^{(0)}M^2.$$

As we mentioned in the previous section, it can be shown that, for a general n

$$P^{(n)} = P^{(0)}M^n$$

where $P^{(n)} = [p_1^{(n)}, p_2^{(n)}]$ and $p_i^{(n)}$ represents the probability of being in S_i after n steps.*

_____

* Kemeny *et al.*, *op. cit.*

Example 8.3.3

With M and $P^{(0)}$ as in Example 8.3.2, we compute

$$P^{(2)} = [p_1{}^{(2)}, p_2{}^{(2)}] = P^{(0)}M^2 = [1/2, 1/2]\begin{bmatrix} 1 & 0 \\ 3/4 & 1/4 \end{bmatrix}$$

$$= [7/8, 1/8]$$

and

$$P^{(3)} = [p_1{}^{(3)}, p_2{}^{(3)}] = P^{(2)}M = [7/8, 1/8]\begin{bmatrix} 1 & 0 \\ 1/2 & 1/2 \end{bmatrix}$$

$$= [15/16, 1/16].$$

We observe that the probability of being in S_1 continues to increase with n.

Exercises 8.3

1. Suppose that the transition matrix for a 2-state Markov chain is $M = \begin{bmatrix} 0 & 1 \\ 1 & 0 \end{bmatrix}$. If you are equally likely to be in S_1 or S_2 at the beginning of a sequence of trials, find

    a. $p_1{}^{(1)}$ b. $p_2{}^{(1)}$ c. $P^{(1)}$ d. $p_1{}^{(2)}$ e. $p_2{}^{(2)}$ f. $P^{(2)}$

2. a. Draw a complete tree diagram illustrating the situation for 2 trials of a 2-state Markov chain with $M = \begin{bmatrix} 1/3 & 2/3 \\ 1/2 & 1/2 \end{bmatrix}$.

    b. Compute $M^{(2)}$ by use of the tree diagram.
    c. Compute $P^{(2)}$ by use of the tree diagram, assuming that $P^{(0)} = [1/2, 1/2]$.
    d. Compute $P^{(2)}$ using matrix methods.

3. In Exercise 5 of Section 8.2, let $P^{(0)} = [2/3, 1/3]$ and find $P^{(1)}$, $P^{(2)}$, and $P^{(3)}$.

4. In Exercise 6 of Section 8.2, let $P^{(0)} = [1/2, 1/2]$ and find $P^{(1)}$, $P^{(2)}$, and $P^{(3)}$.

Suggested reading

J. G. Kemeny, J. L. Snell, and G. L. Thompson, *Introduction to Finite Mathematics*, Prentice-Hall, Inc., Englewood Cliffs, N.J. (1957).

8.4   An insurance example

We conclude this chapter with a short but significant practical example of the use of stochastic matrices.

Suppose that you are employed by the ABC Automobile Insurance Company. The company, upon completion of an extensive study, has concluded that drivers who have had accidents are more likely to have another accident than are drivers who have had no accidents. Faced with increasing repair costs and rising claims, the company has decided to surcharge the premiums of their drivers depending upon their accident history—that is, a policyholder's annual premium will be increased an amount determined by the number of accidents in which he has been involved and held to be at fault.

For simplicity we shall suppose that ABC policyholders have been divided into three categories or states as follows: a policyholder is placed in state S_0 if he has had no accidents, into S_1 if he has had exactly one accident, and into S_2 if he has had two or more accidents as an ABC policyholder. Surcharges will be added to the premiums of drivers in S_1 and S_2 in an effort to force these groups to contribute their fair share of the total premium income.

Your job is to build a mathematical model which will help to predict the number of present policyholders who will be in S_0, S_1, and S_2 after $1, 2, \ldots, n$ years. Stochastic matrices and Markov chains are well-fitted for this task. In Table 8.4.1

State / State	0	1	2
0	.90	.09	.01
1	0	.80	.20
2	0	0	1.00

Table 8.4.1

we list the conditional probabilities of a given policyholder's moving from S_i to S_j in a given policy year, all of which we assume coincide with the calendar year. Thus the probability of having no accidents and remaining in S_0 is .90 for the driver who has had no accidents. The conditional probability of having no accidents and remaining in S_1 is .80 for the driver who has had 1 accident. Similarly, the probability of having exactly one accident and moving to S_1 is .09 for the driver in S_0. The probability of having one or more accidents is .10 (.09 + .01) for the driver in S_0 and .20 for the driver in S_1. Because of our particular classification scheme, drivers in S_2 remain in S_2, as indicated by the fact that $p_{22} = 1.00$. In reality, there could be many more states, one of which could represent drivers who were eliminated as policy-holders because of poor driving records. The typical but fictitious probabilities which are listed analytically illustrate our belief that increasingly poor driving records indicate increasingly poor risks on the average.

For our prediction purposes we use the body of Table 8.4.1 to form the stochastic matrix

$$M = \begin{bmatrix} .90 & .09 & .01 \\ 0 & .80 & .20 \\ 0 & 0 & 1.00 \end{bmatrix}.$$

Let us suppose now that the company had 10,000 policyholders and that management wishes to obtain a probabilistic estimate of the number of these 10,000 policyholders that it can expect to have in each of S_0, S_1, S_2 after three years. With this information and knowledge of the various surcharges, one could estimate the total premium income from these policyholders for year four. We let the original state vector $P^{(0)} = [10000, 0, 0]$ indicating that all policyholders start in S_0. We then compute

$$P^{(1)} = P^{(0)}M = [10000, 0, 0] \begin{bmatrix} .90 & .09 & .01 \\ 0 & .80 & .20 \\ 0 & 0 & 1.00 \end{bmatrix} = [9000, 900, 100],$$

$$P^{(2)} = P^{(1)}M = P^{(0)}M^2 = [9000, 900, 100] \begin{bmatrix} .90 & .09 & .01 \\ 0 & .80 & .20 \\ 0 & 0 & 1.00 \end{bmatrix}$$

$$= [8100, 1530, 370],$$

and that

$$P^{(3)} = P^{(2)}M = P^{(0)}M^3 = [8100, 1530, 370]M = [7290, 1953, 757].$$

Thus, to start the fourth policy year, we would expect that of our original 10,000 policyholders, 7290 would be in S_0, 1953 in S_1, and 757 in S_2. Management may now use this data to help decide what the premium surcharges should be. They may, for example, decide to make the penalty so large that policyholders in S_2 will be economically forced to leave the company rather than continue.

Appendix A

Completeness property of the real numbers

In order to fully describe the real number system we need to make several definitions which were not included in Section 1.3. First, we say that a subset S of R is **bounded below** if there is a real number L such that for each s in S, $L \leqslant s$, and L is called a **lower bound** for S. Similarly, S is said to be **bounded above** if there is a number U such that for each s in S, $s \leqslant U$, and U is then called an **upper bound** for S. Clearly, if a set S has a lower bound L, then it has many lower bounds; for any number $k \leqslant L$ is also a lower bound for S. By way of example, consider

$$S = \{x \mid x \text{ is in } R \text{ and } 5 \leqslant x \leqslant 10\}.$$

Then S is bounded below (5 is a lower bound) and bounded above (10 is an upper bound). The set

$$T = \{x \mid x \leqslant 10\}$$

is bounded above but is not bounded below, while

$$V = \{x \mid 5 \leqslant x\}$$

is bounded below but not above. And, moreover, the set R of all real numbers is neither bounded below nor above. Thus with respect to upper and lower bounds, there are examples of all types of subsets to be found in R.

We say that a number u is a **least upper bound** for a set S provided u is, first, an upper bound for S and, second, if v is another upper bound for S, then $u < v$. (A similar definition may be made for **greatest lower bound**.)

Our final property of the real numbers may now be described by saying that the real numbers are *complete* in the sense that every set S which has an upper bound has a least upper bound. This **completeness property** is the one with which the reader is probably least familiar—and for good reasons. First, it is not a property which everyone finds intuitively obvious (to say the least), and, second, it is not linked to the familiar properties A1–A4, M1–M4, D_1 and D_2. Indeed, the rational numbers $\mathbb{Q}$, which form an ordered field, do not have the completeness property. For consider the set

$$S = \{x \mid x \text{ is in } \mathbb{Q} \text{ and } x^2 \leqslant 2\}.$$

Now S has plenty of upper bounds—17 is one—but has no least upper bound, since if u is an upper bound for S, then $2 \leqslant u^2$; and there are many rational numbers v such that $2 \leqslant v^2 \leqslant u^2$. Any such v is also an upper bound for S and is less than u. Hence S has no least upper bound. The " number" that *ought* to be the least upper bound for S is $\sqrt{2}$, but it, of course, is not rational and thus does not enter our discussion. On the other hand,

$$T = \{x \mid x \text{ is in } R \text{ and } x^2 \leqslant 2\}$$

has $\sqrt{2}$ as least upper bound. The difference here is that S is a subset of the rationals, while T is a subset of the reals.

We have now described our familiar set R of real numbers as a **complete ordered field**. And it is the completeness property which distinguishes R from all other ordered fields. This fact, which is proved in several of the references at the end of Chapter 1, may be loosely stated as: there is one and only one complete ordered field—namely, the real numbers.

Appendix B

Sigma notation and more matrix algebra

B.1 Sigma notation

In our general notation $A = [a_{ij}]$ for matrices, the elements are designated as doubly subscripted a's, the subscripts denoting respectively the row and the column in which the element lies. In order to present proofs of certain algebraic properties of matrices, it is convenient to have a shorthand notation for addition of the elements of a matrix. We use the Greek capital letter $\sum$ (pronounced " sigma ") as our summation symbol, and use it in the following manner.

To indicate the sum of the elements of the third row of the 4×7 matrix $[a_{ij}]$, instead of the usual

$$a_{31} + a_{32} + a_{33} + a_{34} + a_{35} + a_{36} + a_{37},$$

we write

$$\sum_{j=1}^{7} a_{3j}.$$

That is, the symbol stands for the sum (indicated by $\sum$) of all terms of the form a_{3j}, where j (called the index of summation) takes on all integer values from 1 to 7 *inclusive*. In a similar manner

$$\sum_{i=1}^{4} a_{i3}$$

is just an abbreviation for

$$a_{13} + a_{23} + a_{33} + a_{43},$$

which is the sum of the elements of the third column of our aforementioned matrix $[a_{ij}]$.

Consider now the problem of finding the sum of all the elements of the 4×7 matrix $[a_{ij}]$. In longhand, we might write this, summing by rows, as

$$a_{11} + a_{12} + a_{13} + a_{14} + a_{15} + a_{16} + a_{17} +$$
$$a_{21} + a_{22} + a_{23} + a_{24} + a_{25} + a_{26} + a_{27} +$$
$$a_{31} + a_{32} + a_{33} + a_{34} + a_{35} + a_{36} + a_{37} +$$
$$a_{41} + a_{42} + a_{43} + a_{44} + a_{45} + a_{46} + a_{47}.$$

Here the individual row sums are given by

$$\sum_{j=1}^{7} a_{1j}, \quad \sum_{j=1}^{7} a_{2j}, \quad \sum_{j=1}^{7} a_{3j}, \quad \sum_{j=1}^{7} a_{4j}.$$

Thus our sum might be written as

$$\sum_{j=1}^{7} a_{1j} + \sum_{j=1}^{7} a_{2j} + \sum_{j=1}^{7} a_{3j} + \sum_{j=1}^{7} a_{4j}.$$

But even this is cumbersome, so we write more compactly

$$\sum_{i=1}^{4} \left(\sum_{j=1}^{7} a_{ij} \right).$$

The first part $\sum_{i=1}^{4}$ of the above symbol indicates that we are summing four quantities, and each quantity in the sum is of the form $\sum_{j=1}^{7} a_{ij}$. Note that we also could have formed the original sum by columns,

$$\sum_{i=1}^{4} a_{i1} + \sum_{i=1}^{4} a_{i2} + \sum_{i=1}^{4} a_{i3} + \sum_{i=1}^{4} a_{i4} + \sum_{i=1}^{4} a_{i5} + \sum_{i=1}^{4} a_{i6} + \sum_{i=1}^{4} a_{i7}$$

and that this could have also been more briefly written as

$$\sum_{j=1}^{7} \left(\sum_{i=1}^{4} a_{ij} \right).$$

We thus see that in this case the two sums are equal so that

$$\sum_{i=1}^{4} \left(\sum_{j=1}^{7} a_{ij} \right) = \sum_{j=1}^{7} \left(\sum_{i=1}^{4} a_{ij} \right).$$

More generally, for any finite double summation it is true that

$$\sum_{i=1}^{m} \left(\sum_{j=1}^{n} a_{ij} \right) = \sum_{j=1}^{n} \left(\sum_{i=1}^{m} a_{ij} \right).$$

Thus the order of the summation is immaterial and we may write the previous sum (without the parentheses) as

$$\sum_{i=1}^{4} \sum_{j=1}^{7} a_{ij} \quad \text{or as} \quad \sum_{j=1}^{7} \sum_{i=1}^{4} a_{ij}.$$

Let us apply the notation in a simple situation. Suppose that

$$A = \begin{bmatrix} a_{11} & a_{12} & a_{13} & a_{14} \\ a_{21} & a_{22} & a_{23} & a_{24} \\ a_{31} & a_{32} & a_{33} & a_{34} \end{bmatrix} \quad \text{and} \quad B = \begin{bmatrix} b_{11} & b_{12} \\ b_{21} & b_{22} \\ b_{31} & b_{32} \\ b_{41} & b_{42} \end{bmatrix}.$$

The element in the second row, first column of the product AB is:

$$a_{21}b_{11} + a_{22}b_{21} + a_{23}b_{31} + a_{24}b_{41}.$$

Notice that since our element is in the second row, then the row subscript 2 remains fixed on the a's. And since our element is in the first column of the product, then the column subscript 1 remains fixed for the b's. It is the column subscript on the a's and the row subscript on the b's which change from term to term in the sum, so that the sum may be written as

$$\sum_{k=1}^{4} a_{2k} b_{k1}.$$

We conclude this section by noting that the summation index k is completely arbitrary. Thus, for example, the above sum may be written as

$$\sum_{k=1}^{4} a_{2k} b_{k1} = \sum_{s=1}^{4} a_{2s} b_{s1} = \sum_{t=1}^{4} a_{2t} b_{t1}.$$

B.2 Matrix multiplication

In Chapter 2 we gave a rather labored definition of matrix multiplication. In this short section we define matrix multiplication using the $\sum$ notation and give an example. In the following section we prove those properties of matrix algebra which were mentioned in Chapter 2 but not proved there.

Let $A = [a_{ij}]$ and $B = [b_{ij}]$ be respectively an $m \times n$ and an $n \times q$ matrix. Then the product $C = AB$ is defined in that order and $AB = [c_{ij}] = C$ where

$$c_{ij} = \sum_{k=1}^{n} a_{ik} b_{kj}.$$

Example

Let

$$A = \begin{bmatrix} a_{11} & a_{12} & a_{13} \\ a_{21} & a_{22} & a_{23} \\ a_{31} & a_{32} & a_{33} \end{bmatrix} \quad \text{and} \quad B = \begin{bmatrix} b_{11} & b_{12} \\ b_{21} & b_{22} \\ b_{31} & b_{32} \end{bmatrix}.$$

Then

$$C = AB = \begin{bmatrix} \sum_{k=1}^{3} a_{1k} b_{k1} & \sum_{k=1}^{3} a_{1k} b_{k2} \\ \sum_{k=1}^{3} a_{2k} b_{k1} & \sum_{k=1}^{3} a_{2k} b_{k2} \\ \sum_{k=1}^{3} a_{3k} b_{k1} & \sum_{k=1}^{3} a_{3k} b_{k2} \end{bmatrix}$$

$$= \left[\sum_{k=1}^{3} a_{ik} b_{kj} \right] = [c_{ij}].$$

B.3   More matrix algebra

In this section we present in rather terse form the algebraic theorems which were mentioned but not proved in Chapter 2. The last two theorems are linked results, the final one taking a little of the bitterness out of the "divisors of zero" notion mentioned in Section 2.6.

THEOREM B.I

Matrix multiplication is associative.

Proof:

Let $A = [a_{ij}]$, $B = [b_{ij}]$, and $C = [c_{ij}]$ be three matrices which are conformable for multiplication in the order ABC. Let A be $m \times n$, B be $n \times q$, and C be $q \times p$. Then each of the products AB, $(AB)C$, BC, and $A(BC)$ is defined and we wish to prove that $A(BC) = (AB)C$. We first note that A is $m \times n$ while BC is $n \times p$, so that $A(BC)$ is $m \times p$. Moreover, AB is $m \times q$ while C is $q \times p$ so that $(AB)C$ is $m \times p$ also. Thus the products $A(BC)$ and $(AB)C$ at least have the same dimensions. To show that they are equal, we show that a typical element, say in the ith row, jth column of $A(BC)$ is the same as the corresponding element in $(AB)C$. Consider the product BC whose jth column is

$$
\begin{bmatrix}
\sum_{k=1}^{q} b_{1k} c_{kj} \\[2mm]
\sum_{k=1}^{q} b_{2k} c_{kj} \\[2mm]
\vdots \\[2mm]
\sum_{k=1}^{q} b_{nk} c_{kj}
\end{bmatrix}.
$$

Then the element in the ith row, jth column of $A(BC)$ is

$$
\sum_{s=1}^{n} a_{is} \left(\sum_{k=1}^{q} b_{sk} c_{kj} \right),
$$

which may be rearranged as

$$
\sum_{s=1}^{n} \sum_{k=1}^{q} a_{is} b_{sk} c_{kj} . \qquad \text{(Why?)}
$$

Now we calculate the element in the ith row, jth column of $(AB)C$. To do this, first note that the ith row of AB is

$$
\left[\sum_{s=1}^{n} a_{is} b_{s1}, \ \sum_{s=1}^{n} a_{is} b_{s2}, \ \ldots, \ \sum_{s=1}^{n} a_{is} b_{sq} \right].
$$

Thus the ith row, jth column element of $(AB)C$ is computed by forming the product of the ith row of AB by the jth column of C. We thus obtain

$$
\sum_{k=1}^{q} \left(\sum_{s=1}^{n} a_{is} b_{sk} \right) c_{kj} = \sum_{k=1}^{q} \left(\sum_{s=1}^{n} a_{is} b_{sk} c_{kj} \right).
$$

But, as we have seen, the latter may be written as

$$
\sum_{k=1}^{q} \sum_{s=1}^{n} a_{is} b_{sk} c_{kj} .
$$

Since the order of summation may also be interchanged, this may be expressed as

$$
\sum_{s=1}^{n} \sum_{k=1}^{q} a_{is} b_{sk} c_{kj} ,
$$

which is our result for the i, j element in $A(BC)$. Thus corresponding elements of $A(BC)$ and $(AB)C$ are equal and hence $A(BC) = (AB)C$, which is what we wished to prove. $\square$

THEOREM B.2

If A, B, and C are conformable for the product $A(B + C)$ to be defined, then (left distributive property)
$$A(B + C) = AB + AC.$$

Proof:

Suppose A is $m \times n$, and each of B and C is $n \times q$. With $A = [a_{ij}]$, $B = [b_{ij}]$, and $C = [c_{ij}]$ we find that the jth column of $B + C$ is
$$\begin{bmatrix} b_{1j} + c_{1j} \\ b_{2j} + c_{2j} \\ \vdots \\ b_{nj} + c_{nj} \end{bmatrix}.$$
Thus the element in the ith row, jth column of $A(B + C)$ is
$$\sum_{k=1}^{n} a_{ik}(b_{kj} + c_{kj}) = \sum_{k=1}^{n} a_{ik}b_{kj} + \sum_{k=1}^{n} a_{ik}c_{kj}.$$
Now we merely observe that the right-hand side of this equation is the element in the ith row, jth column of the sum $AB + AC$. Thus $A(B + C) = AB + AC$. □

THEOREM B.3

Matrix multiplication is right distributive; that is, for conforming A, B, C, we have $(A + B)C = AC + BC$.

Proof:

The reader should supply his own proof as an exercise.

THEOREM B.4

If the product AB is defined, then $(AB)^T = B^T A^T$; that is, the transpose of a product is the product of the transposes in reverse order.

Proof:

Suppose A is $m \times n$ and B is $n \times q$. Then the element in the ith row, jth column of $(AB)^T$ is the element in the jth row, ith column of AB, and thus is
$$\sum_{k=1}^{n} a_{jk}b_{ki}.$$
Now, the element in the ith row, jth column of $B^T A^T$ is formed by multiplying the ith row of B^T by the jth column of A^T. But since the ith row of B^T is the ith column of B, while the jth column of A^T is the jth row of A, we then have
$$\sum_{k=1}^{n} b_{ki}a_{jk}.$$

But since multiplication of real numbers is commutative, this is the same as

$$\sum_{k=1}^{n} a_{jk} b_{ki},$$

which proves our theorem. $\square$

We note that for the transpose of the product of three matrices, we have

$$(ABC)^T = ((AB)C)^T = C^T(AB)^T = C^T(B^T A^T) = C^T B^T A^T.$$

The theorem may be generalized to any (finite) number of matrices.

In Section 2.6 we observed all sorts of "bad" things about matrix multiplication. First, it is non-commutative (which is bad enough). Secondly, there are many examples of **divisors of zero**; that is, matrices A and B, neither of which is zero but for which $AB = 0$. Now we know that some matrices have inverses and some do not. If A has an inverse then $AB = AC$ implies $B = C$, since we merely left-multiply the first equation by A^{-1} to obtain the second. Thus in case A has an inverse, we have a left cancellation law. But if A has no inverse, then what are we to conclude? Is $B = C$ or $B \neq C$? The general answer to this question is more elaborate than we want to consider in this text, but the next two theorems (really the second one) provide a partial answer in a special setting. Specifically, we will show that if we are given

$$A^T(AB) = A^T(AC)$$

then we may left-cancel the factor A^T to obtain

$$AB = AC.$$

Note that in this result nothing is assumed about the matrix A. It does not have to have an inverse—it does not even have to be square!

First we need a definition. By the **trace of a square matrix B** we mean the sum $\sum_{i=1}^{n} b_{ii}$ of its diagonal elements. Thus the trace of $\begin{bmatrix} 1 & 2 \\ 3 & 4 \end{bmatrix}$ is $1 + 4 = 5$ and the trace of $\begin{bmatrix} -1 & 2 \\ 3 & 1 \end{bmatrix}$ is $-1 + 1 = 0$. Now, by way of introducing our next theorem, notice that while the matrix $A = \begin{bmatrix} 1 & 2 & 3 \\ 4 & 5 & 6 \end{bmatrix}$ has no trace (since it is not square), the matrix $A^T A$, which is calculated as

$$\begin{bmatrix} 1 & 4 \\ 2 & 5 \\ 3 & 6 \end{bmatrix} \begin{bmatrix} 1 & 2 & 3 \\ 4 & 5 & 6 \end{bmatrix} = \begin{bmatrix} 17 & 22 & 27 \\ 22 & 29 & 36 \\ 27 & 36 & 45 \end{bmatrix},$$

is square and its trace is $17 + 29 + 45 = 91$.

THEOREM B.5

If A is any matrix such that the trace of $A^T A$ is 0 then A must consist entirely of zeros.

Proof:

Let $A = [a_{ij}]$ be an $m \times n$ matrix such that the trace of $A^T A$ is 0. (Note that A^T is $n \times m$ and that $A^T A$ is thus a square $n \times n$ matrix.) The first diagonal element of $A^T A$ is computed by multiplying the first row of A^T by the first column of A; but the first row of A^T is the same as the first column of A, so that the first diagonal element of $A^T A$ is

$$\sum_{i=1}^{m} a_{i1}^{2}.$$

Similarly, the second diagonal element of $A^T A$ is

$$\sum_{i=1}^{m} a_{i2}^{2},$$

and in general the kth diagonal element of $A^T A$ is

$$\sum_{i=1}^{m} a_{ik}^{2}.$$

Thus the trace of $A^T A$, which is assumed to be zero, is

$$\sum_{k=1}^{n} \sum_{i=1}^{m} a_{ik}^{2}.$$

However, this is precisely the sum of the squares of all the elements in A, and thus can be zero only if each element in A is zero, which proves our theorem. □

We now apply this result to obtain the previously mentioned

THEOREM B.6

If A, B and C are matrices such that $A^T AB = A^T AC$, then $AB = AC$.

Proof:

We prove this theorem by showing that under the hypothesis the trace of $(AB - AC)^T(AB - AC)$ is zero; so that it will follow from Theorem B.5 that $AB - AC = 0$, which is the result we want. Now consider the product $(AB - AC)^T(AB - AC)$. We unsparingly use Theorems B.2, B.3, and B.4, together with the fact that the transpose of a sum is the sum of the transposes, to obtain

$$
\begin{aligned}
(AB - AC)^T(AB - AC) &= (B^T A^T - C^T A^T)(AB - AC) \\
&= B^T A^T AB - B^T A^T AC - C^T A^T AB + C^T A^T AC \\
&= B^T A^T A(B - C) - C^T A^T A(B - C) \\
&= (B^T A^T A - C^T A^T A)(B - C) \\
&= (A^T AB - A^T AC)^T(B - C).
\end{aligned}
$$

But by hypothesis, $A^T AB - A^T AC = 0$, so that its transpose, which appears as a factor in the last line of the above display, is 0. Thus our original product $(AB - AC)^T(AB - AC) = 0$, and certainly has a 0 trace. Hence, by Theorem B.5, $AB - AC = 0$, so that $AB = AC$. $\square$

Appendix C

Vector spaces

In this appendix we give the general definition of vector space, and several examples of vector spaces which are somewhat different from the ordered n-tuple spaces of the text.

Let F be a field (see Chapter 1) and let $\mathscr{V}$ be a non-empty set with a binary operation $+$ defined on $\mathscr{V}$ such that, for all a, b, c in $\mathscr{V}$

1. $(a + b) + c = a + (b + c)$ $+$ is *associative*
2. $a + b = b + a$ $+$ is *commutative*
3. there is an element 0 in   existence of an *additive identity*
    $\mathscr{V}$ such that
    $0 + a = a + 0 = a$
4. for each a in $\mathscr{V}$ there is   each element has an *additive*
    an element $-a$ in $\mathscr{V}$ such   *inverse*
    that
    $a + (-a) = 0 = (-a) + a$

Further let there be defined an operation of scalar multiplication between elements of the field F and elements of the set $\mathscr{V}$ such that for each x, y in F and a, b in $\mathscr{V}$,

5. xa is an element of $\mathscr{V}$
6. $x(ya) = (xy)a$ *associative*

7. $(x + y)a = xa + ya$ scalar multiplication distributes
                                   over scalar addition

8. $x(a + b) = xa + xb$ scalar multiplication distributes
                                   over vector addition

9. $1a = a$

Then the set $\mathcal{V}$ with its binary operation together with the field F and the scalar multiplication is called a *vector space*. We most frequently say that $\mathcal{V}$ is *a vector space over the field F*.

Now the fields most familiar to the reader are probably the *real numbers*, the *rational numbers*, and the *complex numbers* (readers who have studied modular arithmetic will recall that the integers modulo 5, or modulo any prime, also form a field). Let us now consider some examples of vector spaces over the familiar fields, and note that in each case we specify the set $\mathcal{V}$ (vectors) and its binary operation (vector addition), and we also specify the field F and its scalar multiplication with the member of $\mathcal{V}$. Of course, the example of ordered pairs, or ordered triples, or ordered n-tuples over the reals was *the* example of vector spaces used in the text. We shall not repeat that example here, and only mention in passing that the set of all ordered n-tuples from any field F, with the usual addition and scalar multiplication is an example of a vector space. Moreover, such a space has dimension n, since with 1 as the multiplicative identity of F, the set of n-tuples

$$\{(1, 0, \ldots, 0), (0, 1, \ldots, 0), \ldots, (0, 0, \ldots, 0, 1)\}$$

is easily seen to be a basis.

Example C.1

Let the field F be the field $\mathbb{Q}$ of rational numbers, and let $\mathcal{V}$ be the set of all polynomials of degree $\leqslant 3$ in a single variable t with rational coefficients. Then addition in $\mathcal{V}$ is simply addition of polynomials; that is, to obtain the coefficients of the sum of two polynomials we add coefficients of like powers of t. Scalar multiplication by a member of F is accomplished by multiplying each coefficient of the polynomial by that scalar. For instance, consider the two members

$$v_1 = \tfrac{1}{2} + 5t \quad \text{and} \quad v_2 = -2 + \tfrac{1}{2}t^2 - t^3$$

of $\mathcal{V}$. Their sum is

$$-\tfrac{3}{2} + 5t + \tfrac{1}{2}t^2 - t^3$$

and if we multiply v_2 by $-\tfrac{3}{2}$ (a scalar in $\mathbb{Q}$) then the result is

$$3 - \tfrac{3}{4}t^2 + \tfrac{3}{2}t^3.$$

With these operations in mind, the reader should now go through the list of defining properties for a vector space and assure himself that this set of rational polynomials over the rational field is indeed a vector space. Finally, a word about the dimension of this space. The reader who has studied Chapter 4 will find it easy to see that the set of polynomials

$$\{1, t, t^2, t^3\}$$

is not only linearly independent in this space, but also spans this space and hence forms a basis. Thus the space of all rational polynomials of degree $\leqslant 3$ is a space of dimension 4 (4 being the number of coefficients in such a polynomial). Similarly, for any non-negative integer n, the set of all rational polynomials of degree $\leqslant n$ forms a vector space of polynomials of dimension $n + 1$. Moreover, there being nothing special about the rational field $\mathbb{Q}$, one can form in this way vector spaces of polynomials over any field. Thus one may consider the space of all polynomials with complex coefficients of degree $\leqslant 17$ over the complex field.

Example C.2

As an extension of the previous example, let F be any field and this time let $\mathscr{V}$ be the set of *all* polynomials (no restriction on the degrees) with coefficients from the field F. Again the vector addition is the usual addition of polynomials and the scalar multiplication is defined as before. The reader may readily verify that $\mathscr{V}$ is a vector space over F. Now in this case the matter of dimension needs a word or two of explanation. Consider the (infinite) set

$$\mathscr{B} = \{1, t, t^2, \ldots, t^n, \ldots\}.$$

We say that $\mathscr{B}$ *spans* $\mathscr{V}$ since each element of $\mathscr{V}$ is a linear combination of a *finite* number of elements of $\mathscr{B}$, and we further say that $\mathscr{B}$ is a *linearly independent* set in that any finite subset of it is linearly independent in our usual sense. Thus we are led to say that $\mathscr{B}$ is a basis for $\mathscr{V}$, and, since $\mathscr{B}$ has infinitely many members, we say that $\mathscr{V}$ is an *infinite dimensional vector space over* F.

Example C.3

Let F now be the real number field R, and let $\mathscr{V}$ be the set of all real valued functions defined on the closed interval $[0, 1]$. In $\mathscr{V}$ we define the addition of two functions f and g to be the function $f + g$ whose value at each x in $[0, 1]$ is given by

$$(f + g)(x) = f(x) + g(x).$$

Our scalar multiplication is also the usual one for functions: namely, for any real number r and any function f in $\mathscr{V}$, define rf to be the function whose value at each x in $[0, 1]$ is given by

$$(rf)(x) = rf(x).$$

Then one may easily verify that $\mathscr{V}$ is a vector space over the reals (but we sidestep the question of dimension, because there is not a simple explanation available). To students who have studied the calculus, it will be evident that among the many subspaces of this example is the space of all continuous functions on $[0, 1]$, the space of all differentiable functions on $[0, 1]$ and the space of all integrable functions on $[0, 1]$. The study of such "function spaces" is vital in many areas of both applied and pure mathematics.

Example C.4

In this final example, we should like to point up the fact that the set $\mathscr{V}$ alone does not determine the algebraic character of a vector space. The field F also plays an important role, and to retain $\mathscr{V}$ but change F may make a real difference. To exhibit all this, consider first that the set of complex numbers C (which is a field) may be considered as a vector space over itself; that is, we may think of C as a set of ordered 1-tuples over the field C, with ordinary addition of complex numbers as the vector addition and multiplication of complex numbers as the scalar multiplication. Thus C is a vector space over itself and, since the complex number $1 = 1 + 0i$ is both linearly independent and spans C, then C is a one-dimensional space over C. Now let us keep C as the vector set $\mathscr{V}$, but take the real numbers R as the scalar field (same vector addition; scalar multiplication is simply the multiplication of complex numbers by real numbers). Then C is a vector space over R. But, and this is the point of our example, C is now 2-dimensional over the real field, since over the reals the set

$$\{1, i\}$$

is both a linearly independent and a spanning set for C. Thus by keeping the same vector set and changing the scalar field we have changed the vector space from one of dimension 1 to one of dimension 2.

Answers to odd-numbered exercises

Exercises 1.1

1. a. The set of elements x such that $x - 5$ is a positive integer; $\{6, 7, 8, \ldots\}$.
    b. The set of elements y such that y is a positive integer; $\{1, 2, 3, \ldots\}$.
    c. The set of elements of the form $2x - 1$ such that x is a positive integer; $\{1, 3, 5, \ldots\}$.

3. a. yes, no   b. yes

5. none; 1; no, since $\{\varnothing\}$ contains an element, namely $\varnothing$, while $\varnothing$ contains no elements.

7. $A \cup B = B$; $A \cap B = A$.

9. To show that $A \cap B \subseteq A \cap C$ we need to show that if x is in $A \cap B$ then x is in $A \cap C$. If x is in $A \cap B$ then x is in A and x is in B. Since $B \subseteq C$ and x is in B, x is in C also. Thus x is in A and x is in C, so that x is in $A \cap C$.

11. The subsets of $\{1\}$ are $\varnothing$ and $\{1\}$; thus there are $2 = 2^1$ subsets. The subsets of $\{1, 2\}$ are $\varnothing$, $\{1\}$, $\{2\}$, and $\{1, 2\}$; there are $4 = 2^2$ subsets. The subsets of $\{1, 2, 3\}$ are $\varnothing$, $\{1\}$, $\{2\}$, $\{3\}$, $\{1, 2\}$, $\{1, 3\}$, $\{2, 3\}$, and $\{1, 2, 3\}$; there are $8 = 2^3$ subsets. A set with n elements has 2^n subsets.

Exercises 1.2

1. a. no   b. yes   c. yes   d. no   e. no

3. f, h.

5.

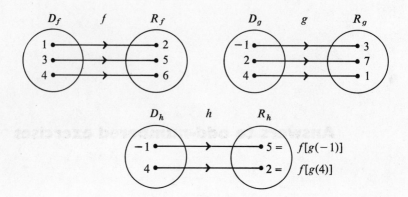

5a. $g \circ f = \{(1, 7)\}$

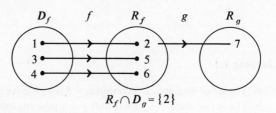

$$R_f \cap D_g = \{2\}$$

5b. $h \circ f = \varnothing$

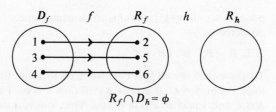

$$R_f \cap D_h = \phi$$

5c. $g \circ h = \{(4, 7)\}$

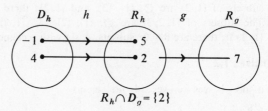

$$R_h \cap D_g = \{2\}$$

Exercises 1.3

1. b. *a*
   c. Yes, the table of sums is symmetric with respect to its main diagonal.
   d. $(-a) = a$, $(-b) = c$, $(-c) = b$.
   e. Must show that $(x + y) + z = x + (y + z)$ for all possible choices of x, y, z in S.

3. a. 0   b. (-5) c. 5

5. c. *b*   e. $c^{-1} = c$; a^{-1} does not exist.

7. For example, $5 - 3 \neq 3 - 5$, and $5 - (3 - 1) \neq (5 - 3) - 1$.

Exercises 1.4

1. a. *T* b. *F* c. *T* d. *T*

3. a. If $1 + 1 = 2$ then $5 + 7 = 3$.
   b. If you have a winning smile, then you chew Black Twist Tobacco.
   c. If one continually overspends his budget then he will eventually be bankrupt.
   d. If we have the Gestapo then we have law and order.

5. a. A sufficient condition for x to be divisible by 12 is that x be divisible by 36.
   b. A sufficient condition for stopping his nose-bleed is to put a tourniquet on his neck.

Exercises 2.1

1. A matrix is a rectangular array of real numbers. In many applications this definition is extended to allow the elements to be complex numbers.

3. Second row, third column.

5. *b*.

7. A–E are each square while F is not square; B has zeros below the left-right diagonal, the only non-zero elements of C and D are on the main diagonal; the elements of E are symmetric with respect to the left-right diagonal.

Exercises 2.2

1. *b*   3. *a, c, d, e, f, g, h, i*   5. *a*   7. *b, h*   9. *a, f*

11. a. $\begin{bmatrix} a & b \\ 0 & c \end{bmatrix}, b \neq 0$ b. $\begin{bmatrix} a & 0 \\ 0 & b \end{bmatrix}, a = b$ c. none exists   d. $\begin{bmatrix} a & b \\ b & d \end{bmatrix}$

13. a. $\begin{bmatrix} 1 & -1 \\ 3 & 2 \end{bmatrix}$

Exercises 2.3

1. $\begin{bmatrix} -1 & -2 & -3 \\ -4 & -5 & -6 \end{bmatrix}$

3. $[6, 4, 4, 7]$

5. Not defined

7. $\begin{bmatrix} 1 & -1 \\ 2 & -3 \\ 3 & -4 \end{bmatrix}$

9. Yes; we may find it by solving the six equations $a_{11} + x_{11} = b_{11}$, $a_{12} + x_{12} = b_{12}$, etc. to form $\begin{bmatrix} 1 & 2 & 1 \\ 7 & 3 & -2 \end{bmatrix}$.

11. a. $A^T = \begin{bmatrix} 1 & 4 \\ 2 & 5 \\ 3 & 6 \end{bmatrix}$, $B^T = \begin{bmatrix} -2 & -8 \\ -4 & -10 \\ -6 & -12 \end{bmatrix}$

13. $[0, 0, 0]$, $[0, 0, 0, 0]^T$, $\begin{bmatrix} 0 & 0 & 0 & 0 & 0 & 0 \\ 0 & 0 & 0 & 0 & 0 & 0 \\ 0 & 0 & 0 & 0 & 0 & 0 \end{bmatrix}$

15. Suppose that both $(-A)$ and B are additive inverses of A. Then, since $A + B = 0$, $(-A) + (A + B) = (-A) + 0 = (-A)$ and $((-A) + A) + B = 0 + B = B = -A$. Thus there was really only one.

17. Show that $B + (-A) = B - A$ is a solution and that if Y is a solution then Y must be $B - A$. See Section 1.3 for the analogous equation for real numbers. Yes.

Exercises 2.4

1. $[32]$ 3. Undefined   5. $[2a + 3b + 4c]$

7. $[2j + 6k - 12k - 24j - 5k] = [-22j - 11k]$ 9. $[b]$

11. $[c]$ 13. Undefined

15. $[a, b, c]$ 17. $[70, 3, 19, 10, -3]$ 19. $\begin{bmatrix} a & b & c \\ 0 & 0 & 0 \\ 0 & 0 & 0 \end{bmatrix}$

21. $\begin{bmatrix} 0 & 0 & 0 \\ 0 & 0 & 0 \\ g & h & i \end{bmatrix}$ 23. $\begin{bmatrix} 0 & b & 0 \\ 0 & e & 0 \\ 0 & h & 0 \end{bmatrix}$ 25. $\begin{bmatrix} a+d & b+e & c+f \\ d & e & f \\ g & h & i \end{bmatrix}$

27. $\begin{bmatrix} ax+dy & bx+ey & cx+fy \\ d & e & f \\ g & h & i \end{bmatrix}$ 29. $\begin{bmatrix} 2 & 4 & 6 & 11 \\ 3 & 1 & 10 & 10 \end{bmatrix}$

31. $\begin{bmatrix} 20 & 11 \\ 18 & 4 \\ 1 & 1 \\ 2 & 2 \end{bmatrix}$ 33. Yes, both are $\begin{bmatrix} 14 & -8 \\ 17 & -10 \end{bmatrix}$

Exercises 2.5

1. $[7] = [2] + [5]$ 3. $[5] = [4] + [1]$

5. $\begin{bmatrix} 5 & 5 \\ 2 & 3 \end{bmatrix} = \begin{bmatrix} 7 & 7 \\ 2 & 4 \end{bmatrix} + \begin{bmatrix} -2 & -2 \\ 0 & -1 \end{bmatrix}$

7. $\begin{bmatrix} 4 & 2 & 10 & 6 \\ 0 & 0 & 0 & 0 \\ 0 & 0 & 0 & 0 \\ 2 & 1 & 5 & 3 \end{bmatrix} = \begin{bmatrix} 2 & 1 & 5 & 3 \\ -2 & -1 & -5 & -3 \\ -2 & -1 & -5 & -3 \\ 4 & 2 & 10 & 6 \end{bmatrix}$

$+ \begin{bmatrix} 2 & 1 & 5 & 3 \\ 2 & 1 & 5 & 3 \\ 2 & 1 & 5 & 3 \\ -2 & -1 & -5 & -3 \end{bmatrix}$

Exercises 2.6

9. $\begin{bmatrix} a_{11} & a_{12} & a_{13} & a_{14} \\ a_{21} & a_{22} & a_{23} & a_{24} \end{bmatrix}$ 11. $\begin{bmatrix} 1/3 & 0 & 0 \\ 0 & 1/3 & 0 \\ 0 & 0 & 1/3 \end{bmatrix}$ 13. $\begin{bmatrix} 0 & 1/3 \\ 1/2 & 0 \end{bmatrix}$

15. No inverse exists.

17. $(A + B)^2 = A^2 + BA + AB + B^2 \neq A^2 + 2AB + B^2$ unless $AB = BA$. The answer is "no" in each case.

19. $A^2 = \begin{bmatrix} 0 & 0 & 1 \\ 0 & 0 & 0 \\ 0 & 0 & 0 \end{bmatrix}, A^3 = 0.$

23. There are an infinite number of solutions; one is $X = \begin{bmatrix} 1 & -3 \\ 1 & 2 \end{bmatrix}$.

Exercises 3.1

1. a. $A = \begin{bmatrix} 1 & -4 \\ -2 & 2 \end{bmatrix}, B = \begin{bmatrix} -5 \\ 4 \end{bmatrix}, X = \begin{bmatrix} x_1 \\ x_2 \end{bmatrix}$

b. $A_1 = \begin{bmatrix} 1 \\ -2 \end{bmatrix}, A_2 = \begin{bmatrix} -4 \\ 2 \end{bmatrix}, B = \begin{bmatrix} -5 \\ 4 \end{bmatrix}$

c. no d. $\begin{bmatrix} 1 & -4 \\ -2 & 2 \end{bmatrix} \begin{bmatrix} -1 \\ 1 \end{bmatrix} = \begin{bmatrix} -5 \\ 4 \end{bmatrix}$

3. a. $A = \begin{bmatrix} 1 & 2 & -1 \\ 2 & -1 & 3 \end{bmatrix}, X = \begin{bmatrix} x_1 \\ x_2 \\ x_3 \end{bmatrix}, B = \begin{bmatrix} 0 \\ 0 \end{bmatrix}$

b. yes

c. $X = \begin{bmatrix} 0 \\ 0 \\ 0 \end{bmatrix}$

5. a. $A(X_1 + X_2) = AX_1 + AX_2 = 0 + 0 = 0$
    b. $A(cX_1) = c(AX_1) = c0 = 0$
    c. $A(c_1 X_1 + c_2 X_2) = A(c_1 X_1) + A(c_2 X_2) = c_1(AX_1) + c_2(AX_2)$
       $= c_1 0 + c_2 0 = 0$

Exercises 3.2

1. trivial   3. It is the *only* solution.

5. a. The solution set consists of the points on a straight line in the plane.
    b. Two straight lines in the plane.
    c. A plane through the origin in 3-dimensional space.
    d. Two planes in 3-dimensional space.
    e. Three planes through the origin in 3-dimensional space.

7. All points not satisfying $x_1 - x_2 = 0$; that is, all points not on the line whose equation is $x_1 - x_2 = 0$. All points not on the line whose equation is $2x_1 + x_2 = 0$. All points except the origin, or $\begin{bmatrix} 0 \\ 0 \end{bmatrix}$.

Exercises 3.3

1. a. $\begin{bmatrix} 1 & -1 & 2 & 4 & | & 1 \\ 0 & 2 & 3 & 7 & | & 2 \\ 6 & 3 & 4 & 5 & | & 3 \end{bmatrix}$ b. Nonsense

    c. $\begin{bmatrix} 2 & 1 & | & 1 \\ 3 & 3 & | & 2 \\ 4 & 7 & | & 3 \end{bmatrix}$ d. $\begin{bmatrix} 1 & 2 & | & 3 \\ 3 & 4 & | & 7 \end{bmatrix}$

3. a. $A^{-1} = [X|\ Y]$

    b. $\begin{bmatrix} 0 & -1 \\ -1 & 0 \end{bmatrix} \begin{bmatrix} x_1 \\ x_2 \end{bmatrix} = \begin{bmatrix} 1 \\ 0 \end{bmatrix}$ has solution $X = \begin{bmatrix} 0 \\ -1 \end{bmatrix}$.

    $\begin{bmatrix} 0 & -1 \\ -1 & 0 \end{bmatrix} \begin{bmatrix} y_1 \\ y_2 \end{bmatrix} = \begin{bmatrix} 0 \\ 1 \end{bmatrix}$ has solution $Y = \begin{bmatrix} -1 \\ 0 \end{bmatrix}$.

    Thus $A^{-1} = [X|\ Y] = \begin{bmatrix} 0 & -1 \\ -1 & 0 \end{bmatrix}$.

Exercises 3.4

1. a. $\begin{bmatrix} 1 & -1 \\ -1 & 2 \end{bmatrix} \begin{bmatrix} 2 & 1 \\ 1 & 1 \end{bmatrix} = \begin{bmatrix} 1 & 0 \\ 0 & 1 \end{bmatrix}$.

b. $X = A^{-1}B = \begin{bmatrix} 2 \\ 3 \end{bmatrix}$; $AX = \begin{bmatrix} 1 & -1 \\ -1 & 2 \end{bmatrix}\begin{bmatrix} 2 \\ 3 \end{bmatrix} = \begin{bmatrix} -1 \\ 4 \end{bmatrix} = B.$

c. $A(A^{-1}Y) = (AA^{-1})Y = I_2 Y = Y = A(0) = 0.$ Thus $Y = 0$ is the unique solution.

3. a. $AA^{-1} = \begin{bmatrix} 1 & -1 \\ 0 & 1 \end{bmatrix}\begin{bmatrix} 1 & 1 \\ 0 & 1 \end{bmatrix} = \begin{bmatrix} 1 & 0 \\ 0 & 1 \end{bmatrix}.$

b. $X = A^{-1}B = \begin{bmatrix} 1 \\ 1 \end{bmatrix}$; $AX = \begin{bmatrix} 1 & -1 \\ 0 & 1 \end{bmatrix}\begin{bmatrix} 1 \\ 1 \end{bmatrix} = \begin{bmatrix} 0 \\ 1 \end{bmatrix} = B.$

c. $A(A^{-1}Y) = (AA^{-1})Y = I_2 Y = Y = AB = \begin{bmatrix} -1 \\ 1 \end{bmatrix}.$

Exercises 3.5

3. a. $\left[\begin{array}{cc|c} 1 & 1 & -1 \\ -1 & 2 & 4 \end{array}\right]$ b. $\left[\begin{array}{cc|c} 1 & 1 & -1 \\ 0 & 3 & 3 \end{array}\right]$ c. $\left[\begin{array}{cc|c} 1 & 1 & -1 \\ 0 & 1 & 1 \end{array}\right]$

d. $\left[\begin{array}{cc|c} 1 & 0 & -2 \\ 0 & 1 & 1 \end{array}\right]$ e. $X = \begin{bmatrix} -2 \\ 1 \end{bmatrix}$

5. From 4.c, $A\begin{bmatrix} 1/2 \\ 1/2 \end{bmatrix} = \begin{bmatrix} 1 \\ 0 \end{bmatrix}$ and from 4.d, $A\begin{bmatrix} -1/2 \\ 1/2 \end{bmatrix} = \begin{bmatrix} 0 \\ 1 \end{bmatrix}$. Thus $A^{-1} =$

$\begin{bmatrix} 1/2 & -1/2 \\ 1/2 & 1/2 \end{bmatrix}$. (See Exercise 3 in Section 3.3.)

7. $X = [1, 2, 1, 2]^T$

Exercises 3.6

1. a. $\begin{bmatrix} -1/3 & 2/3 \\ 2/3 & -1/3 \end{bmatrix}$ b. $\begin{bmatrix} 1 & 1 \\ 0 & 1 \end{bmatrix}$ c. $\begin{bmatrix} -5/2 & 3/2 \\ 4/2 & -2/2 \end{bmatrix}$

3. a. $\begin{bmatrix} 1 & -1 & -1 \\ 0 & 1 & 0 \\ 0 & 0 & 1 \end{bmatrix}$ b. $\begin{bmatrix} 1 & 0 & -1 \\ 1 & 1 & -1 \\ 1 & 1 & 0 \end{bmatrix}$ c. $\begin{bmatrix} -4 & 7 & -2 \\ -3 & 5 & -1 \\ 2 & -3 & 1 \end{bmatrix}$

Exercises 3.7

1. a. $\left[\begin{array}{cc|c} 1 & 1 & 2 \\ -2 & -2 & -4 \end{array}\right] \sim \left[\begin{array}{cc|c} 1 & 1 & 2 \\ 0 & 0 & 0 \end{array}\right].$

$X = \begin{bmatrix} 2-a \\ a \end{bmatrix} = \begin{bmatrix} 2-a \\ 0+a \end{bmatrix} = \begin{bmatrix} 2 \\ 0 \end{bmatrix} + a\begin{bmatrix} -1 \\ 1 \end{bmatrix} = X_P + X_H$

b. $\left[\begin{array}{ccc|c} 1 & -1 & 2 & 3 \\ 2 & -1 & 1 & 3 \\ -3 & 2 & -3 & -6 \end{array}\right] \sim \left[\begin{array}{ccc|c} 1 & 0 & -1 & 0 \\ 0 & 1 & -3 & -3 \\ 0 & 0 & 0 & 0 \end{array}\right].$

$$X = \begin{bmatrix} 0+a \\ -3+3a \\ 0+a \end{bmatrix} = \begin{bmatrix} 0 \\ -3 \\ 0 \end{bmatrix} + a \begin{bmatrix} 1 \\ 3 \\ 1 \end{bmatrix} = X_P + X_H$$

c. $[1 \quad 1 \mid 0]$. $X = \begin{bmatrix} -a \\ a \end{bmatrix} = a \begin{bmatrix} -1 \\ 1 \end{bmatrix}$

d. $\begin{bmatrix} 1 & 1 & 1 & -1 & \mid & 1 \\ -1 & 0 & 3 & 1 & \mid & -1 \\ 1 & 2 & 5 & -1 & \mid & 1 \\ 1 & -1 & -4 & 2 & \mid & 1 \end{bmatrix} \sim \begin{bmatrix} 1 & 0 & 0 & 2 & \mid & 1 \\ 0 & 1 & 0 & -4 & \mid & 0 \\ 0 & 0 & 1 & 1 & \mid & 0 \\ 0 & 0 & 0 & 0 & \mid & 0 \end{bmatrix}$

$$X = \begin{bmatrix} 1-2a \\ 4a \\ -a \\ a \end{bmatrix} = \begin{bmatrix} 1-2a \\ 0+4a \\ 0-a \\ 0+a \end{bmatrix} = \begin{bmatrix} 1 \\ 0 \\ 0 \\ 0 \end{bmatrix} + a \begin{bmatrix} -2 \\ 4 \\ -1 \\ 1 \end{bmatrix}$$

3. a. $a \begin{bmatrix} -19 \\ -11 \\ 1 \end{bmatrix}$ b. $\begin{bmatrix} -19 \\ -11 \\ 1 \end{bmatrix}, \begin{bmatrix} 38 \\ 22 \\ -2 \end{bmatrix}, \begin{bmatrix} -57 \\ -33 \\ 3 \end{bmatrix}$

5. a. 2 redundant equations.

$$X = \begin{bmatrix} 3+b-2a \\ 4-2b-3a \\ b \\ a \end{bmatrix} = \begin{bmatrix} 3 \\ 4 \\ 0 \\ 0 \end{bmatrix} + a \begin{bmatrix} -2 \\ -3 \\ 0 \\ 1 \end{bmatrix} + b \begin{bmatrix} 1 \\ -2 \\ 1 \\ 0 \end{bmatrix} = X_P + X_H.$$

For $a = b = 1$, $X = \begin{bmatrix} 2 \\ -1 \\ 1 \\ 1 \end{bmatrix}$

b. 2 redundant equations. No free variables. $X = \begin{bmatrix} 4 \\ -1 \\ 0 \end{bmatrix}$

5. c. 2 redundant equations. 1 free variable, x_3. $X = \begin{bmatrix} -1 \\ 3 \\ 0 \end{bmatrix} + a \begin{bmatrix} -2 \\ 0 \\ 1 \end{bmatrix}$.

For $a = 1$, $X = \begin{bmatrix} -3 \\ 3 \\ 1 \end{bmatrix}$.

d. 1 redundant equation. x_4, x_5, x_6 arbitrary. Letting $x_4 = c$, $x_5 = b$, $x_6 = a$,

$$X = \begin{bmatrix} 2 \\ 3 \\ -1 \\ 0 \\ 0 \\ 0 \end{bmatrix} + a \begin{bmatrix} 1 \\ -3 \\ -1 \\ 0 \\ 0 \\ 1 \end{bmatrix} + b \begin{bmatrix} -5 \\ -4 \\ 0 \\ 0 \\ 1 \\ 0 \end{bmatrix} + c \begin{bmatrix} 0 \\ -1 \\ 0 \\ 1 \\ 0 \\ 0 \end{bmatrix}.$$

When $a = b = c = 1$, $X = [-2, -5, -2, 1, 1, 1]^T$.

Exercises 3.8

1. a. $X = a\begin{bmatrix} 2 \\ 0 \\ -1 \\ 1 \end{bmatrix} + b\begin{bmatrix} 1 \\ 1 \\ 0 \\ 0 \end{bmatrix}$ b. $\begin{bmatrix} 3 \\ 1 \\ -1 \\ 1 \end{bmatrix}$ c. $\begin{bmatrix} -9 \\ -3 \\ 3 \\ -3 \end{bmatrix}$

3. a. $X = a\begin{bmatrix} -2 \\ 1 \\ 0 \end{bmatrix}$ b. $2, 3, 3 - 2 = 1, 1$ c. $X = \begin{bmatrix} -4 \\ 2 \\ 0 \end{bmatrix}$; yes

5. a. $5 - 2 = 3, 2, 2$ b. $X = \begin{bmatrix} 2 \\ 2b \\ b \\ -3a \\ a \end{bmatrix}$

   c. $X = \begin{bmatrix} 2 \\ 0 \\ 0 \\ 0 \\ 0 \end{bmatrix} + a\begin{bmatrix} 0 \\ 0 \\ 0 \\ -3 \\ 1 \end{bmatrix} + b\begin{bmatrix} 0 \\ 2 \\ 1 \\ 0 \\ 0 \end{bmatrix} = X_P + X_H$

Exercises 3.9

1. a. 2; $X = \begin{bmatrix} 1 \\ 7/3 \\ -2 \\ 0 \\ 0 \end{bmatrix} + a\begin{bmatrix} 0 \\ -7/3 \\ 2 \\ 0 \\ 1 \end{bmatrix} + b\begin{bmatrix} 0 \\ 10/3 \\ -3 \\ 1 \\ 0 \end{bmatrix}$.

   b. 3; $X = [-1/2, 6, 0, 0, 0]^T + a[1/2, -4, 0, 0, 1]^T + b[1/2, 0, 0, 1, 0]^T$
   $+ c[0, -2, 1, 0, 0]^T$.

   c. 0; $X = [1, 3, 2, 2]^T$

   d. 2; $X = [13/5, 0, 1/5, 0]^T + a[-1/5, 0, 11/10, 1]^T + b[1, 1, 0, 0]^T$.

   e. Since $n - m = 3 - 4 < 0$, there will be no solution at all unless at
   least one of the equations is redundant; $X = [1, 1, -1]^T$.

   f. 0; no solution exists.

3. a. $E_1 = \begin{bmatrix} 1/3 & 0 \\ 0 & 1 \end{bmatrix}$, $E_2 = \begin{bmatrix} 1 & 0 \\ -5 & 1 \end{bmatrix}$, $E_3 = \begin{bmatrix} 1 & 0 \\ 0 & 3 \end{bmatrix}$

   $E_4 = \begin{bmatrix} 1 & -4/3 \\ 0 & 1 \end{bmatrix}$

   b. $E_4 E_3 E_2 E_1 = \begin{bmatrix} 7 & -4 \\ -5 & 3 \end{bmatrix}$ c. I_2 d. $E_4 E_3 E_2 E_1 = A^{-1}$.

5. $n - (m - k)$; we choose those variables which are not "fixed" by having one of the "first 1's" in their respective columns.

7. $x_1 = 1$, $x_2 = -2$

9. $B = A_1 - A_2 + A_3$, as we see when we solve $AX = B$ and obtain $X = [1, -1, 1]^T$.

Exercises 4.1

1. a. $\begin{bmatrix} 2 \\ 0 \end{bmatrix} = 2E_1 + 0E_2$ b. $\begin{bmatrix} 3 \\ 5 \end{bmatrix} = 3E_1 + 5E_2$

    c. $\begin{bmatrix} \pi \\ e \end{bmatrix} = \pi E_1 + e E_2$ d. $\begin{bmatrix} 1/2 \\ 3/8 \end{bmatrix} = (1/2)E_1 + (3/8)E_2$

3. The augmented solution matrix is $\begin{bmatrix} 1 & 0 & | & 1 & 3 & 6/5 & -2 \\ 0 & 1 & | & 1 & -1 & -4/5 & 1 \end{bmatrix}$,

    where, for example, $\begin{bmatrix} 1 & -1 \\ 2 & 3 \end{bmatrix} \begin{bmatrix} 3 \\ -1 \end{bmatrix} = AX_2 = \begin{bmatrix} 4 \\ 3 \end{bmatrix} = B_2$.

5. a. yes

    b. $A = \begin{bmatrix} 0 \\ 1 \\ 1 \end{bmatrix}$ and $B = \begin{bmatrix} 1 \\ 0 \\ 0 \end{bmatrix}$ will suffice, although any 2 linear combinations
    of these would serve as well.

    c. $A + B = 1A + 1B$

    d. Let $T = \left\{ Y \mid Y = x_1 \begin{bmatrix} 0 \\ 1 \\ 1 \end{bmatrix} \right\}$ for example.

7. Since $0 + 0 = 0$ and $c(0) = 0$ for all c, $\{0\}$ is a vector space.

9. Since $\begin{bmatrix} 1 \\ 1 \end{bmatrix} = \begin{bmatrix} 1 \\ 0 \end{bmatrix} + \begin{bmatrix} 0 \\ 1 \end{bmatrix}$ is not in S, the set is not closed under addition.
    However, if Y is in S, then Y is of the form $\begin{bmatrix} a \\ 0 \end{bmatrix}$ or $\begin{bmatrix} 0 \\ b \end{bmatrix}$. Any scalar
    multiple of either of these is of the same form and is in S.

11. Let S_1, S_2 be vector spaces with the non-empty intersection $S_1 \cap S_2$.
    If Y_1 and Y_2 are in $S_1 \cap S_2$, then Y_1 and Y_2 are each in S_1 and S_2.
    Since S_1 is a vector space, $Y_1 + Y_2$ is in S_1. Since S_2 is a vector space
    $Y_1 + Y_2$ is in S_2. Thus $Y_1 + Y_2$ is in $S_1 \cap S_2$ and thus $S_1 \cap S_2$ is
    closed under addition. A similar argument holds for scalar multiplica-
    tion.

Exercises 4.2

1. Any vector in S may be expressed as a linear combination of the vectors in T; that is, if $T = \{A_1, A_2, \ldots, A_p\}$ and Y is in S, then $Y = c_1 A_1 + c_2 A_2 + \cdots + c_p A_p$ for some set of scalars c_i.

3. Not all 0; $c_1 A_1 + c_2 A_2 + c_3 A_3 = 0$. ... the only scalars c_i such that $c_1 A_1 + c_2 A_2 + c_3 A_3 = 0$ are $c_1 = c_2 = c_3 = 0$.

5. a. linearly independent   b. $-1 A_1 + \frac{1}{2} A_2 + 1 A_3 = 0$
   c. $-3 A_1 + 2 A_2 + 5 A_3 = 0$ d. linearly independent

7. a. $\begin{bmatrix} 1 & 1 & 1 & -1 & | & 0 \\ 1 & 0 & 0 & -1 & | & 0 \\ 1 & 1 & 3 & 1 & | & 0 \\ 1 & 0 & 1 & 0 & | & 0 \end{bmatrix} \sim \begin{bmatrix} 1 & 0 & 0 & -1 & | & 0 \\ 0 & 1 & 0 & -1 & | & 0 \\ 0 & 0 & 1 & 1 & | & 0 \\ 0 & 0 & 0 & 0 & | & 0 \end{bmatrix}$, so that

   the equation $AC = 0$ has solution $a[1, 1, -1, 1]^T = [1, 1, -1, 1]^T$ for $a = 1$. Thus, $1 A_1 + 1 A_2 + (-1) A_3 + 1 A_4 = 0$, and T_1 is linearly dependent. Any one of the vectors may be expressed as a linear combination of the others since each has a non-zero coefficient.
   b. linearly independent
   c. linearly independent
   d. linearly independent
   e. $2 A_1 + 2 A_2 - 2 A_3 - A_4 = 0$. Thus the set is linearly dependent. $A_4 = 2 A_1 + 2 A_2 - 2 A_3$.

9. Show that each of the vectors in T_1 can be expressed as a linear combination of the vectors in T_2, and vice-versa.

11. There exist c_i, not all zero, such that $c_1 A_1 + c_2 A_2 + c_3 A_3 = 0$. Suppose that $c_2 \neq 0$. Then $c_2 A_2 = -c_1 A_1 - c_3 A_3$ and $A_2 = (-c_1/c_2) A_1 - (c_3/c_2) A_3$.

13. We wish to show that if A is linearly dependent, then so is B. Use the scalars showing dependence of A and assign 0 as a scalar for each element of B not in A. We then have 0 expressed as a linear combination of the elements of B with at least one non-zero scalar; no.

15. Suppose that you have a linear combination of the vectors in the latter set which yields the zero vector. Rewrite the equation as a linear combination of A_1, A_2, A_3 and see that each of the coefficients must be 0 because of the linear independence of $\{A_1, A_2, A_3\}$.

Exercises 4.3

1. linearly independent; spans S.

3. a. true   b. false   c. true

5. a. T_1 is neither linearly independent, nor does it span S.
   b. T_2 spans S but is not linearly independent.

7. $\begin{bmatrix} 2 \\ 1 \end{bmatrix}$ could be replaced (see Exercise 10).

9. $Y = -A_1 + 3A_3 + 2A_4$.

11. Since $\begin{bmatrix} 1 & -1 & 2 & 2 & | & 0 \\ 0 & -3 & 3 & 0 & | & 0 \\ 1 & 1 & 0 & 2 & | & 0 \\ 1 & 0 & 1 & 2 & | & 0 \end{bmatrix} \sim \begin{bmatrix} 1 & 0 & 1 & 2 & | & 0 \\ 0 & 1 & -1 & 0 & | & 0 \\ 0 & 0 & 0 & 0 & | & 0 \\ 0 & 0 & 0 & 0 & | & 0 \end{bmatrix}$, we

conclude that $A_3 = A_1 - A_2$ and $A_4 = 2A_1$. Thus, the dimension is 2 and $\{A_1, A_2\}$ could serve as a basis, as could any two of the vectors except A_1 and A_4.

Exercises 4.4

1. $(1, -1), (3, 4)$. We could express these as matrices $\begin{bmatrix} 1 \\ -1 \end{bmatrix}$ and $\begin{bmatrix} 3 \\ 4 \end{bmatrix}$ and use the matrix to represent both the vector and its coordinates.

3. $(1, 0), (1, 1), (1, -2)$

5. a. any pair
    b. the coordinates are the same as the matrix elements

    c. $\begin{bmatrix} 2 \\ 3 \end{bmatrix} = 0A_3 + 1A_1$, $\begin{bmatrix} 3 \\ 2 \end{bmatrix} = (5/3)A_3 + (2/3)A_1$, $\begin{bmatrix} 1 \\ 0 \end{bmatrix} = 1A_3 + 0A_1$,

    $\begin{bmatrix} 0 \\ 1 \end{bmatrix} = (-2/3)A_3 + (1/3)A_1$

    d. $\begin{bmatrix} 1 \\ 0 \end{bmatrix} = (3/5)A_2 - (2/5)A_1$, $\begin{bmatrix} 0 \\ 1 \end{bmatrix} = -(2/5)A_2 + (3/5)A_1$,

    $\begin{bmatrix} 3 \\ 2 \end{bmatrix} = 1A_2 + 0A_1$, $\begin{bmatrix} 2 \\ 3 \end{bmatrix} = 0A_2 + 1A_1$

    e. $\begin{bmatrix} 6 \\ 6 \end{bmatrix} = (6/5)A_2 + (6/5)A_1$.

7. a. $U = \begin{bmatrix} 1 & 4 \\ 4 & 2 \end{bmatrix}$ b. $X_U = \begin{bmatrix} 2 \\ -1 \end{bmatrix}$ c. $X_U = \begin{bmatrix} -1/7 \\ 2/7 \end{bmatrix}$

    d. $X = \begin{bmatrix} 5 \\ 6 \end{bmatrix}$

Exercises 4.5

1. a. true   b. false   c. true   d. true   e. true   f. true
    g. false   h. false   i. true   j. true   k. true

3. a. 3   b. 0   c. 3   d. 5   e. 1

Exercises 4.6

3. a. no   b. no   c. yes   d. no   e. yes   f. no   g. yes
h. yes

Exercises 5.1

1. -2 3. 0   5. 56   7. 0   9. -24

Exercises 5.2

1. $A_{11} = -3, A_{12} = -1, A_{13} = 2, A_{21} = 3, A_{22} = 1, A_{23} = -2,$
$A_{31} = 3, A_{32} = 1, A_{33} = -2$

3. $A_{21} = 2, A_{22} = 6, A_{23} = 2, A_{24} = -4$

5. $A_{12} = -1, A_{22} = 7, A_{32} = 1, A_{42} = -3$

7. $A_{11} = -4, A_{12} = 10, A_{13} = -1$

9. -5

11. 7

17. $-2 = |A| = |B|. |AB| = 4$

19. $|A| = -18, |B| = 1, |AB| = -18$

21. $|A| = -2, |B| = -21, |AB| = 42$

23. $|A| = 4$

25. $|A| = 0$

27. $|A| = -4$

Exercises 5.3

1. $\text{adj } A = \begin{bmatrix} 2 & -3 \\ -1 & 1 \end{bmatrix}$

3. $\text{adj } A = \begin{bmatrix} 5 & 5 & -5 \\ -14 & -14 & 14 \\ -3 & -3 & 3 \end{bmatrix}$

5. $A^{-1} = 1/2 \begin{bmatrix} -4 & 2 \\ 3 & -1 \end{bmatrix}$

7. $A^{-1} = 1/2 \begin{bmatrix} 11 & -7 & -1 \\ -2 & 2 & 0 \\ -5 & 3 & 1 \end{bmatrix}$

9. $A^{-1} = \begin{bmatrix} 0 & 3 & -1 & -1 \\ 1 & -3 & 0 & 1 \\ 0 & 7 & -3 & -2 \\ -1 & -6 & 4 & 2 \end{bmatrix}$

11. $X = \begin{bmatrix} 11/5 \\ 2/5 \end{bmatrix}$

13. $X = \begin{bmatrix} 1 \\ -1 \\ 2 \end{bmatrix}$

15. $X = \begin{bmatrix} 1 \\ 1 \\ -1 \\ -1 \\ 0 \\ 0 \end{bmatrix}$

Exercises 5.4

1. 1   3. 3   5. 2   7. $r(A) = 3$ 9. $r(A) = 2$

11. $r(A) = 2$ 13. $r(A) = 3$ 15. 2; full rank

17. 3; full rank   19. 3

21. $(AA^T)^{-1} = \begin{bmatrix} 2/3 & -1/3 \\ -1/3 & 1/3 \end{bmatrix}$. The matrix $(A^T A)$ is a 4×4 matrix of rank 2 and hence has no inverse by Theorem 5.4.4.

Exercises 6.2

1. a. $X_U, X_V; X_U, X_V . X_U, V, X_V$ b. $\begin{bmatrix} 5 \\ 5 \end{bmatrix}$ c. $\begin{bmatrix} 13/5 \\ 1/5 \end{bmatrix}$

 d. $U_1 = V_1 - V_2, U_2 = 2V_1 + 3V_2; 2U_1 + U_2 = 4V_1 + V_2$

3. a. $A = \begin{bmatrix} 4 & 7 \\ 3 & 5 \end{bmatrix}$ b. $X_U = \begin{bmatrix} 1 \\ 1 \end{bmatrix}, X_V = \begin{bmatrix} 11 \\ 8 \end{bmatrix}$

 c. $X_V = \begin{bmatrix} 1 \\ 1 \end{bmatrix}, X_U = \begin{bmatrix} 2 \\ -1 \end{bmatrix}$

5. a. $\begin{bmatrix} 1 & 2 & 1 \\ 0 & 1 & 1 \\ 1 & 1 & 2 \end{bmatrix}$ b. $X = \begin{bmatrix} 4 \\ 2 \\ 4 \end{bmatrix}$ c. $X_V = \begin{bmatrix} 4 \\ 2 \\ 4 \end{bmatrix}$

Exercises 6.3

1. linear   3. non-linear   5. non-linear

9. T is linear since $a_1 T(X) + a_2 T(Y) = T(a_1 X + a_2 Y)$

11. $\begin{bmatrix} -a \\ 2a \\ a \end{bmatrix}$

Exercises 6.4

1. $A = I_2;\ \begin{bmatrix} 2 \\ 3 \end{bmatrix}$ 3. $A = \begin{bmatrix} 2 & 1 \\ 1 & 2 \end{bmatrix};\ \begin{bmatrix} 7 \\ 8 \end{bmatrix}$

5. $A = \begin{bmatrix} 1 & 2 \\ -2 & 0 \end{bmatrix};\ \begin{bmatrix} 8 \\ -4 \end{bmatrix}$

7. $A = I_3;\ \begin{bmatrix} -1 \\ 2 \\ 3 \end{bmatrix}$

9. $A = \begin{bmatrix} 1 & 0 & 0 \\ 0 & 1 & 0 \\ 1 & 1 & 1 \end{bmatrix};\ \begin{bmatrix} -1 \\ 2 \\ 4 \end{bmatrix}$

11. $A = \begin{bmatrix} 1 & 1 & 1 \\ 1 & -1 & -1 \\ 1 & 1 & -1 \end{bmatrix};\ \begin{bmatrix} 4 \\ -6 \\ -2 \end{bmatrix}$

13. a. $T\left(\begin{bmatrix} 1 \\ 2 \end{bmatrix}\right) = (17/3)U - (1/3)V;\ T\left(\begin{bmatrix} 2 \\ 1 \end{bmatrix}\right) = (16/3)U - (2/3)V$

    b. $B = \begin{bmatrix} 17/3 & 16/3 \\ -1/3 & -2/3 \end{bmatrix}$ c. $\begin{bmatrix} 5/3 \\ 2/3 \end{bmatrix}$ d. $\begin{bmatrix} 13 \\ -1 \end{bmatrix}$ e. $\begin{bmatrix} 11 \\ 25 \end{bmatrix}$

15. a. $A = \begin{bmatrix} -3 & -4 \\ 4 & 4 \end{bmatrix}$ b. $\begin{bmatrix} 1 \\ 1 \end{bmatrix}$ c. $\begin{bmatrix} -7 \\ 8 \end{bmatrix}$ d. $\begin{bmatrix} 9 \\ -6 \end{bmatrix}$

Exercises 6.5

1. a. 0   b. 4   c. 0   d. 1   e. 10   f. -15

3. $[3/5, 4/5]$

5. a. 0   b. $2\sqrt{5}/5$ c. 0   d. $\sqrt{50}/50$ e. 1   f. -1

7. $[-4/5, 3/5]$ or $[4/5, -3/5]$

Exercises 6.6

1. $A = \begin{bmatrix} 2 & 0 \\ 0 & 2 \end{bmatrix}$

3. a. $A = \begin{bmatrix} 1 & 0 \\ 0 & 0 \end{bmatrix}$, $P\left(\begin{bmatrix} a \\ b \end{bmatrix}\right) = \begin{bmatrix} a \\ 0 \end{bmatrix}$

b. $\begin{bmatrix} 0 & 0 \\ 0 & 1 \end{bmatrix}$, $\begin{bmatrix} 0 \\ b \end{bmatrix}$

c. $\begin{bmatrix} 1/2 & -1/2 \\ -1/2 & 1/2 \end{bmatrix}$, $\begin{bmatrix} (a-b)/2 \\ (-a+b)/2 \end{bmatrix}$

d. $\begin{bmatrix} 1/2 & 1/2 \\ 1/2 & 1/2 \end{bmatrix}$, $\begin{bmatrix} (a+b)/2 \\ (a+b)/2 \end{bmatrix}$

e. $\begin{bmatrix} 1/5 & 2/5 \\ 2/5 & 4/5 \end{bmatrix}$, $\begin{bmatrix} (a+2b)/5 \\ (2a+4b)/5 \end{bmatrix}$

f. $\begin{bmatrix} 4/5 & 2/5 \\ 2/5 & 1/5 \end{bmatrix}$, $\begin{bmatrix} (4a+2b)/5 \\ (2a+b)/5 \end{bmatrix}$

5. a. $\dfrac{1}{2}\begin{bmatrix} \sqrt{3} & -1 \\ 1 & \sqrt{3} \end{bmatrix}$, $\begin{bmatrix} (\sqrt{3}-1)/2 \\ (1+\sqrt{3})/2 \end{bmatrix}$

b. $(1/\sqrt{2})\begin{bmatrix} 1 & -1 \\ 1 & 1 \end{bmatrix}$, $\begin{bmatrix} 0 \\ \sqrt{2} \end{bmatrix}$

c. $\dfrac{1}{2}\begin{bmatrix} -1 & \sqrt{3} \\ -\sqrt{3} & -1 \end{bmatrix}$, $\begin{bmatrix} (-1+\sqrt{3})/2 \\ (-1-\sqrt{3})/2 \end{bmatrix}$

d. $\dfrac{1}{2}\begin{bmatrix} 1 & -\sqrt{3} \\ \sqrt{3} & 1 \end{bmatrix}$, $\begin{bmatrix} (1-\sqrt{3})/2 \\ (\sqrt{3}+1)/2 \end{bmatrix}$

e. $(1/\sqrt{2})\begin{bmatrix} -1 & 1 \\ -1 & -1 \end{bmatrix}$, $\begin{bmatrix} 0 \\ -\sqrt{2} \end{bmatrix}$

f. $\begin{bmatrix} 1 & 0 \\ 0 & 1 \end{bmatrix}$, $\begin{bmatrix} 1 \\ 1 \end{bmatrix}$

7. a. $A = \begin{bmatrix} -1 & 0 \\ 0 & 1 \end{bmatrix}$, $\begin{bmatrix} -a \\ b \end{bmatrix}$, $\begin{bmatrix} -1 \\ 1 \end{bmatrix}$

b. $\begin{bmatrix} 0 & -1 \\ -1 & 0 \end{bmatrix}$, $\begin{bmatrix} -b \\ -a \end{bmatrix}$, $\begin{bmatrix} -1 \\ -1 \end{bmatrix}$

c. $A = \begin{bmatrix} 0 & -1 \\ -1 & 0 \end{bmatrix}$, $\begin{bmatrix} -b \\ -a \end{bmatrix}$, $\begin{bmatrix} -1 \\ -1 \end{bmatrix}$

d. $(1/5)\begin{bmatrix} -3 & 4 \\ 4 & 3 \end{bmatrix}$, $(1/5)\begin{bmatrix} -3a+4b \\ 4a+3b \end{bmatrix}$, $\begin{bmatrix} 1/5 \\ 7/5 \end{bmatrix}$

e. $(1/5)\begin{bmatrix} 4 & 3 \\ 3 & -4 \end{bmatrix}$, $(1/5)\begin{bmatrix} 4a+3b \\ 3a-4b \end{bmatrix}$, $\begin{bmatrix} 7/5 \\ -1/5 \end{bmatrix}$

f. $\begin{bmatrix} 0 & 1 \\ 1 & 0 \end{bmatrix}$, $\begin{bmatrix} b \\ a \end{bmatrix}$, $\begin{bmatrix} 1 \\ 1 \end{bmatrix}$

Exercises 6.7

1. a. Eigenvalues are 0, 1; corresponding to 0 the general form is $a\begin{bmatrix} 0 \\ 1 \end{bmatrix}$;

    corresponding to 1, the general form is $a\begin{bmatrix} 1 \\ 0 \end{bmatrix}$.

    b. Eigenvalues are 0, 3; corresponding to 0 the general form is $a\begin{bmatrix} -1 \\ 1 \end{bmatrix}$;

    corresponding to 3, $a\begin{bmatrix} 1/2 \\ 1 \end{bmatrix}$.

    c. Eigenvalue is 2; general form is $a\begin{bmatrix} 0 \\ 1 \end{bmatrix} + b\begin{bmatrix} 1 \\ 0 \end{bmatrix}$ (all of $\mathcal{M}_{2,1}$)

    d. Eigenvalues: 1, -2; $a\begin{bmatrix} 4 \\ 1 \end{bmatrix}$ corresponds to 1; $a\begin{bmatrix} 1 \\ 1 \end{bmatrix}$ corresponds to -2.

5. a. $c^2 - 4c + 3$; $A^{-1} = \begin{bmatrix} 1 & -2/3 \\ 0 & 1/3 \end{bmatrix}$

    b. $-c^3 + 8c^2 - 14c + 2$; $A^{-1} = 1/2\begin{bmatrix} 11 & -7 & -1 \\ -2 & 2 & 0 \\ -5 & 3 & 1 \end{bmatrix}$

    c. $-c^3 + 3c^2 + 6c + 4$; $A^{-1} = (1/4)\begin{bmatrix} -2 & -1 & 2 \\ 4 & -4 & 0 \\ 0 & 2 & 0 \end{bmatrix}$

Exercises 6.8

1. a. $X^T A X$ where $A = \begin{bmatrix} 1 & 2 \\ 3 & 5 \end{bmatrix}$

    b. $X^T A X$ where $A = \begin{bmatrix} 2 & 1 \\ 0 & -1 \end{bmatrix}$

    c. $X^T A X$ where $A = \begin{bmatrix} 3 & 1 \\ -1 & 1 \end{bmatrix}$

5. a. positive definite   b. positive semi-definite; $(1, -1)$ c. neither; $(0, 1)$ d. neither; $(1, 0)$ e. positive semi-definite; $(2, 1)$

Exercises 7.1

1. Let x_i denote the amount of P_i to be produced. Find x_1, x_2 such that $x_i \geqslant 0$ and

   $5x_1 + 4x_2 \leqslant 480$ (M_1)

   $10x_1 + 8x_2 \leqslant 960$ (M_2)

   $3x_1 + 6x_2 \leqslant 480$ (M_3) and

   $f(x_1, x_2) = 4x_1 + 3x_2$ is maximized.

   Do you notice anything peculiar about the first two constraints?

3. Find $x_{ij} \geqslant 0$ such that

   (M_1) $x_{11} + x_{12} + x_{13}$ $= 1$

   (M_2) $x_{21} + x_{22} + x_{23}$ $= 1$

   (M_3) $x_{31} + x_{32} + x_{33} = 1$

   (J_1) x_{11} $+ x_{21}$ $+ x_{31}$ $= 1$

   (J_2) x_{12} $+ x_{22}$ $+ x_{32}$ $= 1$

   (J_3) x_{13} $+ x_{23}$ $+ x_{33} = 1$ and

   $f(x_{ij}) = 3x_{11} + 5x_{12} + 4x_{13} + 4x_{23} + \cdots + 5x_{33}$ is minimized.

5. Let x_i represent the number of units of c_i to be produced. Find x_i such that $x_i \geqslant 0$ and

   $3x_1 + 6x_2 + 7x_3 + 8x_4 \leqslant 10,000$

   $2x_1 + 5x_2 + 8x_3 + 10x_4 \leqslant 14,000$

   x_2 $\geqslant 250$

   x_3 $\geqslant 500$

   and $f(x_i) = 3x_1 + 4x_2 + 6x_3 + 8x_4$ is maximized.

7. Find $X = \begin{bmatrix} x_1 \\ x_2 \end{bmatrix} \geqslant 0$ such that $AX \leqslant R$ and

   $f(X) = CX$ is maximized, where $A = \begin{bmatrix} 5 & 4 \\ 10 & 8 \\ 3 & 6 \end{bmatrix}$, $R = \begin{bmatrix} 480 \\ 960 \\ 480 \end{bmatrix}$, $C = [4, 3]$.

9. Find x_{ij} such that

   i. $x_{ij} \geqslant 0$ $i = 1, 2$; $j = 1, 2, 3$.

   ii. $x_{11} + x_{12} + x_{13}$ $= 200$

   $x_{21} + x_{22} + x_{23} = 300$

   x_{11} $+ x_{21}$ $\leqslant 200$

   x_{12} $+ x_{22}$ $\leqslant 250$

   x_{13} $+ x_{23} \leqslant 150$

   and $30x_{11} + 38x_{12} + 40x_{13} + 40x_{21} + 35x_{22} + 36x_{23} = f(x_{ij})$ is maximized.

Exercises 7.2

1. a–d.

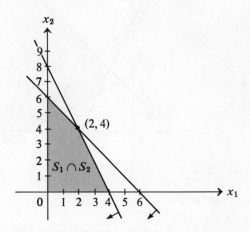

e. $(0, 0)$, $(0, 6)$, $(2, 4)$, $(4, 0)$ f. $0, 12, 10, 4$ g. $f(1, 1) = 3, f(1, 3)$
$= 7, f(3, 1) = 5, f(1, 5) = 11$

3. a–d.

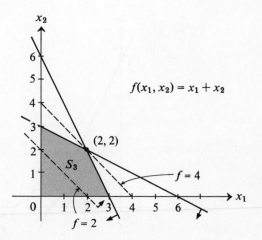

e. $(2, 2)$; $f(2, 2) = 4$
f. $(0, 0)$; $f(0, 0) = 0$
g. any point (x_1, x_2) on the line between $(0, 3)$ and $(2, 2)$

5.

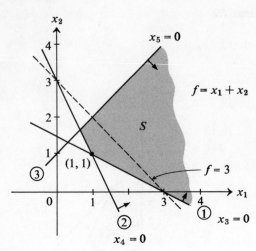

a. see graph
b. $(1, 1), (3, 0), (2/3, 5/3)$
c. $f(1, 1) = 2, f(3, 0) = 3, f(2/3, 5/3) = 7/3$
d. see graph
e. $(1, 1), 2 = f$
f. f has no maximum in S. f can be made as large as you please by, for example, letting $x_2 = 0$ and increasing x_1.
g. the maximum value of g occurs at $(1, 1)$ where $g(1, 1) = -2 = -f(1, 1)$. g has no minimum value over S.

7.

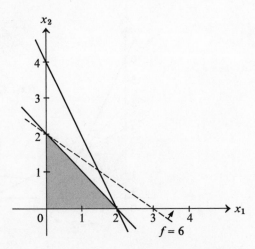

a. The maximum value of f occurs at $(0, 2)$ where $f(0, 2) = 6$.
b. The second constraint was redundant in the sense that it excluded no new points from consideration.

9. Let x_1, x_2 denote the amount of A and B to be produced.
   a. Find x_1, x_2 such that
      1) $x_i \geqslant 0$ $i = 1, 2$
      2) $x_1 + 2x_2 \leqslant 480$ (M_1)
         $3x_1 + x_2 \leqslant 480$ (M_2)
      3) $f(x_1, x_2) = 5x_1 + 4x_2$ is maximized.

   b.
Point	f
O	0
A	960
B	1248
C	800

   c.

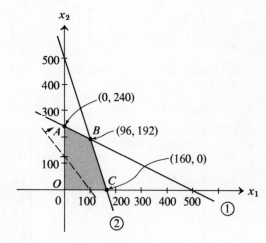

11. $x_1 = 4$, $x_2 = 3$; $f = \$23{,}000$.

Exercises 7.3

1. negative, $2x_1 + 3x_2 + x_3 = 6$, guard, non-negative, not satisfied, slack

3. $2x_1 + x_2 + x_3 \qquad = 6$
   $x_1 + 2x_2 \qquad + x_4 = 6$
   $f(x_1, x_2, x_3, x_4) = x_1 + x_2$ is to be maximized.

5. $\quad x_1 + 2x_2 - x_3 \qquad\qquad = 3$
   $\quad 2x_1 + x_2 \qquad - x_4 \qquad = 3$
   $\quad -x_1 + x_2 \qquad\qquad + x_5 = 1$
   $\quad f(x_i) = x_1 + x_2$ is to be maximized.

7. Find $X \geqslant 0$ such that $AX = R$ and $f(X) = CX$ is minimized.

$$A = \begin{bmatrix} 2 & 1 & 1 & 0 \\ 1 & 2 & 0 & 1 \end{bmatrix}, \quad R = \begin{bmatrix} 6 \\ 6 \end{bmatrix}, \quad C = [1, 1, 0, 0].$$

9. Find $X \geqslant 0$ such that $AX = R$ and $f(X) = CX$ is minimized.

$$A = \begin{bmatrix} 1 & 2 & -1 & 0 & 0 \\ 2 & 1 & 0 & -1 & 0 \\ -1 & 1 & 0 & 0 & 1 \end{bmatrix}, R = \begin{bmatrix} 3 \\ 3 \\ 1 \end{bmatrix}, C = [1, 1, 0, 0, 0].$$

11. a. $(1, 2, 2)$, non-negative b. $(2, 2, -2)$, negative, is not
    c. $(2, 1, 1), (2, 1)$

Exercises 7.4

1. a. $x_1 + 2x_2 + x_3 \quad\quad = 3$
      $2x_1 + x_2 \quad\quad + x_4 = 3$

   b. $A = \begin{bmatrix} 1 & 2 & 1 & 0 \\ 2 & 1 & 0 & 1 \end{bmatrix}$, $X = \begin{bmatrix} x_1 \\ x_2 \\ x_3 \\ x_4 \end{bmatrix}$, $R = \begin{bmatrix} 3 \\ 3 \end{bmatrix}$

   c. See Figure 7.4.2 d. check that $AX_i = R$ e. X_1, X_3
   f. X_1, X_2 g. X_1

3. a. non-basic, basic b. $(1/2, 1/2, 3/2, 3/2)$, yes, no

c.

Point	2-Space Solution	Non-Basic Variables	Basic Variables	4-Space Solution, X^T	Solution Feasible?
O	$[0, 0]$	x_1, x_2	x_3, x_4	$[0, 0, 3, 3]$	yes
A	$[0, 3/2]$	x_1, x_3	x_2, x_4	$[0, 3/2, 0, 3/2]$	yes
B	$[0, 3]$	x_1, x_4	x_2, x_3	$[0, 3, -3, 0]$	no
C	$[1, 1]$	x_3, x_4	x_1, x_2	$[1, 1, 0, 0]$	yes
D	$[3, 0]$	x_2, x_3	x_1, x_4	$[3, 0, 0, -3]$	no
E	$[3/2, 0]$	x_2, x_4	x_1, x_3	$[3/2, 0, 3/2, 0]$	yes

5. a. $A = \begin{bmatrix} 1 & 1 & 1 & 0 \\ 2 & 1 & 0 & 1 \end{bmatrix}$, $R = \begin{bmatrix} 2 \\ 4 \end{bmatrix}$, $A_1 = \begin{bmatrix} 1 \\ 2 \end{bmatrix}$, $A_4 = \begin{bmatrix} 0 \\ 1 \end{bmatrix}$

b.

Point	2-Space Solution	Non-Basic Variables	Basic Variables	4-Space Solution, X^T	Solution Feasible?
O	$[0, 0]$	x_1, x_2	x_3, x_4	$[0, 0, 2, 4]$	yes
A	$[0, 2]$	x_1, x_3	x_2, x_4	$[0, 2, 0, 2]$	yes
B	$[0, 4]$	x_1, x_4	x_3, x_2	$[0, 4, -2, 0]$	no
C	$[2, 0]$	x_2, x_3	x_1, x_4	$[2, 0, 0, 0]$	yes
C	$[2, 0]$	x_2, x_4	x_3, x_1	$[2, 0, 0, 0]$	yes
C	$[2, 0]$	x_3, x_4	x_1, x_2	$[2, 0, 0, 0]$	yes

c. $[1, 1, 0, 1]$, basic, feasible

Exercises 7.5

1. a. $\begin{bmatrix} 5 \\ 29 \end{bmatrix}$ b. 29   c. $\begin{bmatrix} 6 & -1 \\ -5 & 1 \end{bmatrix}$ d. $a = 5, b = 29$

3. a. $\begin{bmatrix} 3 \\ 1 \end{bmatrix}$ b. $\begin{bmatrix} 4 \\ 4 \end{bmatrix}, 4$ c. $\begin{bmatrix} 4 \\ -8 \end{bmatrix}, -8$ d. $\begin{bmatrix} 1 \\ 1 \end{bmatrix}, 1$ e. 4

5. a. $x_1 A_1 + x_2 A_2 + x_3 A_3 + x_4 A_4 = R$

    c.

Point	Basic Variables	B	B^{-1}	X_B	X^T	x_{B1}
O	x_3, x_4	$[A_3, A_4] = \begin{bmatrix} 1 & 0 \\ 0 & 1 \end{bmatrix}$	$\begin{bmatrix} 1 & 0 \\ 0 & 1 \end{bmatrix}$	$\begin{bmatrix} 3 \\ 3 \end{bmatrix}$	$[0, 0, 3, 3]$	3
A	x_2, x_4	$\begin{bmatrix} 2 & 0 \\ 1 & 1 \end{bmatrix}$	$\begin{bmatrix} 1/2 & 0 \\ -1/2 & 1 \end{bmatrix}$	$\begin{bmatrix} 3/2 \\ 3/2 \end{bmatrix}$	$[0, 3/2, 0, 3/2]$	3/2
B	x_2, x_3	$\begin{bmatrix} 2 & 1 \\ 1 & 0 \end{bmatrix}$	$\begin{bmatrix} 0 & 1 \\ 1 & -2 \end{bmatrix}$	$\begin{bmatrix} 3 \\ -3 \end{bmatrix}$	$[0, 3, -3, 0]$	3
C	x_1, x_2	$\begin{bmatrix} 1 & 2 \\ 2 & 1 \end{bmatrix}$	$\begin{bmatrix} -1/3 & 2/3 \\ 2/3 & -1/3 \end{bmatrix}$	$\begin{bmatrix} 1 \\ 1 \end{bmatrix}$	$[1, 1, 0, 0]$	1
D	x_1, x_4	$\begin{bmatrix} 1 & 0 \\ 2 & 1 \end{bmatrix}$	$\begin{bmatrix} 1 & 0 \\ -2 & 1 \end{bmatrix}$	$\begin{bmatrix} 3 \\ -3 \end{bmatrix}$	$[3, 0, 0, -3]$	3
E	x_1, x_3	$\begin{bmatrix} 1 & 1 \\ 2 & 0 \end{bmatrix}$	$\begin{bmatrix} 0 & 1/2 \\ 1 & -1/2 \end{bmatrix}$	$\begin{bmatrix} 3/2 \\ 3/2 \end{bmatrix}$	$[3/2, 0, 3/2, 0]$	3/2

Exercises 7.6

1. $[1, -1], [1, 0, 2, 0], -1$

3. a. $B_1 = [A_3, A_4], X^T = [0, 0, 4, 4]; B_2 = [A_2, A_4],$
       $X^T = [0, 4/3, 0, 8/3]. B_3 = [A_2, A_1], X^T = [1, 1, 0, 0];$
       $B_4 = [A_1, A_3], X^T = [4/3, 0, 8/3, 0]$
    b. $C_{B_1} X_{B_1} = 0, C_{B_2} X_{B_2} = 8/3, C_{B_3} X_{B_3} = 3, C_{B_4} X_{B_4} = 4/3.$
    c. $[1, 1, 0, 0]^T$ with $f = 3$.
    d. $C_{B_i} X_{B_i} = 0, 0, 1, 4/3; [4/3, 0, 8/3, 0]^T$ with $f = 4/3$.

5. a. At O, $C_B X_B = 0$; at A, $C_B X_B = -3/2$; at C, $C_B X_B = -4$; at E,
       $C_B X_B = -9/2$.
    b. E c. $[3/2, 0, 3/2, 0], f = -9/2$.

7. a. At O, 0; at A, 12; at C, 14; at E, 12

    b. $\begin{bmatrix} 2 \\ 4 \end{bmatrix}$, 14   c. $[2, 4, 0, 0]^T$

Exercises 7.7

1. a. $x_3 = 6 - 2x_1 - 3x_2$, $x_4 = 6 - 3x_1 - 2x_2$.
    b. x_3, x_4, x_4; x_4; x_2, x_4
    c. x_2; x_3, x_1, decrease, x_3, x_3; $x_2, x_1, x_2 = 6/5 - (3/5)x_3 + (2/5)x_4$, $x_1 = 6/5 + (2/5)x_3 - (3/5)x_4$

3. the optimum BFS is $[1, 1, 0, 0]^T$ with $f = 3$

5. a. positive   b. a, negative   c. $-6/c$, $0 - e(6/c)$, $5 - (6/c)a$
    d. $x_4 < 0$

Exercises 7.8

1. a.

C			4	3	0	0
B	$C_B{}^T$	R	A_1	A_2	A_3	A_4
A_3	0	6	2	3	1	0
A_4	0	6	③	2	0	1
$c_J - z_J$		0	4	3	0	0

b. no, 3, positive   c. A_1 d. feasibility, A_4; 3

e.

C			4	3	0	0
B	$C_B{}^T$	X_B	Y_1	Y_2	Y_3	Y_4
A_3	0	2	0	5/3	1	-2/3
A_1	4	2	1	2/3	0	1/3
$c_J - z_J$		8	0	1/3	0	-4/3

;

$x_{B1} = 2$, $y_{12} = 5/3$, $y_{24} = 1/3$

f. $1/3$, A_2; $6/5$, 3; x_3, $5/3$

g.

B	$C_B{}^T$	X_B	Y_1	Y_2	Y_3	Y_4
	C		4	3	0	0
A_2	3	6/5	0	1	3/5	−2/5
A_1	4	6/5	1	0	−2/5	3/5
$c_j - z_j$		42/5	0	0	−1/5	−6/5

;

4, 0, −2/5

3. The optimal tableau is

B	$C_B{}^T$	X_B	Y_1	Y_2	Y_3	Y_4
	C		3	1	0	0
A_3	0	3/2	0	3/2	1	−1/2
A_1	3	3/2	1	1/2	0	1/2
$c_j - z_j$		9/2	0	−1/2	0	−3/2

Exercises 7.9

1. $[X_B \mid Y]$, R, A_j.

3. a. The optimal tableau is the third; $X^T = [1, 1, 0, 0]$

B	$C_B{}^T$	X_B	Y_1	Y_2	Y_3	Y_4
	C		1	2	0	0
A_2	2	1	0	1	3/8	−1/8
A_1	1	1	1	0	−1/8	3/8
$C - Z$		3	0	0	−5/8	−1/8

5. a. We would choose the vector with the most negative $(c_j - z_j)$ value.

   b. Since we are only maintaining feasibility with this criterion, it has nothing to do with the type of problem being solved. Therefore it would not change.

7. a. The optimal tableau is the third: $X^T = [96, 192, 0, 0]$.

	C	5	4	0	0
B	$C_B{}^T$	X_B	Y_1	Y_2	Y_3	Y_4
A_2	4	192	0	1	3/5	−1/5
A_1	5	96	1	0	−1/5	2/5
C − Z		1248	0	0	−7/5	−6/5

9. a. The optimal tableau is the fourth; $X^T = [3, 1, 0, 3, 0]$.

	C	2	3	0	0	0
B	$C_B{}^T$	X_B	Y_1	Y_2	Y_3	Y_4	Y_5
A_4	0	3	0	0	3	1	−2
A_2	3	1	0	1	−1	0	1
A_1	2	3	1	0	2	0	−1
C − Z		9	0	0	−1	0	−1

c. $B = [A_4, A_2, A_1]$ d. 3, −1, 2

Exercises 7.10

1. $x_1 + x_2 + x_3 \qquad = 3$
    $-x_1 + 2x_2 \qquad - x_4 + x_5 = 4$

3. The optimal tableau is the third; $X^T = [4, 3, 0, 0, 0]$.

	C	2	5	0	0	M
B	$C_B{}^T$	X_B	Y_1	Y_2	Y_3	Y_4	Y_5
A_2	5	3	0	1	−3/2	−1/2	3/2
A_1	2	4	1	0	2	1	−2
C − Z		23	0	0	7/2	1/2	∞

5. The optimal tableau is the fourth; $X^T = [1, 1, 0, 0, 1, 0, 0]$.

	C	1	1	0	0	0	M	M
B	$C_B{}^T$	X_B	Y_1	Y_2	Y_3	Y_4	Y_5	Y_6	Y_7
A_1	1	1	1	0	1/3	−2/3	0	−1/3	2/3
A_5	0	1	0	0	1	−1	1	−1	1
A_2	1	1	0	1	−2/3	1/3	0	2/3	−1/3
$C-Z$		2	0	0	1/3	1/3	0	∞	∞

Exercises 7.11

3. $CX = c_1 x_1 + c_2 x_2$; $ZX = z_1 x_1 + z_2 x_2$.
$CX - ZX = (c_1 - z_1)x_1 + (c_2 - z_2)x_2$. Since each $x_i \geqslant 0$ and each $(c_i - z_i) \leqslant 0$, the entire sum is non-positive; that is, $CX - ZX \leqslant 0$ or $CX \leqslant ZX$.

Exercises 8.1

1. a. $p(H) = p(T) = 1/2$ b. all of the probabilities are 1/4
3. The matrices in (b), (d), (e), (g) are stochastic
9. a. −1/3, 1   b. $[1/2, 1/2]$ c. 1/9, 1

Exercises 8.2

1. a. 1   b. 0   c. 1/3   d. 2/3
3. a. 2/9, 7/9   b. 7/27, 20/27
5. a. $\begin{bmatrix} 2/3 & 1/3 \\ 1/3 & 2/3 \end{bmatrix}$ b. $\begin{bmatrix} 5/9 & 4/9 \\ 4/9 & 5/9 \end{bmatrix}$

Exercises 8.3

1. a. 1/2   b. 1/2   c. $[1/2, 1/2]$ d. 1/2   e. 1/2   f. $[1/2, 1/2]$
3. $P^{(1)} = [5/9, 4/9]$
    $P^{(2)} = [14/27, 13/27]$
    $P^{(3)} = [41/81, 40/81]$

Index